AMERICAN GUIDE TO
Infant & Child Care

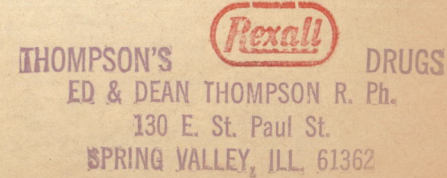

THOMPSON'S *Rexall* DRUGS
ED & DEAN THOMPSON R. Ph.
130 E. St. Paul St.
SPRING VALLEY, ILL. 61362

Copyright 1969 © Robert McMichael, Inc.,
12 East 44th Street, New York, N.Y. 10017.

Cover photo by Doris Pinney, Photo Library. Other photos by Kathryn Abbe, FMG; Tom De Santo, Scoville Mfg. Co.; Phoebe Dunn, DPI; Robert Goldstein; Tana Hoban, DPI; John G. Horey; Lew Merrim, Monkmeyer Press; Stephen Munz; H. Armstrong Roberts; Josef Schneider; Bob S. Smith, Rapho Guillumette; Suzanne Szasz; Doris and Roy Pinney, Photo Library; Vivienne; Pride Trimble Co.

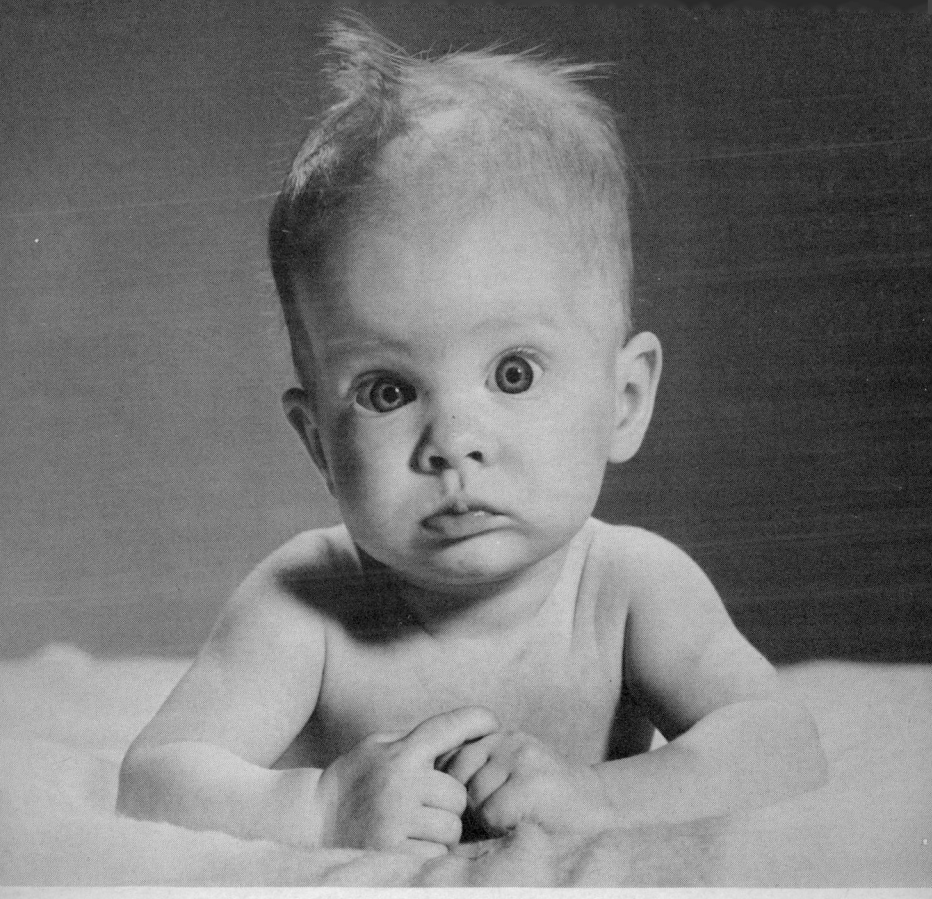

AMERICAN GUIDE TO
Infant & Child Care

With an introduction and supplements by
Carl C. Fischer, M.D., F.A.A.P., F.A.C.P.

Robert McMichael, Inc., New York

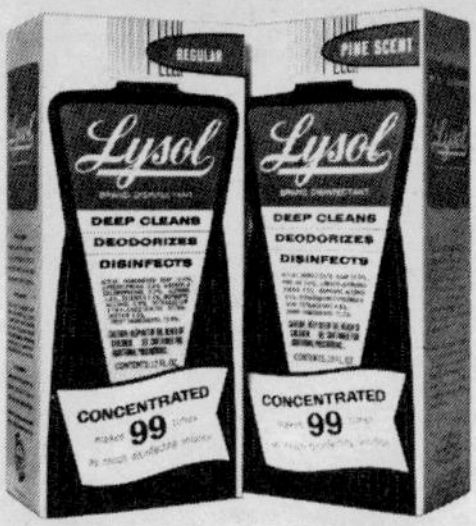

The original ounce of prevention

Use a little Lysol next time you clean or do the laundry. It prevents all sorts of things from getting started—even in a spotless home.

Add a few ounces to your wash —and diapers come out sanitized. Lysol kills bacteria that can lead to diaper rash.

Add Lysol Brand Disinfectant to your cleaning water. It kills germs that cause odors.

Since Lysol kills disease germs, it could just help prevent an illness from getting started in your house.

A little LYSOL® gets things a lot more than clean

© 1970 LEHN & FINK PRODUCTS

Contents

CHAPTER   PAGE

Introduction

1. **The most important things** 1
   Shaping a child's world...Your baby *is* different... What to expect of the doctor

2. **The newborn baby** 5
   How the skin should look...The shape of the head... How are the eyes?...Chest, navel, and breasts...The genitals...To circumcise or not?...Arms and legs... What his motions mean...If you feel "blue"...Are the older children upset?...Get a birth certificate!

3. **Feeding the baby** 21
   First feedings...Breast or bottle?...Work out a system ...Removing milk by hand...Food for the nursing mother...Foods other than milk...Spitting up and vomiting

4. **Facts about formulas** 40
   Types of milk used...Planning the formula...Making the formula...Preparation Method 1...Preparation Method 2...Other methods...Giving a bottle... Should you reuse a bottle?

5. **Other routines of baby care** 57
   What bowel movements reveal...How much sleep?... Bed and bedclothes...Where to sleep...Sleeping position...If he cries a lot...Bathing the baby...The skin and scalp...Care of the genitals...Clothing for the

baby... How to wash and fold diapers... Laundering his clothes

6. **Special problems of new mothers** 86
    The low-birth-weight baby... If he must get care at home... The baby who's handicapped... Get help early ... Moving to a new home... Going to the hospital... Should new mother take job?

7. **Keeping the child healthy** 102
    What determines size?... Caring for his teeth... Proper food for children... You and your child's doctor

8. **Preventing disease and accidents** 117
    Polio... Smallpox... DPT injections... Measles... Keep record of immunizations... Other preventive measures... Safety at home... Burns and fire... Falls ... Poisons... Suffocation and choking... Water hazards ... Safety in automobiles

9. **When your child is sick** 133
    Amusing the convalescent... Home nursing techniques ... Feeding the sick baby... General care

10. **Common diseases and disorders** 144
    The baby's mouth... Don't always blame teething... Tongue-tie... Defective vision... Crossed eyes... Inflamed, tearing eyes... Respiratory infections... Asthma ... Communicable diseases... Heart trouble... Skin ailments... Allergic skin conditions... Intestinal and genital ills... Emergencies... Mouth-to-mouth resuscitation ... Inducing vomiting... Convulsions... Bites and stings ... Broken bones... Particle in eye... Common communicable diseases... Less common infectious diseases

11. **One to four months** 178
    How he will develop... To schedule the day... Introducing solid foods... Going places with the baby... The babysitter or maid

12. **Four to eight months** 189
    Learning to talk ... He begins to play ... He may have fears ... A playpen is useful ... Feeding becomes more grown up ... Three meals a day ... When to stop boiling things ... The baby's chair ... A tooth may appear ... Sleeping patterns are set ... Thumbsucking and other comforts

13. **Eight to twelve months** 207
    Discipline in little ways ... Changes in feeding ... Weaning the baby ... When he starts to walk ... What kind of shoes? ... A look ahead ... Plan your next baby

14. **Ages one and two** 221
    Take stock at first birthday ... He becomes a toddler ... Early experiences count heavily ... Walking enlarges his world ... The age of accidents ... "Growing pains" ... Sleeping habits change ... Feeding the toddler ... Sucking may continue ... When to start toilet training ... He learns to talk ... Toddlers play with everything ... Managing a toddler ... Your babysitter

15. **Ages three and four** 271
    Fathers become important ... When parents disagree ... Brother-and-sister quarrels ... Jealousy occurs in families, too ... Learning right from wrong ... Learning to tell the truth ... Imaginary companions ... He has new fears ... In search of answers: sex ... More questions: death ... Teaching good behavior ... Play at 3 and 4 ... Aids to having fun

16. **The mother's personal well-being** 312
    Hair ... Skin ... Teeth and nails ... Diet ... Weight ... Bathing ... Exercise ... Side effects ... Clothes ... Time off

    Notes and records 333

    Index 340

Introduction

Guiding the progress of the new infant through the vitally important first four years of his life is one of the happiest experiences parents can share. But if parenthood is new to them, doubts and fears may overshadow their joy.

Many worrisome questions arise in their minds, for instance: "Just what should we expect of our youngster at this age?" "What to do for minor rashes?" "How warm should the baby's bath water be?" "When are vitamins supposed to be added to his food?" "Is it normal for our formerly placid and agreeable baby to become a little monster at age two, who shouts 'No!' to everything we ask of him?"

INFANT & CHILD CARE answers these and myriad other questions that arise daily. And it does so with authority, since it is based on the latest guides of the United States Government. It includes in slightly condensed form not only most of the material in the Children's Bureau publication, "Infant Care," but also that part of its publication, "Your Child From 1 to 6," covering the period through age four. The Children's Bureau is part of the Social and Rehabilitation Service of the U.S. Department of Health, Education, and Welfare.

The only material in this book not derived from the Government guides cited are my supplements to it and Chapter 16 on the mother's personal well-being, by Nancy R. Jones.

There is often more than one "right" way to take care of a child. So the guidelines given here can be applied with some flexibility. They will help you not only to anticipate your little one's actions and needs at various stages, but also to recognize when there's a problem and when there isn't.

You'll find predictions of the progress you may expect by certain ages. But don't be distressed if your child doesn't achieve all these predictions within the times mentioned. Each youngster has his own pattern of growth and development and will do best if allowed to achieve his goals at his own pace. Only when this pace is unusually different from what appears normal, need you ask your doctor about it.

Attention to your youngster's emotional needs is every bit as important as that paid to his physical welfare. If you give him your love and affection, you will also be giving him the inner security he needs to carry him over the rough spots and to assure him a strong foundation for the future.

During the years from birth to four, a child develops much faster than during any other period of his life. He learns to use his hands, to walk, to talk, and to care for himself to some extent. He also begins to learn how to relate to those around him. If, during these years of unbelievably rapid progress, he is fortunate in having the guidance of firm yet understanding and loving parents, his chances of developing into a well-adjusted older child and adult are infinitely improved.

The Government guides on which INFANT & CHILD CARE is based reflect the contributions of many parents and of more than 100 professionals in such specialties as pediatrics, child psychology and psychiatry, nutrition, child development, vision, safety, orthopedics, nursing, and parent education.

The guides were written by Laura L. Dittman, specialist in growth and development, under the direction of Marian M. Crane, M.D. They were reviewed before publication by Steward A. Clifford, M.D.; Woodruff L. Crawford, M.D.; Matthew Debuskey, M.D.; Alfred H. Washburn, M.D.; and Myron E. Wegman, M.D. — all well-known authorities in their fields.

This book cannot take the place of a physician. It is intended, rather, to supplement the doctor's care and to help you carry on in his absence.

A new baby is so little, and seems so fragile and vulnerable to hazards, that parents are often overanxious about their handling of him. If you're one of those who haven't yet developed all the know-how you'd like, this book can give you "instant experience" in taking care of the baby and encouraging his development. We hope it will help you to be at ease with him and to enjoy these wonderful, quickly-fleeting years.

CARL C. FISCHER, M.D.

Dr. Carl C. Fischer has had 40 years' experience in the specialty of pediatrics, both practicing it and teaching it. As president of the American Academy of Pediatrics (1960–1961), chairman of its Council on Pediatric Practice since 1963, and professor and chairman for more than 25 years of the Department of Pediatrics of Philadelphia's Hahnemann Medical College and Hospital, he has made an outstanding contribution to the science of pediatrics and to the health of the children of this country. His supplements to this book have been set in the form of boldface captions to distinguish them from the text of the Government guides.

1. The most important things

Now that your baby is here, the important thing is to enjoy him. Enjoying the baby may seem much too simple a recipe when your mind is full of feedings, birth weight, and how to get some sleep. But in the long run, your pleasure in him will be the most precious gift you can receive—and give. Through your enjoyment of him as a baby, he becomes an adult who can give enjoyment to others and experience joy himself.

At first, all your feelings run high. Pleasure and delight are mixed with wonder and doubt. You check your baby over and over, discovering the tiny fingernails, the arching eyebrows, a little blemish on the forehead. And those enormous feet! As the days go by and he responds to what you do for him, you feel more sure of yourself; and love grows between you.

No doubt you are astonished at how powerful such a little thing is. The whole world appears to revolve around him. His arrival has, in fact, changed the world. And with his coming is born not only a living being, but a whole chain of new relationships. First, of course, is the new relationship between you and him. Next, you will find a different relationship in your marriage. Through a child, a husband and wife share the worries and delights of introducing a new life to the ways of the world. Commonplace things become fresh again as they see them through the wide-eyed gaze of a baby: the pattern of sunlight on a wall, the bounce of a bright ball, a dandelion.

SHAPING A CHILD'S WORLD

Some of the baby's qualities are settled before he is born and cannot be changed. But by the environment you provide his personality is shaped. Through his experiences with you and your family (the people who are most important to him), the baby learns the dimensions of the world. He sees it as a safe and kind place, or as unpredictable, hard, and empty. Hopefully, behind the bottles and the wet diapers and the shots are strong, loving, and dependable parents.

YOUR BABY *IS* DIFFERENT

Babies differ enormously in temperament. Each has his own ways. Life around him affects each baby differently, too. One baby may be placid and easygoing. He'll practically sleep through his bath and seem unaware of household noises from the first. Another may be sensitive to the slightest changes around him, waking with a start as you tiptoe out of the room. He wiggles and squirms, and seems to resent being held. Still another baby is most happy when being held, and likes to have people fussing over him.

We know that certain things are good for babies, and we try to provide them. Food and rest, comfort and reassurance, clean and healthful surroundings, and care when sick are all important. From the outset, you experiment with your baby to find how to apply what you know in the way that suits him best.

When you hit on the rhythm and the little techniques that

make the baby most comfortable, you bring him satisfaction and pleasure. And he's sure to bring you satisfaction and pleasure, too. It's a circle.

Sometimes, you may feel that the baby isn't altogether yours. Grandparents brag about "their" new baby. Friends chime in. Along with their pride and excitement, the well-wishers want to tell you how things should be done, and it's easy to become confused by too much free advice.

WHAT TO EXPECT OF THE DOCTOR

Often the suggestion is made that you check with your doctor. Many questions cannot be answered about babies in general; decisions must be made about *your* baby in particular. And there is wisdom in seeing the doctor to keep the baby well instead of seeing him only when the baby is sick. You may consult a pediatrician (a specialist in the care of babies) at his office or at a well-baby clinic conducted by your local health department. Or you may choose a general family doctor. On your regular visits to the doctor during the baby's first year, you can ask questions you've saved between visits. Jot them down so you won't forget them.

The doctor will help you plan the baby's diet. He will check the baby to be sure he's growing properly. He can discover special problems early, such as difficulties with vision, hearing, or feet. In many cases, early treatment can make the problem much less serious or can correct it entirely. The doctor can also help you anticipate changes in the behavior of the baby so you'll know what to expect next. And he'll see that the baby is given protection against diseases that formerly took the lives of many children.

The physician or nurse will keep a record of the height

and weight of your baby at each visit. You'll look forward to hearing how much he has gained, as one indication that things are going well.

Getting him weighed at the regular checkup is often enough. If you happen to have scales at home, you may want to weigh him more frequently. But there are many other signs that he is growing:

His thin arms and legs become more firmly padded. The belly takes on a nice roundness; soon he can scarcely see over it. His cheeks plump out. His color is good. Eyes are bright. His hair—if he has any—is soft and gleaming.

As time goes by, he stays awake more and eats and sleeps in a regular pattern. He is active and energetic, calling to you vigorously, responding to the sights and sounds around him.

2. The newborn baby

Your new baby probably is 18 to 21 inches long. He may weigh anywhere from 2 or 3 pounds to 10 or more. Around 7 pounds is the average in this country. Boys are apt to be a little heavier than girls. If a baby weighs less than 5½ pounds, he may need special care (discussed later).

Everybody inquires about a baby's birth weight as if it were a magic number of some sort. Truth is, a baby probably weighs less than what his father is announcing to his friends, because a few days after birth most babies lose weight for a time. This loss, mostly water, may be up to 10 per cent of the birth weight.

Many babies gain again toward the end of the first week, and will have regained their original weight by the end of the second week. Some other babies, equally healthy, may just begin to regain at the end of the second week.

Whatever his weight or height, though, your new baby is sure not to look like the babies pictured on magazine covers. Those babies are probably 3 to 6 months of age. Yours may seem to have a head too big for his body and not much of a neck. You wonder what color his eyes really are. Once you get him home from the hospital, you settle down to take a good look at what you've got.

It may be helpful to know in some detail how a new baby looks; for many of the initial worries of parents are about perfectly normal things.

One of the first things you notice about your newborn is his mouth. While his eyes are closed much of the time and his nose is so tiny that it's hardly noticeable, his mouth immediately catches your attention, for it's seldom still. It will quiver, then yawn, then maybe emit a full-blown sneeze. Or you may notice brief sucking movements, or pursing, of the lips. Even when the baby lies quietly, wrapped in his light blanket, his mouth is as responsive to inner and outer stimuli as the antennae of a butterfly.

When you remove the blanket and diaper, the baby becomes more active. A simple motion of an arm or a leg, or both legs moving together, will be followed by general twistings of his whole body. For no apparent reason, his body may jerk, or an arm or leg may twitch, or his jaw may quiver. Breathing may slow down and be very quiet, then become quick, strong, and regular again.

HOW THE SKIN SHOULD LOOK

A lively pink underlies the skin color of most babies, even very dark-skinned ones. At birth, the skin is protected by a creamy-looking covering that comes off readily when sponged with water, or soon dries and disappears by itself. The velvety appearance of the skin may be increased by a covering of downy hair, especially on the back. Some babies have dry or scaling skin. That is perfectly normal.

Blotchy patches on the eyelids, forehead, or back of the neck are common. They may stand out more when the baby cries. These mottled areas disappear gradually in most cases.

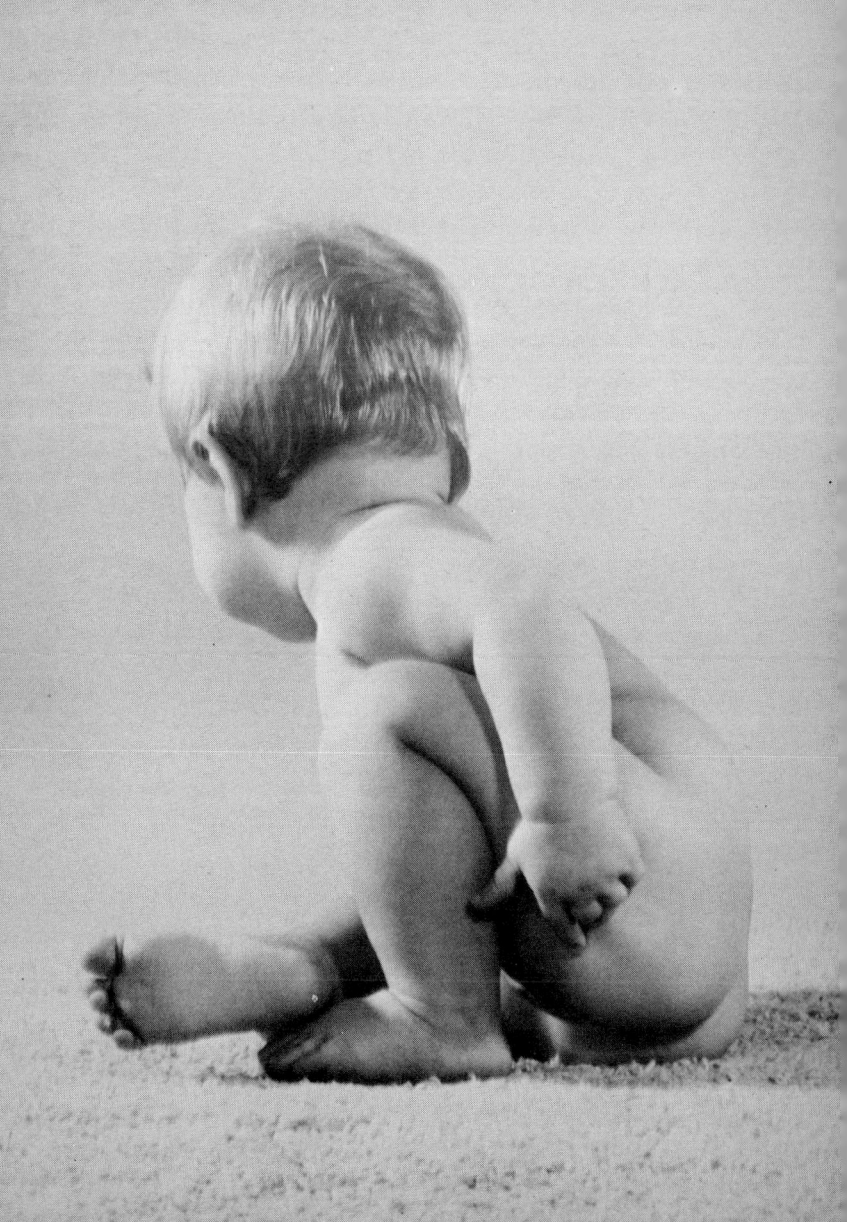

Those on the back of the neck are more apt to remain, but they become hidden by the hair. In folklore, these were called "stork bites."

Other types of birthmarks may be present, too. Your doctor can tell you what—if anything—can be done about them. Birthmarks are *not* caused by anything the mother saw or did while she was pregnant.

There may be a dusting of white spots or blisters across the baby's nose or on his forehead. These are plugged sweat and oil glands which will open naturally in time. A few days after birth, many babies have a light rash covering the body, arms, and legs. The rash will clear and nothing needs to be done about it. Some babies, especially those with dark skins, have deep-bluish areas of color on the back. These are caused by extra pigment in the skin and are not a sign of bruising.

Other babies develop a yellowish tinge to the skin within a few days after birth. This is called jaundice, but is usually not a sign of trouble. The yellow shows that the baby's body is getting rid of the extra supply of red blood corpuscles he needed before he was breathing air. The red blood cells release a yellow pigment when they die off, and this colors the tissues for a time. A few babies may need special treatment if the color gets too intense. Tell your doctor if the yellow appearance deepens, if it does not clear by the end of the week, or if it occurs at any time later in infancy.

THE SHAPE OF THE HEAD

Every parent wants to be sure his baby's head is all right. It may be beautifully oval in shape. But more often, it will resemble—as one father described it—an old, tired softball. If the skull bones have been squeezed during birth, there may be "molding" or uneven lines. Some swelling may remain for a time, but will go away.

Portions of the skull have not hardened into bone. This is fortunate because the incomplete areas allow for some squeezing during birth, and later for growth as the baby's brain becomes larger. A tough elastic membrane covers the soft spots, which are called fontanels. One of these is large enough to be noticeable. It is on top of the head. Occasionally you will notice a pulse moving the membrane up and down.

Mothers are sometimes afraid to wash the soft spot. So the baby collects a little halo of scaly crust ("cradle cap"). But the spot isn't as tender as it appears, and the scalp can—and should—be washed thoroughly without worry.

You may also notice lines or ridges where the bones of the skull join together, somewhat like seams. These smooth out. They are not noticeable if your baby has thick hair, but stand out if he's bald. Don't despair yet if your baby girl doesn't have curly locks. During the first year, some of the first crop of hair will wear off and be replaced.

In the first days of life, many babies can lift their heads up briefly from the mattress as they lie on their stomachs. For some time, though, whenever you're holding the baby, his head will need the support of your hand or arm.

HOW ARE THE EYES?

Your baby may keep his eyes shut most of the time. But if you lift him into a sitting position, his eyes are apt to fly open like a doll's. At birth, light-skinned babies have blue-gray eyes, dark-skinned babies have brown eyes. The blue-gray are subject to change, though; so it may be some months before you're sure what color they will be.

Sometimes the newborn doesn't get his eyes completely open for a day or two. Then, the lids may be puffy. There may be some white or yellow discharge. (Let the doctor know if it does not clear up in a few days.) In addition, there may be a red spot or two in the eye caused by the breaking of a tiny blood vessel during birth. (This will clear up without any trouble.) Although the eyes may water a bit, he may not have true tears until he is 4 to 6 weeks old.

CHEST, NAVEL, AND BREASTS

The baby's chest is about as big around as his head. It is barrel shaped, high, and round. By contrast, the hips and belly seem flat and small, and you wonder what to hang the diaper on.

Next to the soft spot on top of the head, the stump of the umbilical cord usually troubles parents most. It is unfortunate, in a way, that we talk about the navel "healing," for it is not an injury to the baby. The doctor cuts the cord several inches away from the body, and the baby feels nothing. As the stump dries up, it turns black. Then it drops off, sometime between 1 and 3 weeks. For another 2 or 3 days, you may notice that the skin stays moist. Usually, keeping it clean and dry is sufficient. You may sponge the area with alcohol to aid in drying. Occasionally, the doctor will use a medicine to dry it up if it continues to ooze.

The base of the navel appears swollen in many babies. This is a type of hernia, resulting from a small separation of the muscles of the abdomen. Although you may be alarmed if the hernia balloons up when the baby struggles or cries, it will not cause him pain or be harmful to him. Just let him wear the usual baby clothing—diaper and shirt. As a rule, by the age of 3, but sometimes not until 5 or 6, the muscles of the abdomen develop strength and power, and the hernia disappears.

In the first few days after birth, breasts of both boys and girls may be swollen and contain a little liquid. This is perfectly normal and soon goes away. Nothing should be done—no squeezing, massaging, or ointment.

THE GENITALS

At birth, the sex parts of both boys and girls may appear puffy and swollen. It is not uncommon for a little girl to show a white secretion from the vagina for a week or two after birth. It is produced by the presence of the mother's hormones temporarily in the baby's body. You may not even notice it unless there is a bloody tinge; this is also related to hormones and will not continue.

The baby boy's scrotum may not contain the two firm kernels of the testicles. Sometimes your touch or a cold draft will cause the testicles to withdraw from the sac of the scrotum into the boy's body. Whether or not the testicle is in the scrotum ("descended") does not matter at this age.

Occasionally, the scrotum continues to look swollen. Not infrequently a water sac forms, then disappears without treatment. But any swelling that develops in this area should be seen by a doctor, for it may or may not be a hernia. Unlike most hernias in the region of the navel, a hernia in this region usually needs prompt attention.

TO CIRCUMCISE OR NOT?

Before or shortly after the birth of the baby—once you knew he was a boy—you decided about circumcision. To circumcise or not is usually a matter of choice or religious preference. Circumcision is the simple procedure by which the collar of the skin covering the end of the penis is removed. You can talk it over with your doctor.

Circumcision is usually done shortly before the baby leaves the hospital, although sometimes it is performed at the time of delivery. Folded gauze with a bit of petroleum jelly may be kept wrapped around the penis for a time after circumcision. A bit of blood may ooze now and then. Don't be troubled by a pinkish tinge to the diaper; but if real bleeding should start, get your doctor's advice.

ARMS AND LEGS

Hands and feet have a network of lines that make fine prints for identification. These wrinkles are somewhat like those on your hand when kept in water a long time.

Hands and feet may be darker than the rest of the body — crimson to bluish purple. Against a paler leg or arm, they appear as bright flags of color. Toes, too, are deeply colored. They seem like afterthoughts: little beads strung across the foot. Toes that overlap are fairly common. Don't worry if you can't find all the toenails. They may be slow to appear.

The baby's legs show the effect of the position he was curled up in before birth. For some time they bow out. Feet, too, are held in — pigeon-toed. With time and use, they straighten.

WHAT HIS MOTIONS MEAN

The best inventory in the world of how the new baby looks fails to tell you how very well equipped he is to live in his new surroundings. He can do all that's important — and even some extra things, too. What could be more effective than the ability to breathe, to eat, to sleep, and to call you by crying?

At birth, a normal baby usually flinches under a bright light and may try to follow it in an irregular way. But he probably sees little or no detail. When a few weeks old, he will see detail better. By then he can keep his eyes focused for quite a while and will respond to expressions.

He can hear and will respond also to noises. Some babies are startled even by the click of a light switch. He can taste and smell. His tongue automatically pushes foreign matter out of his mouth, as you'll see later when you try to put a spoon in.

Surprisingly, he can hunch about a little; and if placed on his belly he tends to squirm toward the corner of the crib. It worries him greatly if he feels he's lost support. He reacts immediately with a clutching motion that involves his whole body. He likes best to be handled surely and firmly. When he loses this sense of security, he may throw his arms wide, open his hands, spread his fingers, and try to encircle something to hold onto. At the same time, he may draw up his legs and give a sharp cry or look startled. As you learn to move more slowly and smoothly, you won't upset him in this way so often; and, with time, he can take it better, too.

IF YOU FEEL "BLUE"

In the weeks after the baby is born, it is not at all unusual for a new mother to have some days of feeling depressed and weepy. Perhaps these so-called baby blues are noticed more now that mothers leave the hospital so soon after the baby's birth. They're eager to get home, of course, to take charge of things. But all at once they feel quite alone. Formerly, the "blues" hit when mother and baby were safe in the hands of an experienced hospital staff.

There are many reasons why depression may occur. If

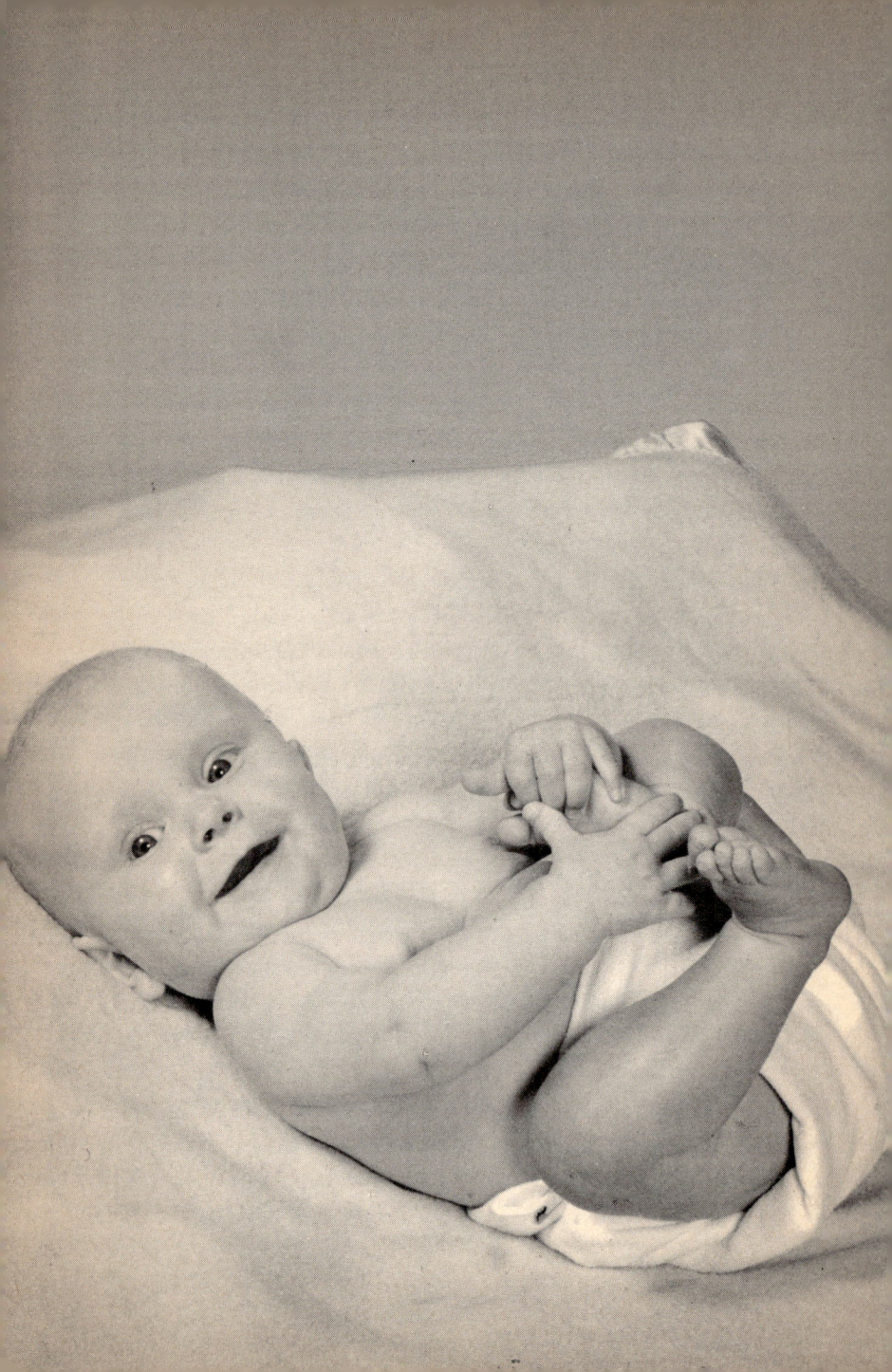

you find yourself on the verge of tears for no apparent reason, you are actually being quite reasonable. The blues may be no more complicated than the letdown most of us feel after any long-awaited moment has come—and gone (e.g., Christmas). Physical changes within the mother's body may also trigger and deepen depression. (Hormones secreted during pregnancy, for one thing, are no longer needed.) Then there's the wornout feeling that follows any sudden change in schedule, when the supply of available energy may not match the increased demands of the day—and night. Sometimes the problem is disappointment in the sex of the newborn. She's just not the blue-eyed, blond boy you mentally pushed in a baby carriage during the months of pregnancy.

Of course, there are sometimes *real* problems to be faced. For instance, the baby may not be off to a good start. He may have a physical defect. This is naturally a source of deep concern until you can take the measure of it and learn just what it will mean to you and the baby.

If it has been necessary to leave your newborn in the hospital for awhile after you have come home, there is the pain of separation, even when you know the baby will be returning home eventually. The empty crib becomes a rebuke that somehow you didn't manage things better; though commonsense tells you that it is not your fault. In such cases, you may find it helpful to talk with your doctor, a visiting nurse, a social worker at the hospital, or a counselor at your family service agency.

Sometimes new parents feel a touch of mourning. It's hard to explain a feeling of loss after you've gained something so real; but it occurs in many a man and woman. It may be loss of the former husband or wife, exchanged for the mother and father you've become. It may be loss of the freedom you felt was yours before.

Probably the best way to deal with ordinary baby blues is to be reassured that many mothers have them and they are temporary. Try to keep your days as simple as possible, and ask nothing of yourself beyond the essentials. Treat yourself to all the extra help you can afford. Let thank-you notes and birth announcements wait until you have strength for them. When you can get out, indulge yourself in a trip to the beauty parlor, or whatever makes you feel fresh.

Be sure to snatch a moment each day for you and your husband together. It may be time out for an extra cup of coffee at breakfast, a shared moment as you fold diapers, a giggle over the silly look on the baby's face as he hiccups. Understand that fathers have moments of depression, too. Often they feel inadequate to the responsibilities of fatherhood. A wise mother will let her husband share in the routines of the baby's care.

Without meaning to, an unthinking mother can get so possessive over her baby that she won't let anyone touch him or share her concern. Then she's dismayed when others lose interest in him.

ARE THE OLDER CHILDREN UPSET?

Are there older children in the family? If so, they may get depressed, too—for some of the same reasons as their parents. It's easy to oversimplify the attitude of the older child and say he's just jealous. But his feelings are more complicated than that.

He may have experienced a letdown also. He waited so long for a baby brother to play with. And now, instead of a playmate, this wrinkled, crying thing has appeared. He can't even get close to it without someone exclaiming, "Don't hurt the baby!" or "Don't touch!"

He may also be disappointed in the sex of the baby. "Guess what? We got a girl at our house," complains Junior, aged 4, disgustedly.

The older child suffers a feeling of loss as well. Even though he has been told about his mother's trip to the hospital and about the new baby she's had, he can't really be prepared for the deepness of his hurt. He feels he's exchanged the mother he once had for one who's now absorbed in the care and progress of another. He can't be sure there's love enough to go around, and he doesn't want to share it anyhow. Actually, he's angry at his parents for getting somebody to take his place; yet he's afraid to show his anger toward them, lest he lose them altogether.

Such strong feelings usually burst forth somehow. The older child may express his resentment toward his parents by taking it out on the baby. He may start to pat his little sister or brother and somehow wind up hitting or pinching instead. He may become dawdling and helpless, whining or tearful.

If his parents want a baby so badly, he may try to be one himself, and revert to crawling, asking for a bottle, wetting his pants. Or he may become noisy and aggressive, showing off to get the attention he feels should be his. Or he may attempt to hide his anger and withdraw into stiff silence.

Such behavior from the firstborn can be pretty frustrating to his parents. Having forgotten how much time a new baby requires, they despair of having enough energy to meet the demands of both babies. Without thinking, they may be tempted to punish the older child for his noisy or selfish ways, not realizing this only convinces him he has lost their understanding and love.

There are many ways to help the other child who feels so deserted. If you try to see things through his eyes, you will find the way to help him best. A 2- or 3-year-old may *need* a chance to be a baby again. He'll soon return to more grownup ways when he is reassured that you care about him, too. Let him be the star whenever you can. Praise him for his helpfulness. Let him do things for you and the baby (but don't make him feel like an errand boy). Now, by the way, is the time for his father to step in as the more available companion and friend.

A somewhat older child may have outside interests and companions. See that he has a chance to keep up with them. Be sure that everything he asks for is not met with "In just a minute" or "Not now."

After the first few weeks you and the baby will be on a more predictable schedule. Then you can give the older child his due and arrange some time for him when the baby is left out. He gets an ice cream cone, but the baby does not. He goes to the zoo, but the baby is too little.

The older child will have to make his own way with the baby, though. The two of them must work out their own relationship. So let them get to know each other without your hovering interference, except where safety is a factor. If you've been able to accept the older child's distress calmly, he'll be able to move beyond the grip of hurt and anger and toward a lasting bond with the small intruder. As time goes by, he'll take heart in having a partner in mischief — now two of them to keep you on your toes.

GET A BIRTH CERTIFICATE!

The certificate of birth is legal proof of the date of your child's birth and citizenship. Throughout life, he will need this proof of identity. It is required when a child enters school, requests a driver's license, goes to work. It may be needed to

prove his right to vote, to marry, to draw social security benefits, to hold office, inherit property, or obtain a passport to travel in foreign countries.

If the baby is born in a hospital, the staff will see that necessary information is sent to the local health department or registrar of births. In the event that you have not selected a name for the baby before you leave the hospital, be sure to add it to the official record later. If the baby is born at home, the midwife or doctor (or the parent if no one assists at the birth) is required by law to report the birth to the local authorities.

You will be officially notified when the record of your baby's birth is on file. Some states send a copy of the registration. If any of the information is wrong, be sure to get it corrected immediately. In some states, the birth certificate is sent only on request and for a fee. There is practically always a charge for a second copy, so keep your baby's certificate in a safe place.

If you do not receive notice of the proper registration in a few weeks, check on it. Call the hospital or local health department. Or write to your state health department, which is usually located in the capital city.

3. Feeding the baby

Getting enough to eat and feeling safe and warm are what a new baby needs. When food and love are equally available, he tends to thrive. It's fortunate that both can be given at the same time.

When he's hungry, the baby yowls. Not just his stomach but his whole world is empty. Then you come along with the complete answer: food. Be it breast or bottle, the nipple is the source of most of his happiness. He plunges into sucking. His rigid body relaxes. The room, so recently filled with his crying, is still . . .

For both you and the baby, milk is more than nourishment. Feeding becomes a language between you. You tell the baby that when he is so desperately hungry, you will bring him food. He begins to learn that whatever he needs, you will be there to try to supply it. These are his first lessons: that you are a trustworthy person; that the world is a safe and dependable place.

At first, he simply cannot wait. But as the days go by, he finds the promise of food and comfort in your footstep in the hall, in the click of the icebox door. He can now wait a minute. From your patient giving to him, he learns a bit of patience himself. And in the moments of contented fullness after his feeding, he begins to study your face, to pat the bottle or fondle the breast, to look about. From this safety and peace he dares to reach out.

Your baby talks to you, too, through his behavior with the food you give him. As he begins to respond to you, you grow in regard for him. He takes the food and gives back his trust and love. Through this giving and receiving, the feeling of belonging to each other develops.

FIRST FEEDINGS

Usually a baby is allowed to rest for the first 12 hours after birth. Then he is offered a drink of sweetened water. If he is born at home, you can fix his first drink by measuring 3 ounces of boiled water (6 tablespoons) into a bottle that has been boiled. Add one teaspoon of sugar and shake gently to dissolve.

Use a nipple that has been boiled. Cool the water to a comfortable temperature. The water is given more as a trial run than because the baby will be especially thirsty. He may enjoy it, and he may not. Don't force him to take it. In fact, never force a baby to take anything.

When he's about 24 hours old, the baby is given his first milk feeding. Thereafter, he's fed every 3 or 4 hours for the first weeks. He may be hungry at some feedings and not so eager at others. The actual amount of milk taken at the first few feedings isn't important. These are practice sessions for you both.

You'll probably find it convenient to feed the baby each time in the same place, for you can then have handy all the little things you need. Whether you are breast or bottle feeding, get yourself comfortable. Arrange pillows to support your back, and try to make the feeding a refreshing time for you as well as the baby. If you sit, select a comfortable chair that will let you hold the baby with some support for your arm. Rocking chairs must have been invented for these sweet moments. Find a way to support your feet, too, with a hassock or footstool.

To get the baby started, press a little milk onto his lips. If he's frantically nuzzling about, stroke the cheek nearest the nipple and he will turn toward it. If you touch the opposite cheek, he'll turn away.

When the baby stops sucking, it's time to give him a chance to release any air he has swallowed along with the milk. You can "bubble" or "burp" him in any number of ways. Some bubble easily when lifted to the shoulder and patted on the back. It doesn't take a whack. Others burp best when laid across the knee, stomach-side down, and patted or rubbed. You may like to hold the baby on your lap, in a sitting position, his back against your chest. Some milk may come up along with the swallowed air, so have a clean diaper or cloth ready. These bubbling moments are good times just to enjoy the feel of the baby. They're an excuse to cuddle.

After the swallowed air is released, and he's had a rest, the baby may feel hungry again and continue to nurse for a time. Then he may turn away from the nipple, fall asleep, or let the milk run out of his mouth. It's tempting to try to rouse him to get in just a bit more, but he knows better than you how much he can hold at any one feeding; so don't urge him. He'll let you know when he's hungry again.

Occasionally, a baby does not burp, no matter how you hold him. If so, put the reluctant bubbler back to bed on his right side. This permits the stomach to hang loose, and soon allows the release of any trapped air.

In the first few weeks, it's hard to predict just when the baby will want to be fed. Usually, it will be anywhere from 2½ to 4 hours after the beginning of the last feeding—around the clock. Restlessness or crying sooner than 2 hours after a feeding probably does not indicate hunger, although this is not a hard-and-fast rule. Toward the end of the first 2 weeks, most infants begin to settle down to feedings from 3 to 4 hours apart.

You may find yourself worn out after the first feedings. Chances are, you try so hard to get the milk into the baby that you make sucking movements with your own mouth, you push or wiggle the bottle, or you jiggle the baby to keep him awake as he drifts off to sleep. You discover, after you lay the baby down, that you've been working with every muscle in your body. You can't help it at first, but at least you can be aware that every other mother does the same thing.

The trick is to get enough sleep between times yourself. Be assured that the uncertain feeding hours will become more fixed and regular soon. Let everything go at first except the baby and the necessary laundry. It's even better if you can have someone help out with the other duties so you can conserve your energy for the baby. Have regular visiting hours and keep company away at other times. Banish callers who tire you out. Try to nap when the baby is sleeping. He won't remain such a tyrant for long.

Indulge yourself in all the tricks you know to make sleep come at odd hours—a warm bath or a cold one; something to eat or drink; darken the room; ask the neighbors to be quiet—whatever works for you.

BREAST OR BOTTLE?

Before the baby's birth, you probably decided whether you would feed him by breast or bottle. This is the kind of decision you have to make on the basis of your inner wishes, not on what

A mother who wants to breast-feed her baby and who feels she may need help can get it from La Leche League. The League offers information and encouragement at meetings of its local groups. It also publishes a bimonthly newsletter and a manual entitled, "The Womanly Art of Breastfeeding." To find the nearest La Leche League group, write headquarters at 9616 Minneapolis Ave., Franklin Park, Ill. 60131.

other people say. Either method is all right as long as you feel right about it. The feelings seem to be more important than the kind of milk. Almost every mother will have enough milk for her baby; almost every baby will thrive on a formula.

Nobody has ever improved on the formula that the breast secretes to nourish the baby. But lots of women have doubts about trying to breast-feed anyhow. This is understandable, for practically nothing in our lives today prepares a woman to feel natural about this task. Some of the doubts concern the baby, some concern the mother. All are perfectly normal.

As to the breast-fed baby, you wonder how you'll know if he's getting enough to eat, since you don't have the reassurance of watching the milk line go down in a bottle. What's more, it takes faith to believe that as the baby eagerly nurses, your milk supply will increase to meet the demand. At least you are free from worries about the quality and suitability of the breast milk supply—for breast milk almost always agrees with the baby, and it is always clean and ready.

Many of the reasons mothers give for not wishing to breast-feed the baby may be related to their wish to be less tied to him all the time. In a way, it is similar to the reaction of most women when they realize they are pregnant. Along with elation and delight, they usually feel some misgivings and regrets.

Losing your figure should not be one of your worries, though. Many people blame breast-feeding for body changes that are, in fact, the result of overeating, inactivity, increasing age, or pregnancy itself.

Changes in the breast occur because of pregnancy. The woman who nurses and the one who doesn't end up with the same kind of breast tissue. And as far as breast size is concerned, the full contour is one that many women prize.

A good supporting brassiere is as important during breast-feeding as it was during pregnancy. If you can afford to buy two or three, do. Many types on the market today snap in front, permitting you to expose one breast or the other without removing your clothing. Here, a style of dress that buttons down the front is most convenient.

Nursing, in itself, does not prevent the return of the regular menstrual cycle, although it may delay it a bit in some women. Nor will it prevent another pregnancy.

If you decide to breast-feed, you will want to have privacy at your first trials. You have a right to experiment with the technique alone. At some point, though, you may want to ask for some helpful guidance from a nurse. Because of her training and experience she can give you expert suggestions.

WORK OUT A SYSTEM

First, wash your hands and breasts carefully with soap and water. Then wipe off the nipples with cooled boiled water. Lift the breast in such a way that the baby can get the nipple, touching his cheek to get him to turn toward you. Help him to get his lips well over the tip of the nipple and onto the surrounding darkened area, which is called the areola. Here are placed the little reservoirs which, when pressed, eject a spray of milk through the nipple so the baby gets a rewarding return for his effort. If the baby sucks only on the tip of the nipple, he is not apt to get much milk. Besides, he will bruise the tender tissue and cause it to become sore.

For a few days, the breasts secrete a yellowish liquid called colostrum. Gradually this is replaced by the more typical whitish milk. Mother's milk does not look like cow's milk. It is more watery-looking and bluish. But this does not mean it is not "rich" enough.

Usually, it works well to alternate the breast you offer first at each feeding; that is, start out with the right breast one time, the left the next. At first, let him suck for 5 to 10 minutes. Later, the baby will get much of the milk out of the breast in 10 to 15 minutes, but he may spend somewhat longer sucking.

In the additional sucking period, milk will no longer flow freely, but may be coming a few drops at a time. Don't let the baby idly suck so long that your nipples become sore. But he should be allowed to nurse for a time after the first easy gush of milk. Additional sucking will empty the breast completely, which will stimulate it to produce more milk. This delicate signaling between the demand and supply causes the mother to manufacture milk in increasing amounts as the baby's appetite increases.

The baby enjoys this additional sucking, too, after his first hunger spasms are quieted. He may drowse, then wake and suck, sighing and perhaps yawning. This is a good time to "burp" the baby, patting him to release any swallowed air. If he's still hungry, offer him the second breast. However, at the next nursing time, the one offered last should be the first, so that it, too, will be completely emptied. To help you keep track, you can place a safety pin on your brassiere to mark the side to use first.

Take care of the nipples by drying them carefully after nursing, and keep them dry by placing a clean cloth or pad in the brassiere. Half a sanitary napkin makes a good pad. Replace the cloth as it becomes damp from leaking milk.

Some mothers find it helpful to let the nipples become thoroughly dry after nursing the baby by leaving them exposed to the air for 5 minutes or so, several times a day. The warmth of an ordinary light bulb held 6 inches or so from the breast may feel soothing.

A little soreness of the nipples at first is to be expected, but if the soreness persists or the nipples become cracked, you'll want to take prompt action. Feeding times come swiftly around, and there is little chance for the soreness to heal between times. Get help from your doctor.

He may prescribe medicine to use or suggest that you use a nipple shield to protect the nipple. In such cases, the baby is actually nursing from a rubber nipple placed in a plastic or rubber funnel which is held against the breast. A nipple shield should be carefully washed and then boiled between usings, just as any other artificial nipple needs to be cared for.

REMOVING MILK BY HAND

Occasionally you may need to remove milk from your breasts by hand. Hand removal is helpful if the nipples become sore or cracked. If the breast becomes so firm the baby has difficulty in getting hold of the nipple, you can remove some milk from the engorged breast by hand. If you have more milk than the baby can use in the first weeks of life, hand removal relieves the tightness of the breast and keeps the milk coming.

Later on, you may want to take milk to keep for the baby if you will be away at feeding time. If you plan to use the milk you remove, it should be caught and stored in containers which have been boiled. Your doctor may want you to boil this milk before giving it to the baby, unless you are going to use it immediately.

Hand removal, or "expressing" milk, is easy to do, but it is somewhat hard to describe. It is best if you can get someone to show you how to do it. Ask at the hospital, before you leave, or ask a visiting nurse who will come to your home. In brief, the method is as follows:

Wash your hands thoroughly with soap and water. Place

thumb and forefinger on the edges of the darkened area near the nipple. Press your fingers in toward the ribs, then raise the breast with your whole hand. Open and close the fingers and thumb in a scissors motion, rapidly (60 to 100 times per minute). At first the milk will come out in a fine spray; then in drops. Continue until no more drops come out, probably from 5 to 20 minutes. Your fingers should not slip forward on the breast or the skin may become irritated. It is not necessary to touch the nipple.

FOOD FOR THE NURSING MOTHER

In general you will be well nourished if you continue the well-balanced diet you followed in pregnancy, with some increase in the amount of the protective foods as the baby takes more milk. This means additional milk; lean meats; green, leafy vegetables; and citrus fruits. Add more liquids to your diet, too. Nursing mothers should not be fearful of gaining an excessive amount of weight if they follow this routine.

If your diet calls for a quart of milk a day, it is easiest to get the equivalent of a quart when you drink part of it. With some care in planning, you can use a good part of the daily ration in dishes such as cream soup, creamed vegetables, cereal with milk, puddings, and other desserts such as ice cream and milk sherbet. The amount of milk in these dishes ranges from a quarter to a half cup per serving.

Those who object to the creamy taste of whole milk, or who have a tendency to gain weight, can use skim milk. It has fewer calories, but furnishes less vitamin A than whole milk. Dry skim milk (nonfat dry milk) is an economical form of milk for both drinking and cooking. Some mothers like to add it to the milk they drink. One cup of fluid milk plus about ¼ cup of dry skim milk powder gives as much protein and calcium as 2 cups of fluid milk.

Cheese in its many forms can be used in place of part of the milk. However, some kinds of cheese such as cream cheese and cheese spreads do not have as much calcium as whole milk. One of the reasons why milk is so strongly recommended for the nursing mother is that it is a rich source of readily absorbed calcium. It is an important source of protein and vitamins also. Some milks have vitamin D added. This vitamin helps to make the best use of the calcium.

Before the baby was born, you were cautious about taking certain drugs or medicines because they would be carried to the baby. The nursing mother needs to continue to be careful about taking certain medicines which would reach the baby through her milk. Sleeping medicine, aspirin, laxatives, and others aren't really good for your baby. Check with your doctor before taking any medicine. If you find that certain foods you eat don't agree with the baby, omit these for the time being. Doctors differ in their opinions about a woman's smoking and drinking alcoholic beverages during the time she is nursing her baby.

In the first week or so, trying to get the baby started on the breast may be discouraging. Be assured that most mothers who decided to bottle-feed are discouraged at times, too. The main difference is that they are more apt to blame the baby or the formula; those who breast-feed are more apt to blame themselves. It may take several weeks to get nursing well established. Keep offering the breast first even if you supplement it with a formula. In time you and the baby will develop a routine which is comfortable and satisfying to you both.

The best aids to a continued, full supply of milk are probably plenty of rest, a good strong baby who sucks eagerly, and plenty of confidence that you will work it out. Of course it isn't always possible to get plenty of rest or be free from worry, but as you move from day to day with the baby, everything is likely to become easier.

Buy a few bottles and nipples even if you are breast-feeding. Have two or three of the 4-ounce bottles for water and for orange juice later, and one or two of the 8-ounce bottles for an occasional or regular bottle of formula.

You may wish to shift to bottle-feeding after a few weeks or months. Many mothers do. Others continue to breast-feed until the baby is ready to drink all of his milk from a cup, often at 8 or 9 months. Whenever you make a change in your method of feeding or in the food itself, do it gradually. The baby has learned to depend on the old, familiar way of getting milk, and may resent your efforts to change him suddenly. If you become ill, or there is some reason why it would be injurious to you or to the baby to continue breast-feeding, check with the doctor.

FOODS OTHER THAN MILK

Water: Babies need a lot of liquid for their size, but they get most of what they need from the milk they drink. However, occasionally offer your baby a drink of water which has been boiled and cooled, especially in hot weather. He may not take much, or he may drink an ounce or two. If he is fussy between feedings, a sip of water may help to quiet him. The easiest thing to do is to fix one 8-ounce bottle of boiled water each day. Put a clean nipple on it each time you give it to the baby. Keep water you have boiled in a special place and never offer a clear solution to a baby without being sure it is his water. Poisonous liquids, left in jars about the kitchen, have been mistakenly

DAILY FOOD PATTERN FOR THE NURSING MOTHER

	Type of food	Each day
Milk group	Milk	4–6 cups
	Dairy products such as cheddar cheese, cottage cheese, and ice cream	May sometimes be used in place of milk
Vegetable-fruit group	Select from those rich in vitamin C, such as grapefruit, orange, tomato (whole or as juice, canned or fresh), raw cabbage, green or sweet red pepper, broccoli, fresh strawberries, guava, mango, papaya, cantaloupe	2 servings
	Select from those rich in vitamin A. (You can pick them out by their dark green or deep yellow color.) They include apricots, broccoli, cantaloupe, carrots, greens, pumpkin, sweet potatoes, winter squash	1 or more servings
	Others, including potatoes	2 or more servings
Meat group	Meat, poultry, or fish	1–2 servings
	Dry beans, peas, peanut butter	Occasionally in place of meat
	Eggs	1
Bread and cereal group	Whole grain or enriched bread; restored breakfast cereals; and other grain products, such as cornmeal, grits, macaroni, spaghetti and rice	3–4 servings
Other foods	Foods such as sugars, oils, margarine, butter, and other fats which may be used in cooking, to complete meals and to provide additional food energy and other food values	
	Vitamin D in some form, if your food does not provide an adequate amount	According to your doctor's instructions

offered to babies. Mark the water bottle in some distinctive way so that there can be no doubt.

Vitamins: Babies need enough vitamins C and D in their diet for growth of bones, teeth, and healthy tissues. Milk does not naturally contain sufficient amounts of either, although today you can buy fluid whole milk and evaporated milk to which vitamin D has been added. The label will tell you how much; 400 International Units is the usual amount in a quart of whole milk or a tall can of evaporated milk. Unless your baby can be counted on to take a full quart of milk a day, the doctor may wish you to supplement the vitamin D added to his milk to be sure he is getting enough. Ask him which type of vitamin D preparation to use, how much to give, and how long to continue giving it.

Continued overdose of vitamin D can be harmful, so follow your doctor's instructions or check the dosage on your bottle carefully. If you wish, you may simply squirt the measured amount of vitamin preparation into the baby's mouth, using the dropper attached to the cap of the bottle. He'll be less apt to choke if you aim at cheek or tongue, rather than the back of the throat.

As the baby grows older, and tends to clamp down on anything put into his mouth, don't use a dropper made of glass. By then, you may wish to pour the required amount into a teaspoon. You can give such concentrates when the baby is undressed for his bath, since spilled oil then won't stain the clothing.

Vitamin C, also known as ascorbic acid, occurs naturally in oranges and other citrus fruits, and to a lesser extent in tomatoes and some other fresh vegetables and fruits. Breast milk contains vitamin C in small amounts, if the mother's diet includes foods

Neo-Synephrine goes to work to bring breathing comfort faster than any tablet or capsule possibly can. Used soon enough, it can help prevent those 3 A.M. earaches and troublesome sinus infections children may get with a cold. Because Neo-Synephrine begins to shrink swollen nasal passages almost on contact, breathing space increases, mucus can drain, and children start to eat and sleep better. So effective—yet gentle enough even for infants. That's why doctors have been recommending Neo-Synephrine for over 30 years. **Available as spray or drops in strengths for every member of the family: 1/8% for infants; 1/4% for children; 1/2% and 1% for adults.**

Neo-Synephrine® HCl
Brand of phenylephrine HCl

the nasal decongestant brand most recommended by doctors...for noses of all ages

makes breathing room

in stuffy places

rich in the vitamin. But to be on the safe side, and to teach babies early to like foods that have vitamin C in them, even breast-fed babies are given citrus fruit while they are very young.

The baby should receive 30 milligrams of the vitamin, daily, from some source. Frozen and canned orange juice compare favorably with the fresh-squeezed fruit juice, but some bottled or canned "orange drinks" are not an adequate substitute. Unless vitamin C has been added, canned pineapple, apple, and prune juice have too little of the vitamin to be depended upon as a good source. Vitamin C can be bought in the form of ascorbic acid drops.

Orange juice is probably the most common source given to babies. At first, the baby can take but a small amount of orange juice, but it is a good idea to start giving it early so he can become accustomed to the taste. Begin by giving one teaspoon of strained juice mixed with an equal amount of boiled water. Cool the water before adding the juice, because heat may destroy the vitamin C. If this mixture agrees with the baby, you can increase the amount. Add a teaspoon of diluted juice every week or so, until you are giving 4 tablespoons of diluted juice every day. Then you can begin to leave out some of the water, replacing it with juice, until he is taking 4 tablespoons of undiluted orange juice. By 8 to 10 months of age, you can increase to 6 tablespoons (3 ounces). From the early weeks, you can give orange juice by spoon or cup. Juice tends to clog the nipple, even if strained, and both mother and baby get upset if the nipple holes are clogged.

Many doctors suggest that the baby be given vitamin C drops until he is old enough to take at least 2 ounces (4 tablespoons) of undiluted orange juice each day. If the baby appears to be allergic to orange juice or other citrus fruit juices, you can keep on giving the drops.

Orange juice can cause spitting up and other disturbances if infants are allergic to it. In such cases, use vitamin C drops.

Vitamins A and B are usually present in sufficient quantity in the baby's normal diet of milk and cereal.

SPITTING UP AND VOMITING

A good many babies spit up some of their milk after eating, especially at first. Some do it rarely, others frequently. The channel between the stomach and mouth of the young baby is very loosely closed so that movement or normal churning of the stomach is sufficient to throw back some of the stomach contents.

There's a difference between vomiting and spitting up. Spitting up is more like spilling over. It is a nuisance, but nothing to worry about. Babies usually outgrow this tendency as they spend more time upright in sitting or standing.

Vomiting is another matter. If the baby's milk is returned forcibly and in large amounts, with spasms of his body, check with the doctor. Vomiting in newborn babies might indicate that there is something wrong with the digestive tract. Vomiting in a baby of any age may be an early sign of illness.

The one who spits up may need more careful bubbling to remove excess air in the stomach, which, as it rolls up, carries milk with it. If the baby does not burp, place him on his right side when you put him down. Air is expelled more readily in this position. Spitting up may follow overfeeding. Some babies need to be handled very gently after feeding. If the baby seems happy and healthy, you need not worry about the tendency to spit up. Just be sure to have a diaper or clean cloth over your shoulder when you handle him to protect your own clothing from the sour smell which partially digested milk always has.

Occasionally, for no apparent reason, an entire feeding may come rolling back out. The baby appears unconcerned and is otherwise healthy. Do not pick up a baby while he is vomiting. Leave him lying down, face toward the mattress, and hold his feet higher than his head in order to permit the vomit to roll out completely. Afterwards you may wish to give him another bottle. If it is forcible vomiting or accompanied by signs of illness such as fretful crying, fever, or rash, withhold further milk. Call your doctor and inform him of the symptoms.

Hiccups often follow a feeding, with or without spitting up. If they persist, give an ounce or two of water, plain or slightly sweetened.

4. Facts about formulas

Milk, other than breast milk, has to be specially prepared to make it suitable for feeding babies. Water and sugar, or another carbohydrate, are added. It is heated to make it more digestible and to free it from disease germs. This mixture is called a formula.

As a rule today, cow's milk is used in making the formula, although if it does not agree with your baby, the doctor may suggest another kind.

TYPES OF MILK AND SUGAR USED

At first, milk seems to be a familiar item you know all about, but there are many different ways to treat milk, and you will want to know what different processes actually mean. Some of the common terms you hear are:

Pasteurized: By this process, fresh milk is heated to kill harmful organisms.

Homogenized: Under pressure, milk is forced through tiny jets in such a way that the cream is broken into small particles and will no longer separate. Homogenized milk is always pasteurized.

Raw milk is not considered safe for drinking until it has been heated, as in pasteurization. The simplest way to heat raw milk is in an open saucepan, stirring constantly. Heat it to 165°, measured by a dependable cooking thermometer, or until it comes to a gentle boil. Remove from the heat, place the saucepan in cold water, and stir until cool. Fast cooling is important.

Vitamin D milk is whole or skim milk which has vitamin D added — 400 International Units per quart.

Evaporated milk is whole milk from which slightly more than half of the water has been removed. It is homogenized, fortified with vitamin D, and sterilized during the canning process. Evaporated milk forms fine curds in the stomach and is, therefore, easily digested.

Evaporated milk will keep for months before the can is opened, and is cheaper than fresh milk. It is available in cans of two sizes: a tall can containing 13 fluid ounces and a small one with $5^{1}/_{3}$ ounces. An equal amount of water will bring the canned milk to about the same proportions as fresh milk: 26 ounces for the tall (a quart is 32 ounces) and about a cup and a third for the small. Once you open the can, treat it as you would fresh milk, by using it within 2 days and keeping it cold. Always wash the top of the can with soap or detergent and water before punching a hole in the lid. Use a thoroughly clean can opener. The triangular punch-type opener, designed for beverage cans, is readily washed. Make two small holes on opposite sides of the lid.

Condensed milk is not used for babies because it has too much added sugar.

Dry milk comes in two types. Dry whole milk is made by removing water from whole milk. In unopened tin cans it will keep many months. Once opened, the powder absorbs moisture quickly. Because it does not keep well and is hard to mix, it is not readily available in stores today. Dry skim milk (nonfat dry milk) is made by removing the fat as well as water from fresh milk. When the fat is removed, the fat-soluble vitamin A is also removed. Skim milk is not recommended for feeding babies as a rule, but it may be prescribed by a doctor under certain circumstances.

Prepare dry milk according to the directions on the label. Use a clean, dry spoon to remove milk from the tin or box. To get lumps out of the powder and water mixture, use an egg beater or mixer.

Special milks, modified for infant feeding, are sold under many different trade names. Fresh milk is altered in some way—by adding sugar, vitamins, and sometimes minerals; by making the fat or protein higher or lower; by substituting other fats for milk fat. Then the milk is evaporated or dried. Modified milk can be mixed into a formula rather easily. It may cost more than evaporated milk. Modified milk may be useful if you are traveling or have no place to keep prepared formula.

Goat's milk is sometimes used if a baby is sensitive to cow's milk. It has a fine curd, and the fat particles are so small that the cream will not separate—it is naturally homogenized. Goat's milk is available in fluid, evaporated, and powdered form. This milk should be handled like cow's milk—kept cold and used promptly. Raw goat's milk should be pasteurized or boiled.

Substitutes for milk are sometimes prescribed by the doctor if the baby cannot take milk. It may be soybean, meat, or an artificial product. If it is necessary to use a milk substitute for feeding your baby, you will want to follow the doctor's instructions carefully. Vitamins and minerals may be required to make the formula contain all the food value the baby needs.

Sugars for infant feeding: Plain white sugar, brown sugar, or corn sirup may be used to make the baby's formula. Corn sirup comes in the dark or light type. The light type is usually used. Once the bottle of corn sirup is opened, it should be kept covered and cool. A harmless mold may form on the top of the bottle if it is kept on the shelf. Either light brown or dark brown sugar can be used in the formula. Measure it by packing the sugar on the spoon with a table knife.

Sugars which differ, chemically, from common table sugar are often used in infant feeding. They are more expensive but sometimes a doctor will prescribe them for a special reason. They are not as sweet, nor do they contain as many calories. One tablespoon of table sugar is equal to 2 tablespoons of dextrin or maltose preparations.

PLANNING THE FORMULA

At about 24 hours of age, a baby is given his first feeding. Thereafter, he is fed every 3 or 4 hours. For the first feedings, you can divide the "first" formula into 8 bottles of 2 ounces each or 6 bottles of about 2½ ounces each. As soon as he takes all the milk at most of his feedings, increase the amount you put in the bottle by about half an ounce to an ounce. If he seems ready to sleep through a nighttime feeding, you can prepare one less bottle and divide the extra formula among the other bottles. Soon, however, he will probably show that he is ready for an increase in the total amount of his feeding, and you can change the formula so as to offer him more. The increase you offer may be more than he actually needs, so do not urge him to empty the bottle if he seems not to want it. By the fifth or sixth day he should be offered 3 ounces or so at a feeding.

As time goes by, you will want to give a somewhat more

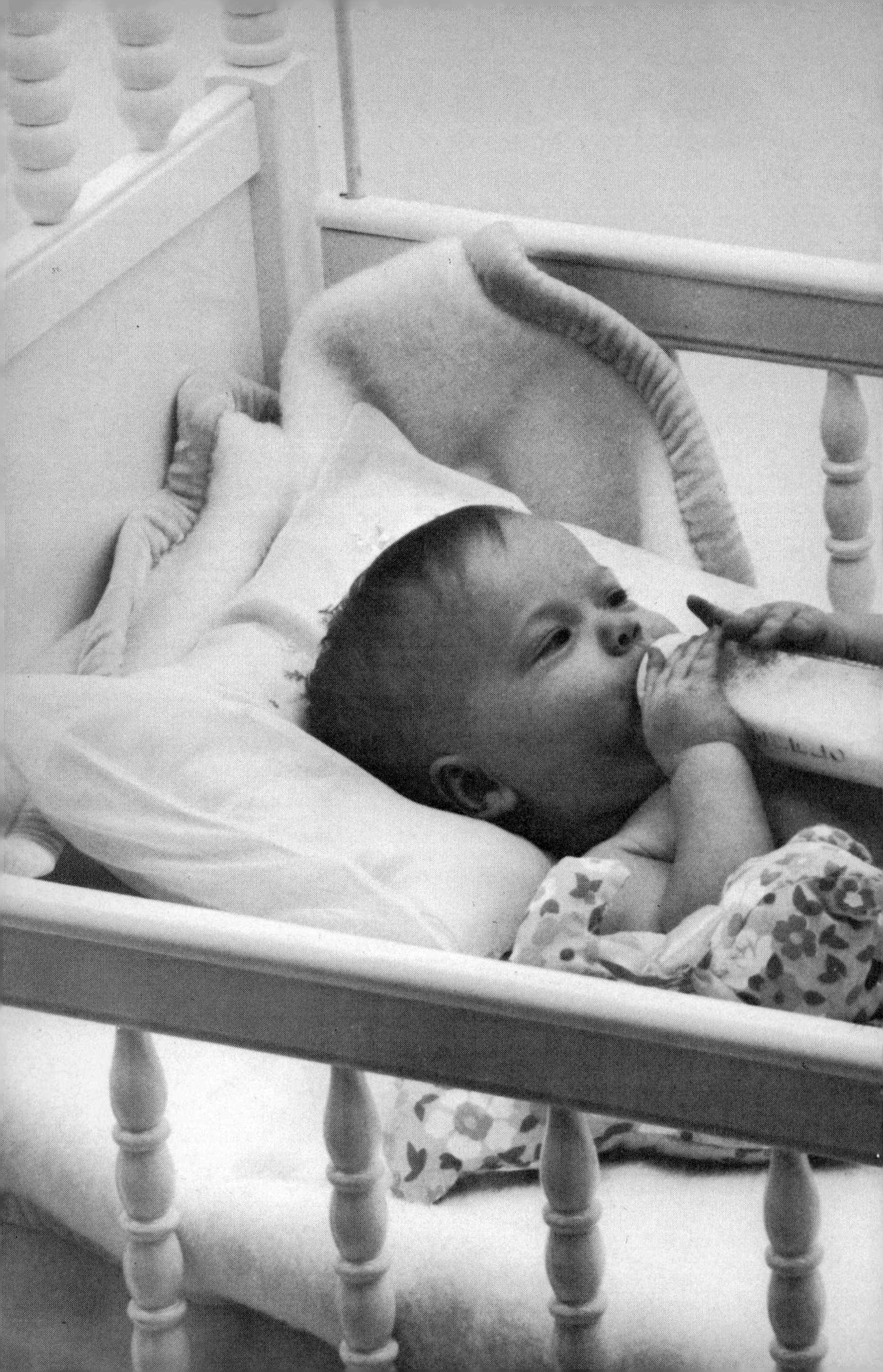

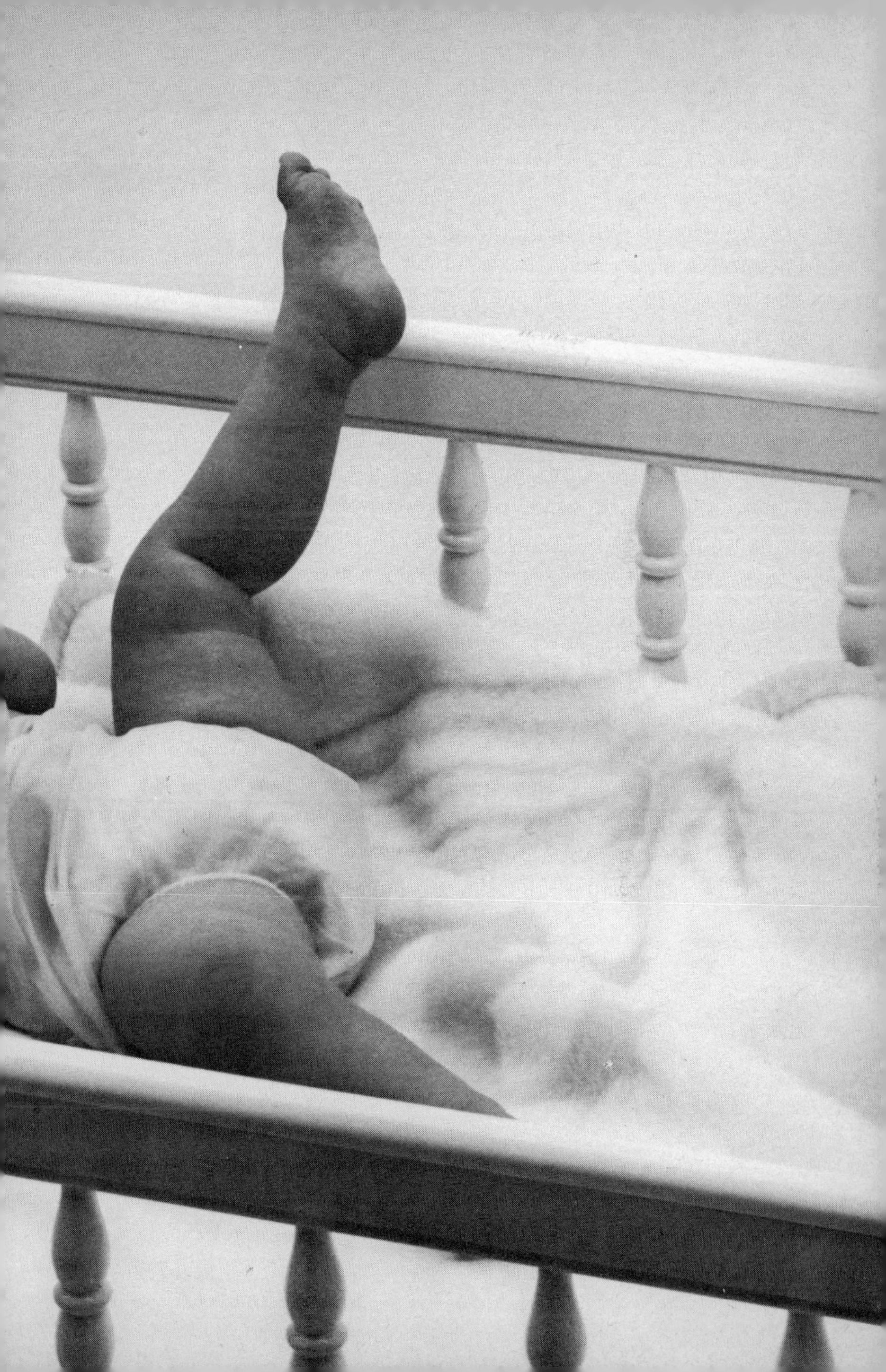

concentrated formula as well as a larger amount per feeding. But do try to have the advice of a doctor on formula changes instead of trying to plan the baby's feeding yourself.

If you use evaporated milk in the formula, there is a shortcut for measuring that may be helpful. A large can contains 13 ounces, the amount suggested for one of the later formulas. One and a half large cans is approximately 19 ounces, the amount of water suggested for this formula.

After the first week or two of life, your baby will probably take about 1 ounce of evaporated milk or 1½ to 2 ounces of fresh milk (properly diluted with water) per pound of weight. That is, a 10-pound baby will probably take about 10 ounces of evaporated milk or 20 ounces of whole milk daily. Tell your doctor if he usually takes less than this. When he gets to where a quart of formula a day doesn't keep him happy, increase the amounts of cereal and other foods.

After the baby begins to take solid food you can gradually cut down on the water and sugar in his formula until he is getting equal parts of evaporated milk and water with no sugar, or undiluted fresh whole milk.

MAKING THE FORMULA

The following items are what you will need:

Bottles: start with a dozen 8-ounce bottles because you'll have some breakage. Heat-resistant bottles cost more, but will last longer. Wide-mouth bottles are easiest to clean. It is convenient to have two or three small bottles (4 ounce) to use for water, orange juice, and first feedings.

Nipples: to fit the kind of bottles you have, either small or wide-mouth. It is convenient to have enough nipples so that

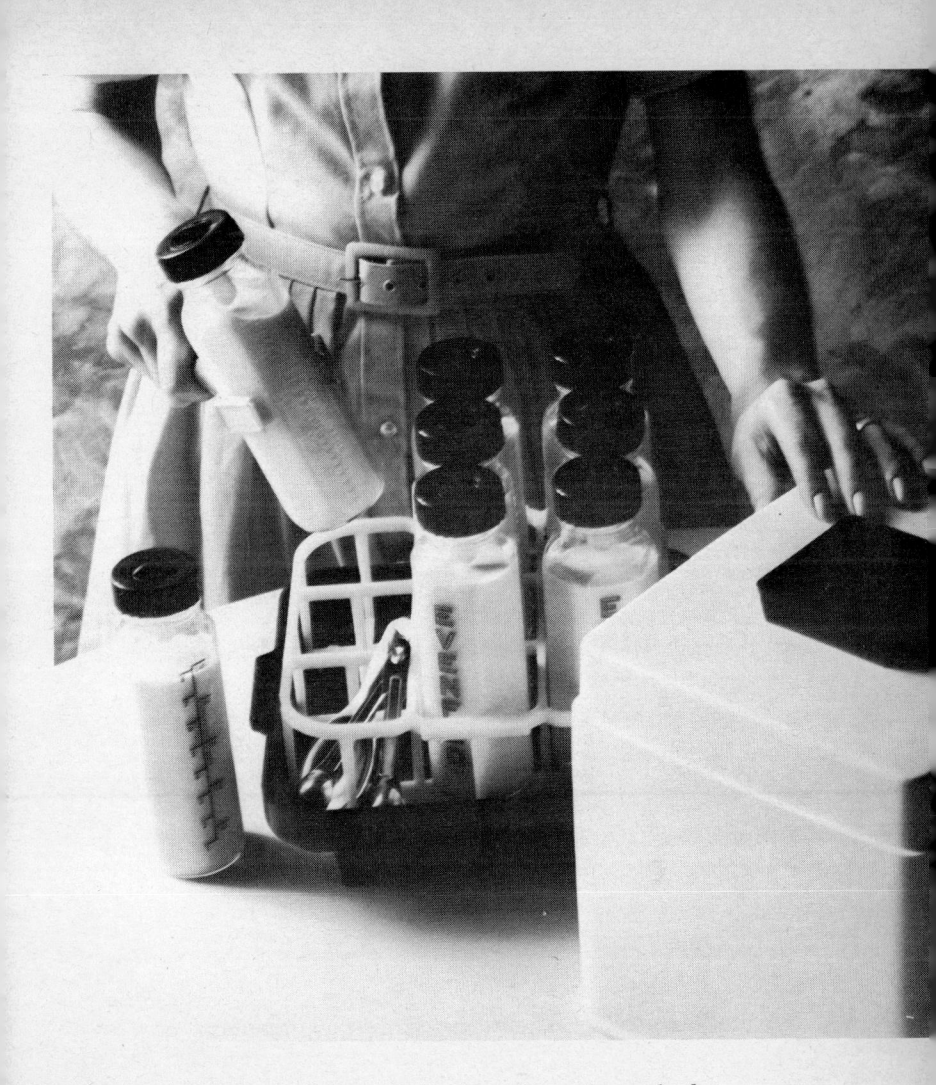

In some of the larger cities if a mother is unable to breast-feed her baby but the doctor wants him to have breast milk, it can be obtained from a breast-milk station. It is also possible to rent an electric breast pump to extract the milk and transfer it to sterile bottles if the doctor feels this method is preferable.

you will only have to boil them once a day. This will mean having one for each feeding, and each drink of water or orange juice.

The holes in the nipple may need to be made larger, especially at first. The baby may have become accustomed to the soft, well-used hospital nipples, while yours at home are new and stiff. Older babies can suck more vigorously, but smaller ones require an easier flow. When the bottle is tipped, milk ought to come out of the nipple one drop right after another.

To enlarge the hole in the nipple, heat a small needle in the flame of a match until it is red hot. To hold the needle, the eye can be forced into a cork or eraser end of a pencil. Then pass the hot needle through one or more holes in the nipple. If you use a needle which is too large, the resulting hole will let milk come out too fast and the baby will choke.

Covers for the nipples: you can buy nipple caps of glass, plastic, aluminum, or paper. You can make caps out of brown or waxed paper or other paper stiff enough to stand up away from the nipples. Fasten homemade caps with string or a rubber band. Leave the cap in place until you are ready to use the bottle.

Kettle for boiling equipment: you may wish to buy a kettle especially made for boiling baby bottles. It will have a tight-fitting cover and a rack inside to hold the bottles. Any kettle or can large enough to hold the bottles and other equipment will do, however. If your kettle does not have a special rack, you can work out a substitute to hold the bottles off the bottom. You can punch holes in a pie tin and set it in upside down, or place a folded cloth on the bottom.

Bottle brush with a long handle and stiff bristles to scrub the inside of the bottles. Get one which is bent at the tip, or bend yours, so that the bristles reach the edge of the bottom of the bottle.

A set of standard measuring spoons.

A measuring cup, marked in ounces.

A funnel which can be boiled.

A long-handled spoon.

Can opener that punches holes (if you use canned milk).

Pair of tongs is convenient to handle hot bottles and other sterile equipment.

2-quart saucepan with a pouring lip to mix formula in. When a baby is small, a glass quart measure is very convenient. A wide-mouth jar will do.

Small saucepan with a lid in which to boil and keep the nipples, if you are preparing the formula as in Method 2, which follows. Since it is so easy to let the pan of nipples burn dry, always time the boiling with a timer.

There are two different methods by which you can make the formula safe for the baby. In Method 1, the formula is mixed in clean utensils, poured into clean bottles and then sterilized by heating. In Method 2, the formula is boiled and then put into bottles which have been sterilized. Each method has advantages and disadvantages.

PREPARATION METHOD 1

1. Wash your hands. Then wash all equipment with hot water and detergent. Use the bottle brush to clean the inside of the bottles, the nipples, and the nipple covers if they are reusa-

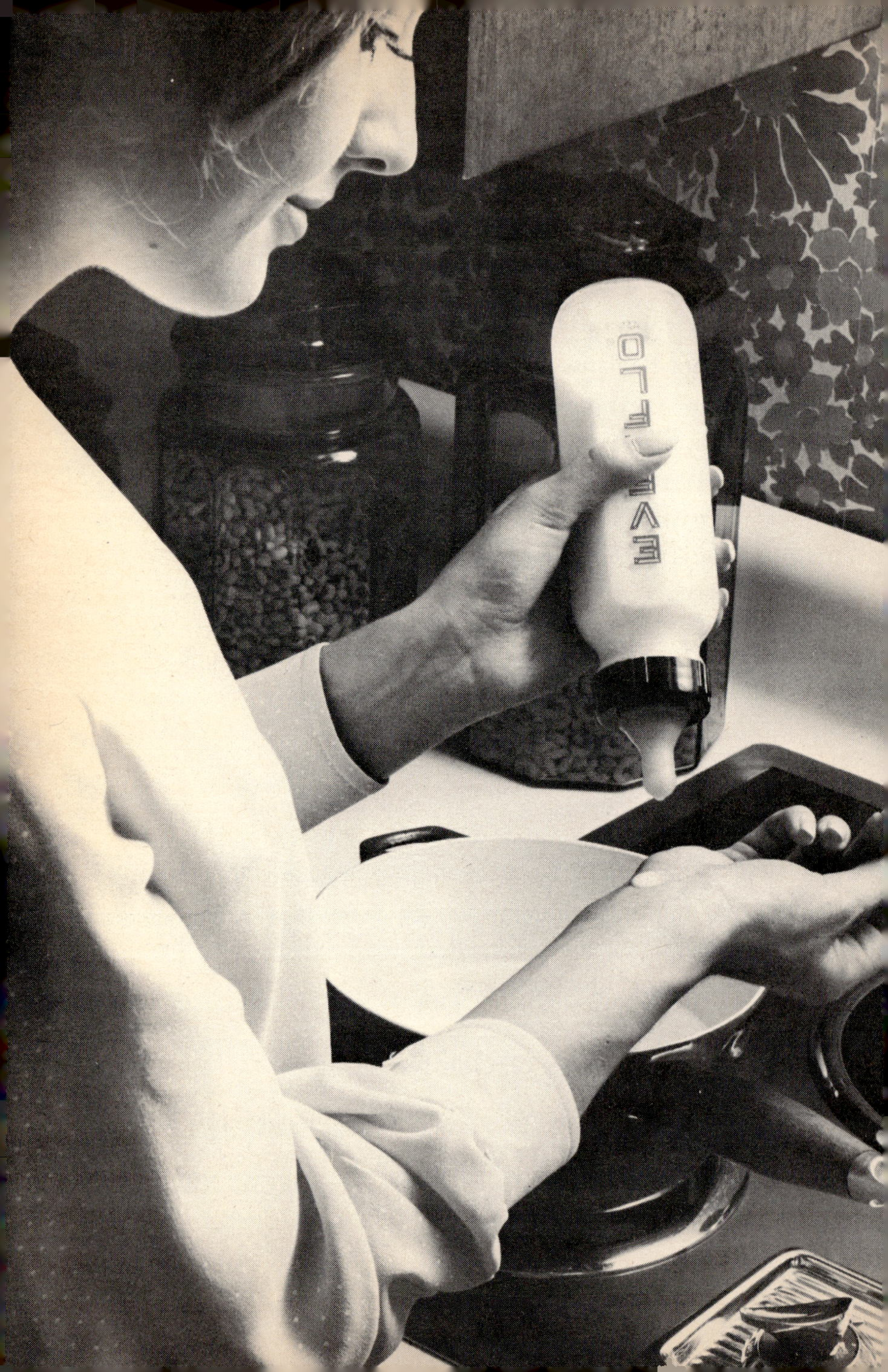

ble. Squeeze water through the nipple holes. If the holes are clogged, unclog them with a clean toothpick or other sharp tool.

2. Rinse all the equipment in clean hot water and drain.

3. Measure the milk, water, sugar or sirup, and pour into the clean saucepan, quart measure, or jar. You can use water from the faucet. Draw a knife across the sugar spoon to make the measure level. If you use evaporated milk, wash the top of the can with soap or detergent and water, and rinse in running hot water before opening the can. Shake whole milk that is not homogenized to mix the cream thoroughly.

4. Use the funnel to pour formula into the number of bottles the baby is likely to need before you mix formula again. Enough for 24 hours is convenient. Formula can be kept up to 48 hours under proper storage conditions. Pour clean drinking water for the baby into a small bottle and boil it along with the bottles of formula. Place nipples on the bottles. If you are using wide-mouthed bottles which have a separate screwtop cap, you can place the nipple on the bottle, holes pointing downward, screw on the top, and then turn the cap back a quarter turn. If you leave it tight, the cap may blow off during the heating.

5. Place a wire rack, overturned pie tin or folded washcloth in the bottom of the kettle which you are using as a boiler. Stand the filled bottles upright in the container. Add water (hot or cold) until it reaches the level of the milk or water in the bottles, whichever is lower. Cover with tight-fitting lid and bring the water to a boil. When it is bubbling actively, time it for 25 minutes by the clock.

6. When the bottles are cool enough to handle, put clean covers over the nipples if they are exposed. Tighten the cap on wide-mouth bottles and store with nipples inverted. Place the bottles in the refrigerator.

PREPARATION METHOD 2

Before you start, wash your hands. Then boil the equipment. If you boil the equipment before you make the formula, the utensils will have a chance to cool before you must handle them.

1. Wash the bottles, nipple covers, funnel, nipples, spoon, pans, and everything else you will be using thoroughly in hot water with a detergent. Force water through the nipple holes. With the bottle brush, scrub the inside of the nursing bottles, nipple covers, and inside and outside of the nipples.

2. Rinse everything well.

3. If the kettle you use has a rack, set each bottle in place, upside down. Fit the funnel, tongs, spoons between the bottles. There may be room to put the nipples in also. If so, put them in a clean jar with a perforated lid and put the jar in upside down. Or tie them in a cheesecloth bag.

If your kettle has no rack, place an inverted pie tin or folded cloth on the bottom, and lay the bottles on their sides with the other equipment on top.

4. If the kettle has a rack and a tight-fitting cover, pour in 1 or 2 inches of water and replace the cover. Bring to a boil. Let it boil for 5 minutes by the clock.

If the kettle does not have a tight-fitting lid, put in enough water to cover everything. It will take some time to come to a boil. Let it boil for 5 minutes. You may wish to dip out some of the water after it has finished boiling so that the contents of the kettle will cool more quickly. Leave things in the kettle until you are ready to use them.

If you did not boil the nipples with the other things, do them separately. Drop the nipples into boiling water in a small pan, cover, and let them boil for 5 minutes. Pour the water off and leave the nipples in the covered pan until you use them. You may prefer to store them in a jar with tight-fitting lid, both of which have been boiled. It wears nipples out to leave them soaking in water or to boil them too long.

The next step is to boil the formula. You do it as follows:

1. Measure the water, milk, and sugar or sirup into the large saucepan. Add an ounce or so more water than your formula calls for to make up for the amount lost in evaporation as the mixture boils. If you use granulated sugar, level off measuring spoon with the back of table knife. Whole milk that is not homogenized should be well shaken to mix the cream before measuring. If you use evaporated milk, wash the top of the can with soap or detergent and water, and rinse it off well before opening it. Some doctors suggest that evaporated milk, when first opened, does not need boiling. It can be added to the boiled water and sugar when the mixture is still warm.

2. Bring the mixture of water, milk, and sugar to a boil and keep it bubbling gently for 3 to 5 minutes. Stir constantly with the large stirring spoon. Keep stirring after you remove it from the fire to make it cool faster and to keep a scum from forming.

3. Take nursing bottles out of the kettle without touching the tops. If you have a funnel, remove it from the kettle without touching inside or rim and place in one of the bottles. Use tongs, if you have them, for both the bottles and the funnel.

4. Divide the milk mixture among the number of bottles the baby is likely to need.

5. Put boiled rubber nipples on the bottles without touching the rim of the bottles or the nipple except by the tab or base edge. Chances are, you'll spill more than one bottle before you get the hang of it. Cover the nipples immediately with nipple caps and put the bottles in the refrigerator.

OTHER METHODS

If you are short of bottles or refrigerator space, use one of the following variations of Method 2:

1. Store the day's formula in a boiled quart jar and fill one clean bottle at a time, as needed.

2. Put water-sugar mixture into boiled bottles. Add boiled milk just as you are ready to feed the baby.

3. Prepare one bottle at a time. Wash and scald with boiling water the bottle, nipple, spoon, and can opener. Put boiled water, sugar, and boiled milk or freshly opened evaporated milk into the bottle just before using it. Shake thoroughly. You can boil several bottles in advance (as in Method 2) and leave them filled with boiled water until you are ready to use them.

Evaporated milk or a modified milk for babies can be used directly from the can. Once opened, however, the remainder should be boiled before use.

GIVING A BOTTLE

When it is time to feed the baby, you may want to warm the bottle in a saucepan of water. It isn't necessary for the water to boil. If you are using screwtop bottles, adjust the nipple for use before heating. You can leave the protective cover on a narrow-mouth bottle as you warm it.

Before giving warmed milk to the baby, always test the temperature of the milk by shaking a few drops from the nipple on the inside of your wrist. The milk should not feel hot. Most babies don't mind cool milk, but they do object if it is too hot. It is not necessary to rewarm the milk during the feeding even though the baby takes 30 to 40 minutes to finish.

After a bottle has been used, rinse it with cool water and

Today's new mother has a choice of two types of pre-mixed baby formula:
(1) the liquid or powder concentrate to which she adds sterile water
and (2) the ready-to-use formula she simply pours into a bottle (or
buys already bottled). Neither type when unopened needs refrigeration.

wash it thoroughly. Leave it filled with water until you are ready to prepare the formula. Rinse the nipple by squeezing water through it. Keep it in a covered jar with the other used ones until you are ready to prepare the feedings again.

Always hold the baby as you feed him. He needs the comfort of your arms, and the little adjustments you can so easily make keep the feeding smooth and pleasant for him. It gives you a few minutes' rest, too. Withdraw the nipple if the milk is coming too fast or he indicates that he wants to stop to rest briefly. Tip the bottle so the nipple is filled with milk. Then he doesn't swallow a lot of air as he sucks.

If you do prop a bottle occasionally when the baby is older, be sure to stay nearby to help out if trouble occurs. When the flow of milk does not correspond perfectly to the sucking-swallowing rhythm of the baby, he must get rid of the nipple to avoid choking. If the bottleholder has no give, the baby can draw in additional milk as he struggles to be free, which can actually cause him to drown in milk. There is also the risk that he will inhale droplets into his lungs which can cause pneumonia.

SHOULD YOU REUSE A BOTTLE?

There's no hard-and-fast rule to guide you about the use of a bottle which has once been offered to the baby and not finished. Ideally you would never use a bottle the second time because bacteria multiply so rapidly in milk which has been warmed.

If you're going someplace and need to take a bottle along, keep it cold. Put it in an insulated bag and surround the bottle with ice. Or wrap the thoroughly chilled bottle completely in about 10 layers of newspaper. It is not wise to heat a bottle and carry it for later use.

5. Other routines of baby care

With most new jobs the beginner learns one part of the task at a time. When he masters that part, he graduates to the next. Not so with the new mother. Once the baby is here, everything begins all at once—feeding, sleeping, bathing, washing the clothes, and so on.

It's comforting to know that you soon master it all, and can settle down to enjoy the baby. Caring for him becomes easier all the time, rather than harder. Another comforting thing to remember is that the baby is a lot tougher than he looks. He doesn't even notice that you are inexperienced, and he keeps right on growing.

WHAT BOWEL MOVEMENTS REVEAL

The first bowel movements of a baby consist of sticky, greenish brown to black material, which has collected inside the body before birth. Gradually, the bowel movement becomes lighter in color. If the baby has not had any bowel movement by the time he is 2 days old, tell the doctor.

By about the seventh day, the bowel movements of the baby

will be the characteristic yellow color produced by a milk diet. Both the color and the consistency will vary from one baby to the next, and depend partly on the kind of milk he gets. A breast-fed baby tends to have soft and mushy, perhaps quite loose, yellow to orange movements. They may change from yellow to green on standing in the air. They may have a rather acid odor. Cow's milk formula produces movements more pasty and formed, light yellow to brown, with strong sour milk odor and some curdy lumps.

The number of movements a day will vary, too. Some babies have a movement after or during each feeding at first, then taper off. Two or three stools a day become about the average. A breast-fed baby may have more frequent movements. This seems to be perfectly normal for them.

If there is a sudden change in the consistency or odor of the movements, observe the baby carefully. One or two movements may be out of the ordinary, yet the baby will remain perfectly well. Several abnormal movements, however, are a signal that something is wrong.

Of special concern is a sudden change to loose, watery movements with liquid which stains the diaper beyond the area of solid matter. This diarrhea may be caused by a good many things, including improper feeding, the beginning of a cold, or infection in the bowel or elsewhere in the body. If you are breast-feeding, a laxative you have taken will affect the baby's stools. Get advice from your doctor promptly if the baby has frequent loose movements. Diarrhea may be mild and easily corrected, but it can become a serious problem in a young baby.

Your good routine care of the baby will go a long way toward preventing diarrhea. Keep him out of crowds of people and away from visitors who have colds. Be sure to prepare the milk carefully, and keep it under safe and sanitary conditions. Keep all flies away from your kitchen and be sure the drinking water is pure. If other children in the family have intestinal upsets, keep their dishes separate from the baby's things, and do not let them handle the baby or the baby's food.

Movements of a hard consistency are rarely found with a breast-fed baby. Cow's milk has a greater tendency to produce a firm mass. The fact that a baby has hard movements, however, is no cause for worry unless the baby has pain when passing them. Some people have the mistaken notion that a hard bowel movement is the same as constipation and they give babies medicines which are not good for them. Never use a laxative or an enema unless the doctor orders it. Never give oily preparations, such as mineral oil, to a baby since there is danger that he may choke on it and draw it into his lungs.

In most cases, you can correct a tendency to hard stools by giving the baby more water or juice or, if he's taking them, more fruits and vegetables. Prune juice, sieved or strained prunes and figs may help to keep bowel movements soft.

Occasionally, you may notice small streaks of blood in the stool of a baby who passes hard movements. Check to see if there is a crack in the anus, or outlet, of the bowel. If so, you may wipe the area with baby cream or lotion which contains lanolin. You may need to put some cream or an ointment prescribed by the doctor just beyond the opening into the rectum. Check with the doctor for help in correcting the condition, because it is unfortunate if the baby begins to associate pain with passing a bowel movement.

Also call the doctor if you notice larger amounts of blood or any other markedly unusual appearance of the movement.

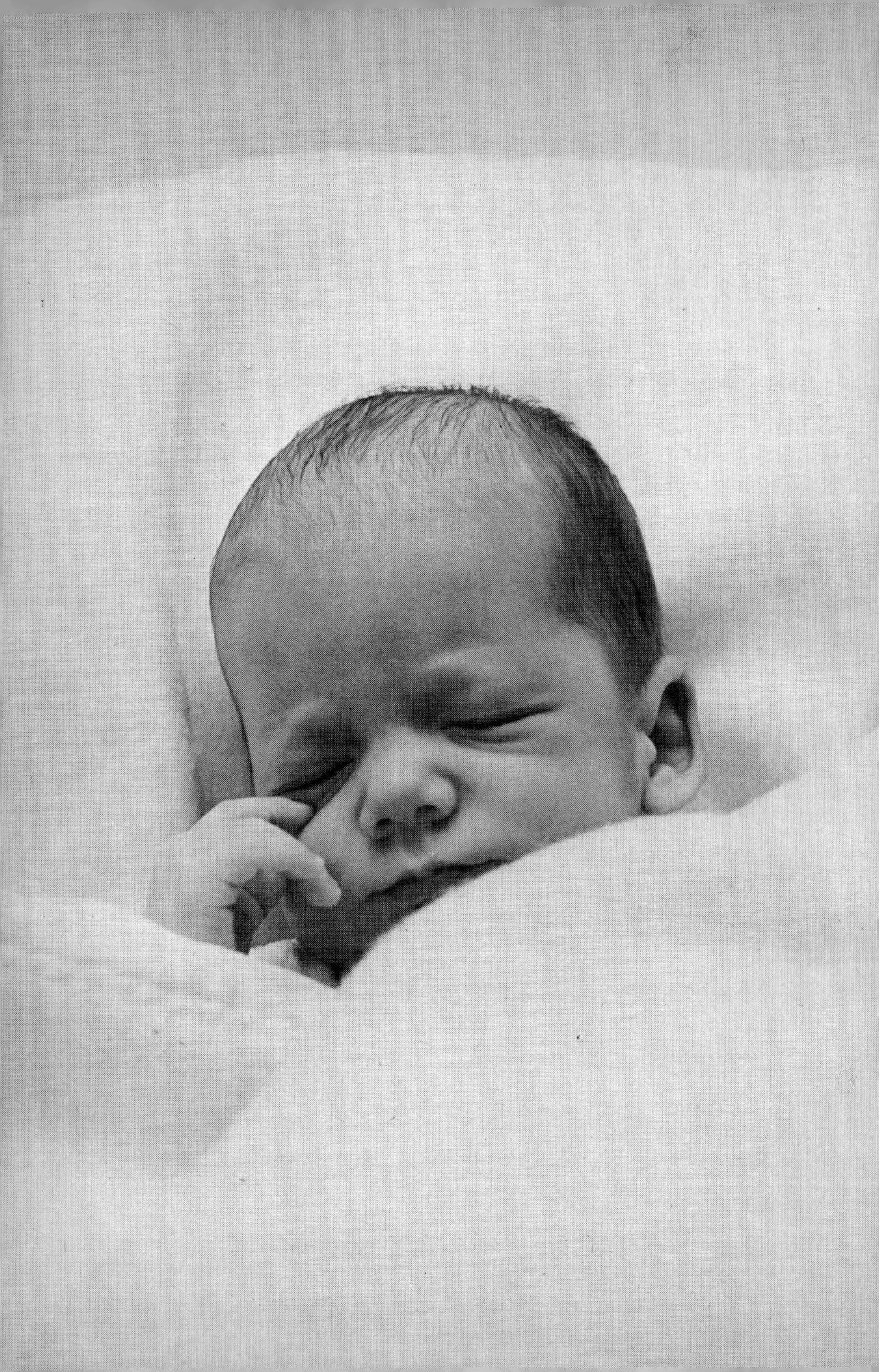

HOW MUCH SLEEP?

The amount of time your baby will spend in sleep is a highly individual matter. All babies sleep less as time goes by, but from the outset one baby may always sleep a great deal more than another, yet both are healthy and normal. Babies are said to sleep from 20 to 22 hours a day at first, but some sleep a great deal less.

Actually there are different kinds of sleeping patterns in the same baby. There's the sound sleep, accompanied by deep regular breathing, interrupted now and then by a startle or jerk. This may be followed by irregular sleep with shallow breathing alternating with slow, deep breathing. There may be many movements of the whole body. Later you note a drowsy state, with irregular breathing. The baby opens and closes his eyes, may make a few sucking movements with his mouth, then yawns. From this drowsy state, he may move again into deep sleep, or become more active, finally kicking or whimpering. After a time, he goes into pre-cry stretching, the corners of his mouth pull down, his chin dimples, and the eyes screw up; there's a pitiful quiver of the chin. Next—a full-blown call to you. For food? Attention? Dry pants? As time goes by, you'll learn to read the cries quite accurately. At first, it may be hard to tell just what he wants.

BED AND BEDCLOTHES

Since the baby spends a lot of time sleeping, he should have his own bed. Someone may loan you a bassinet for the first few weeks, or you can get by with a padded laundry basket or box. Just be sure the place to sleep has sides on it so the baby won't roll out, and be sure the padding is firm and extends to the sides of the box or bed so the infant can't get caught in the crack.

If you are going to buy a bed for the baby, you might as well start out with the standard size crib (54 by 27 inches) which will last for several years. However, if you are going to move the crib out of your room at night, you may decide to get a smaller one which will roll more easily around corners.

Check the spaces between the bars of the crib to be certain they will not let the baby's head go through. Make sure the sides, if removable, lock securely in place. Get a firm, well-made mattress, with inner spring if you can. Instead of a mattress, padding can be made of blankets folded to fit the bed or box. Tack the folds in place with stitches of yarn or cord at intervals over the pad.

Even if the mattress you buy is covered with waterproof material, you will find it useful to have waterproof sheeting to go over it. Sooner or later, the mattress cover will crack and urine may seep into the mattress or leak into the airholes.

Waterproof sheeting is usually rubber, plastic, or a fabric coated with flannel. You can buy it by the yard and cut pieces long enough to tuck in at the edges of the mattress. It is convenient to have two pieces, to provide for daily washing. Smaller squares of flannel-coated rubber sheeting or cotton quilted pads are useful under the baby, and in your lap as you hold him. The baby should not lie directly on rubber or plastic. Do not use thin plastic bags to cover sheet or mattress.

Get sheets for the bed long enough to tuck in generously so they don't pull out easily as the baby becomes more active. Fitted bottom sheets are a convenience.

The baby does not need a pillow and should not have one. It is good to have blankets of several kinds. Flannel squares are used so regularly when the baby is little that they are listed under clothing. Somewhat warmer blankets are needed, too. Many parents like to place the baby into a sleeper of warm fabric, which can be bought or made. Use a sweater underneath if the nights are really cold. The covers, in other words, are put on the baby instead of on the bed. Then you're not worried about his becoming uncovered in the night.

WHERE TO SLEEP

It's a good idea to start the baby with sleeping arrangements you can keep throughout childhood. This means you'll expect him to sleep alone, in his own bed. And, after the first weeks of infancy, he should not be sleeping in the same room with you if you can possibly make other plans. In fact, some parents admit they get better rest themselves if the baby's crib is not in their room from the beginning. Most babies will let you know well enough by their loud and determined crying if they really need you. Babies are noisy roommates. You lie awake, waiting for the next gurgle or snort, wondering if he's going to cry or not. It's hard to get the sleep you deserve. Furthermore, the presence of an outsider, even a baby, can be an unwelcome intrusion between married people.

It may be tempting to take the baby to bed with you when you are feeding or calming him at night, but it is unwise to do so. There is some danger that an infant can be smothered in the bedclothing or pillows or hurt by an adult rolling over. There are problems of another kind. The baby finds it pleasant to have you so near, and may decide to move in. He'll do his best to make it a regular thing. And a permanent bedfellow —especially one who is apt to wet the bed—becomes a pest.

You're sure to resent it eventually, and the baby will be even more troubled by your later refusal to let him in with you. Better not to start at all.

Place the crib out of drafts. It is not necessary to have the windows open in his room as long as there is enough ventilation from an adjoining one.

SLEEPING POSITION

Most babies like to sleep on their stomachs, hunched up, with knees tucked under. It is probably the best position in which to place the baby since mucus, milk which is spit up, or vomit will roll out without choking him. Some babies, though, are firm about preferring their backs. Whichever position you place the baby in, move him about from time to time; or reverse the crib. Spending a great deal of time in one position may tend to flatten the bones of the head or face when they are still soft. However, if the head should become misshapen, or the hair worn away, it will become more normal when the baby spends more time upright.

IF HE CRIES A LOT

There's an old folksong that asks: "How can you have a baby with no cryin'?" It's a good line to remember.

Often a baby will settle on a certain time of day to "sound off." This is apt to be the late afternoon or early evening, when the household is more active and everybody is busy—and tired. Daddy comes home, dinner must be prepared, other children are more demanding. Sometimes you may be able to switch around the feeding or the hour you bathe the baby, and persuade him to pick out another—and more convenient—time of day to fuss. But you may just have to put up with it for a month or so. As he becomes able to amuse himself and use up energy in other ways, and as his body processes become more settled, the fussy periods will taper off.

If your baby cries a good deal, however, he should be checked by a doctor. If he's bottle-fed, sometimes a change in the formula is helpful, although usually a baby will adapt himself to any standard milk mixture. The doctor may suggest more food, or less; he may find other physical causes for the baby's distress.

At first, you may feel each time the baby cries that he's hungry. He is apt to try to ease any pain or discomfort by stuffing a fist into his mouth or by making sucking movements, since these have brought him pleasure. This convinces you that it must be hunger. If it has been a couple of hours since a feeding, or if he took but little at his most recent feeding, food may be the answer. It's worth trying to rule out other things, though, for not all cries are from hunger and inexperienced parents may tend to overfeed the baby. The obvious things to check are whether or not he's wet (although lots of babies don't mind soaked diapers a bit); or has a pin sticking in him (they hardly ever do, but it's worth looking); or is thirsty, cold, or in an uncomfortable position. Maybe he just needs to hear your voice or be patted to remove an uncomfortable air bubble.

Sometimes the baby will cry briefly, and settle down if left alone. And some regularly fuss for 10 minutes or so as they are going off to sleep. If you rush in to pat or prod, you postpone sleeping even longer.

When a baby has hard crying periods soon after being fed, he may be called "colicky." Many babies have colic during the first 3 or 4 months. It is less frequent after that. "Colicky" is the word usually used to describe a baby who cries hard, with a cry unmistakably that of pain. He may draw his arms and legs up, his face gets red, and his abdomen may feel hard while he's having cramps that make him scream.

Frequently, these attacks come on just after eating, though not always after every feeding. Some babies behave this way only after the late afternoon or evening feedings. Evidently a good many things can cause this discomfort. Unfortunately, not much can be done many times about the causes. Some of them, such as an immature digestive system, time alone will take care of.

Colic begins to taper off, usually by the third month, almost always by the fourth or fifth. Many babies with colic gain regularly despite all their fuss.

The hardest part is to keep your fatigue and annoyance from being communicated to the baby and everybody else in the household. Cross feelings are contagious. The baby is irritable and fussy, about what, nobody can figure out. The parents try everything—hot water bottles, rocking, patting, bubbling, and so on. Nothing works. Grandmother adds her ideas. So do the neighbors. Daddy hates to come home. Things get tense. Eventually, the baby's crying makes the mother angry. She may be angry at herself because she thinks she is not succeeding in the job of being a mother—and it's a very important job to most women once they embark on it; or she may be angry at the baby for not responding well when she is doing the best she knows how. Her anger and tension are felt by the baby, and he becomes more fussy and cross. Tension circles between mother, father, and baby. It spreads out to grandmother and back again.

If you should find yourself in such a knot, perhaps the best thing is to stop and take stock. It does help a little to know, if you can believe it, that this round-the-clock crying of "colic"

Baby care your mother never even dreamed of.

No more juggling a wet slithery baby and a cake of slippery soap.
You belong to the Baby Magic Generation.
You'll bathe your baby with safe sweet Baby Magic Bath.
An easy to hold bottle.
Squeeze.
Out comes a gentle liquid cleanser made just for babies. And perfect for babies.
Baby Magic Bath cleans babies better than soap.
It has a lotion-like conditioner to help protect against chafing and dry skin.
It's medicated with hexachlorophene to fight against diaper rash.
No old fashioned cake of soap ever cared for a baby like this.
In fact, perhaps your baby's very first bath in this world, right there in the hospital, was in the safe happy bubbles of Baby Magic Bath.
Yes. Things are different in this brand new Baby Magic Generation.
Protection. That's what's different.

PRODUCT OF THE MENNEN COMPANY

will decrease as the baby grows older. Try to remember, too, that the baby is not being stubborn or naughty. There is something bothering him even though you can't fix it. Whatever you do to make the baby feel more comfortable is a good idea. It will not spoil the baby if you do your best to make him feel better. Try to remove your own outside sources of tension and upset. Cut out unessential jobs. Let the housework slide. And get a babysitter or neighbor so you can be out of the house for a little while. The baby's crying won't bother anyone else as much as it does you, and you'll feel better able to cope if you have a breather now and then.

BATHING THE BABY

Bathtime will become a thoroughly satisfying experience as the baby grows older. He will enjoy freedom from clothes which hamper his movements, and he'll stretch and kick, crowing with delight. Merely getting clean is the least of his concerns. He becomes a real showoff and it is a pleasant moment to share with older children in the family. Try to make a space in your busy day so that you, too, can enjoy playing with the baby who is so alert and happy—enjoying his damp sweetness as you pat him dry, and the clean soap smell clinging to his scalp.

It will take some time to work up to this point of high glee over baths, though. At first, you may wish to lightly sponge him with a cloth, wrung out in warm water. Pay special attention to keeping the face and buttocks clean. You may want to use cotton moistened with water, baby lotion, or mineral oil to cleanse the buttocks which are soiled.

After a week or two, when you are feeling up to it and the navel is healed, you can begin a more complete bath routine.

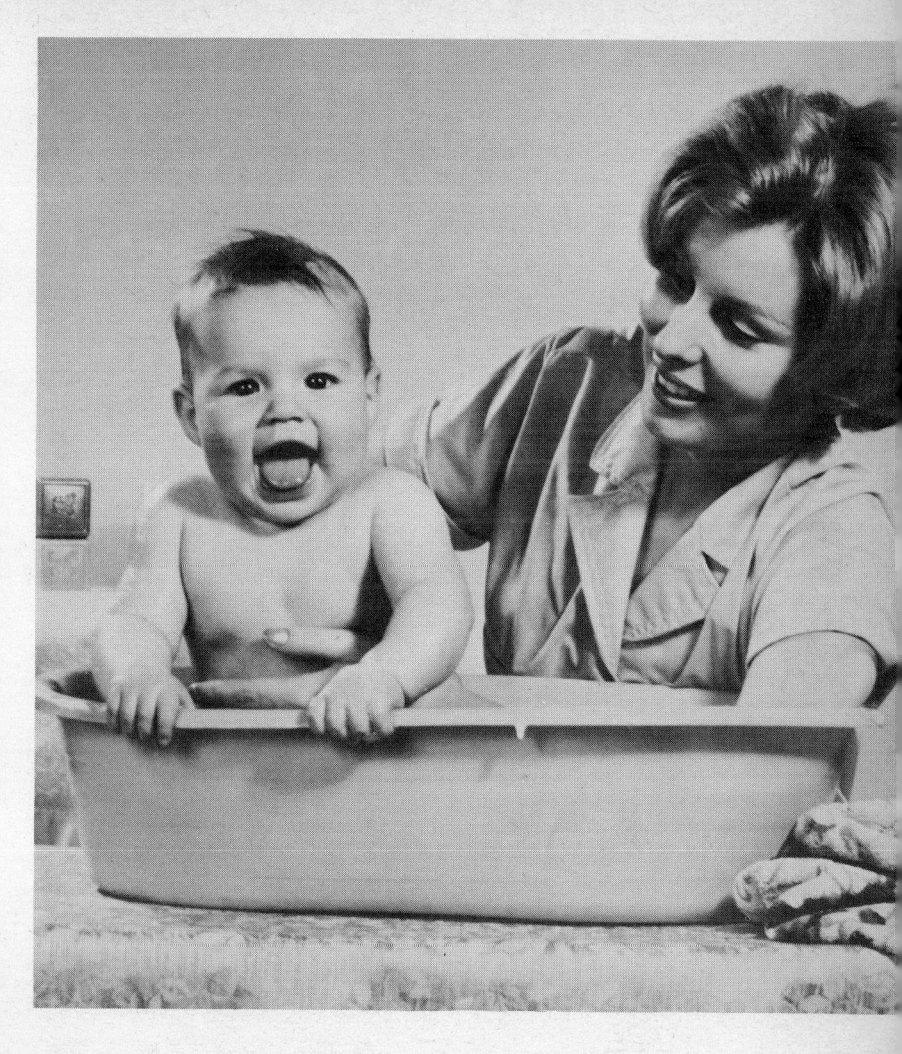

When it's time for the baby's bath, first collect everything you'll need: soap, towel, diaper, clean shirt. Then get the baby. It's not safe to leave him unattended in the bath even for a moment, since a moment is all it would take for him to slip out—or under. If the phone rings or you *must* get something, take him with you.

How does pHisoHex® make skin surgically clean?

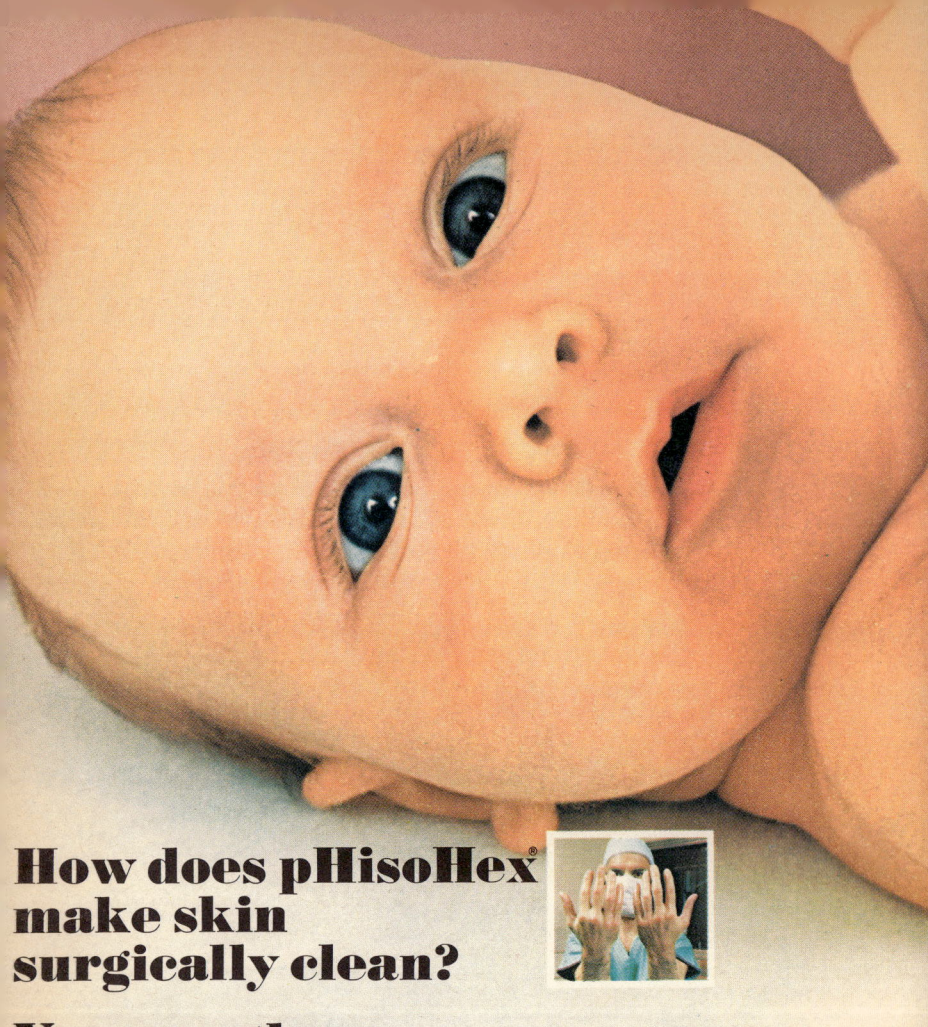

Very gently.

pHisoHex is used regularly in hospitals to bathe newborn babies. It cleanses and degerms baby's skin. Builds up protection against harmful skin bacteria that may cause skin infections and aggravate diaper rash. And this protection lasts for hours after washing. Mothers, too, need pHisoHex. It degerms the skin, removes bacteria that can spread infections. No soap, no medicated soap, can do as much for skin. Surgeons use it. Why don't you?

The more complete way to care for skin.

There's no hurry about it. Plan the bath before a feeding. Bathing too soon afterwards may make him spit up.

Select a place to bathe the baby which is warm, free from drafts, and has a work surface of a convenient height. The kitchen may be the warmest room in the house. A room temperature of 75° to 80° is enough.

Some mothers like to have a special folding type of bath table for the baby. It will have a hinged cover which becomes a convenient surface for changing or dressing the baby. If you're crowded and can't have an extra piece of furniture around, you may prefer to use the bathroom sink or a plastic or enamel dishpan set on the kitchen drainboard. Pad the surface where you work with folded towels or a light blanket. It's hard to handle a baby in a standard adult bathtub and it's mighty uncomfortable to stoop over.

It is handy to keep all bath supplies in a shallow baking pan or tray. You'll need:

Cake of mild soap for use on the baby only.

Pieces of absorbent cotton in a jar with a cover.

Washcloth (or squares of old soft cloth).

Small towel or diaper to put in the bottom of the tub (to keep the baby from sliding on the wet surface).

Larger towel to dry the baby (soft flannel, terry cloth or jersey).

Clean clothes: diaper, shirt, pins, nightgown.

Warm mineral oil, powder or lotion if you use such.

It is helpful if you can be shown how to bathe the baby while you are still in the hospital or by a public health nurse who will come to your home. Nothing really prepares you for dealing with a slippery baby, though, except the reassurance of some practice yourself. The trick is to use only a little water in the tub (2 to 3 inches) at first, be sparing with the soap, and take your time. For the first baths, you can rinse soap off the baby with a cloth wrung out in water without lowering him into the tub. Later, you'll find a grip you can trust. One way is to slip your hand under the baby's back, supporting his head with your wrist or arm, the fingers of the hand crossing to the baby's armpit on the side away from your body. Then you'll have the other hand free to soap, or rinse his body or scalp.

A good bathing routine is as follows: Pour a few inches of warm water into the tub, testing it with your hand or elbow. It should feel a little warm to your skin (96° to 104°). It will cool off rapidly, you know. Place a folded cloth in the bottom of the tub. Remove the baby's clothing, except for the diaper perhaps, and throw a light blanket or clean diaper over his shoulders. You may hold him in your lap or lay him on the flat surface. Wash his face with clear water on a damp cloth. He'll hate this, so be quick. Clean the eyelids gently, working from the nose outward. Wipe the outer ear with the washcloth folded over your finger, and cleanse behind the ears, too. Leave the mouth alone.

Once or twice a week, soap the baby's scalp with a lather you have worked up in your hand, rubbing your palm gently over his head and working the soap into the scalp. Remember, don't worry about the soft spot. It is covered with a tough membrane. Rinse off the soap with a wet washcloth—at least two swabbings. Or hold the baby's head over the tub, and cup your hand into the water, bringing some over onto his head. Keep soapy water out of the baby's eyes. As you become more sure of yourself, you can place the baby in the tub for rinsing his head. Dry the face, ears, and scalp thoroughly.

Next soap the body, removing the diaper if you have not already done so. You may find it easier to soap your hand than

Ammens wants you to stop treating diaper rash

We want to help you *prevent* diaper rash instead.

Medicated AMMENS® Powder helps prevent diaper rash in more ways than even the best-known baby powder. Here's why you should use AMMENS with every diaper change:

Diaper rash happens when bacteria go to work in your baby's wet diapers. AMMENS has a mild medication to fight those bacteria. The best-known baby powder doesn't have it.

AMMENS has another mild medication to put an antiseptic coating on your baby's skin. The best-known baby powder doesn't have that, either.

And AMMENS also has corn starch, to absorb more moisture than the best-known baby powder's talc can absorb.

Those same ingredients in AMMENS *can* treat diaper rash. But why treat what you may be able to prevent in the first place?

© 1969 Bristol-Myers Co.

A sprinkle of prevention is worth a pound of cure

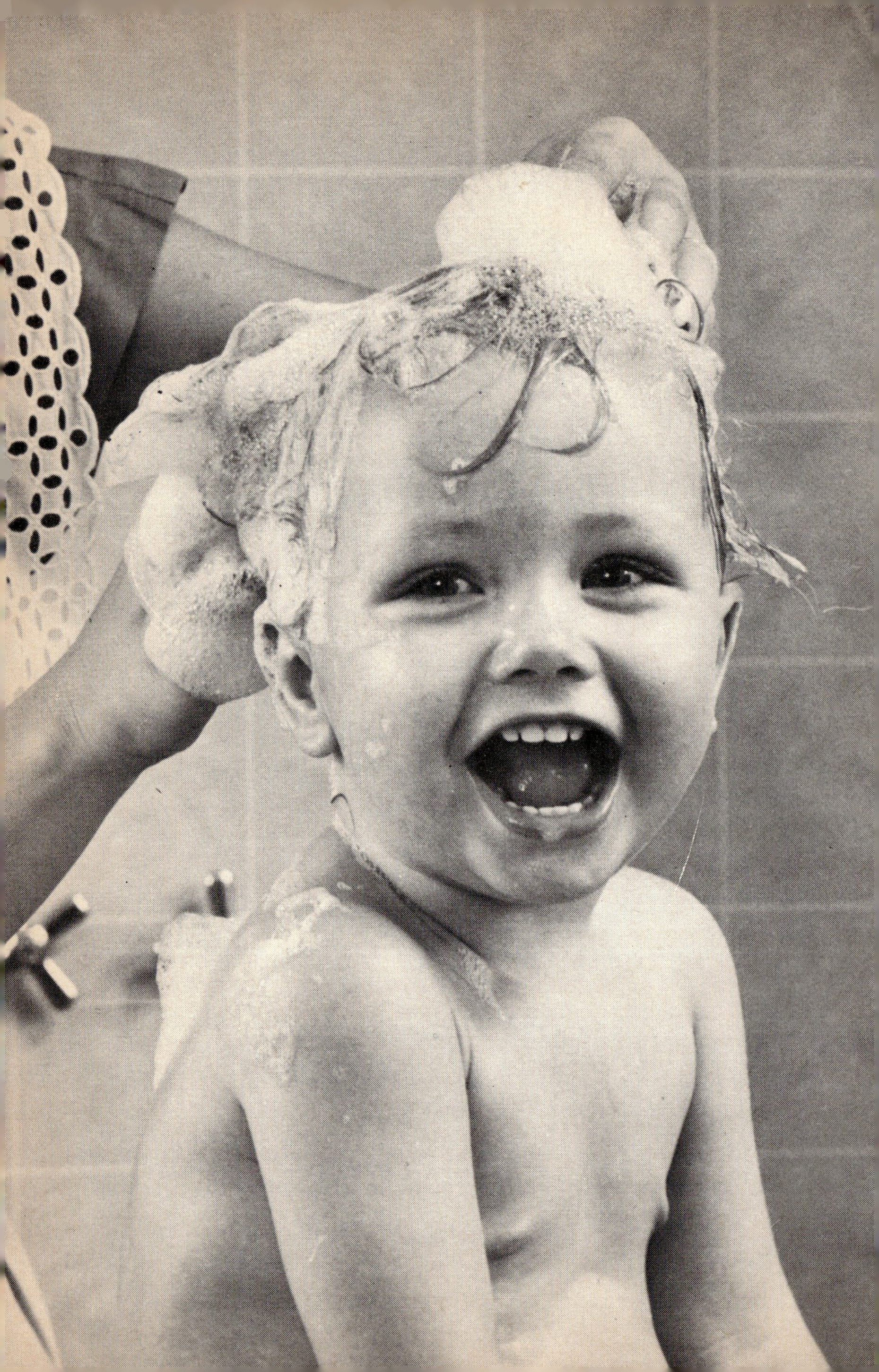

to use a drippy cloth. Reach into all the creases. Clean the genitals. A piece of cotton dipped into warm water is sufficient to clear away the white cheesy material that may collect in the folds of the labia of a girl, around the end of the penis of a boy. Then remove all the soap, either by wiping carefully with a wet washcloth or lowering the baby into the tub for a rinse.

As you bathe the baby, you may notice long finger and toe nails which need trimming. It's a good idea to wait until he's asleep before attempting to cut the nails because the baby is so apt to jerk, or fight against the restraint you impose on him. Cut the nails straight across, without attempting to shape them. A nail clipper is good for this. Take care not to cut too deeply into the cuticle.

You may wish to use a lotion or mineral oil on the baby's buttocks. Apply it with a ball of cotton. Be sure to wipe away any excess. Some mothers like to use a dusting of baby or medicated powder, especially in the creases and folds of buttocks and neck. Place powder onto the palm of your hand or onto a cotton ball and apply lightly. It is not wise to shake powder directly onto the baby, for he may inhale the fine particles, which are harmful to the lungs. A can containing any powder at all does not make a safe toy for a baby.

It does no harm to skip the bath, especially when the house is cold, you are tired, or the baby seems sick. Give the baby a complete change of clothing daily and wipe off his face and hands now and then. In hot weather, a bath or sponging several times during the day makes him more comfortable.

THE SKIN AND SCALP

The frequent shampoo you give the baby should keep his scalp in good condition. If a greasy crust known as "cradle cap" appears, you will want to clear it up promptly with special attention. Soften the crust with petroleum jelly or mineral oil at night and wash the baby's head thoroughly in the morning. Or apply a thin solution of baking soda and water to the scalp. Leave it on over night and shampoo in the morning.

Diaper rash: Any irritation of the skin in the region of the diaper is loosely referred to as diaper rash, although it may be caused by a variety of things. If the skin does not clear after you have tried the simple measures which follow, check with the doctor. Aside from the discomfort which persistent chafing causes the baby, raw areas in the skin are prone to infection and should have medical attention.

Good routine care of the diapers and reasonably frequent changes will go a long way toward preventing sore buttocks. At one time or another, most babies have some breaking out that disappears with nothing more than changing the diaper somewhat more often. Oil doesn't stick long enough to be much of a waterproofing. And some ointments have a tendency to remove the new skin when they are removed. If there are open sores, do not use any medicine without consulting your doctor.

If the rash lasts more than a day and seems to be spreading or becoming more sore, it is well to give special attention to care of the diapers. To kill bacteria which may be present use heat. Boil them, iron with a hot iron, or dry them in the sun. Some home dryers reach temperatures high enough to destroy the bacteria which grow readily in urine-soaked cloth. The doctor can suggest a special chemical to use in washing diapers. It is safe to use with the rest of the baby's laundry if you wish.

If the baby has diaper rash, do not use rubber or waterproof pants. Some babies can stand wearing these (or "soakers" made of knitted fabric). Others are irritated by more than occasional use. At the first sign of irritation, leave them off. In fact,

© Leeming Division, Chas. Pfizer & Co., Inc., New York, N.Y.

Chances are, your new baby will get diaper rash.

Will you know what to do?

Desitin® Ointment is the diaper rash medicine more doctors recommend than any other—the one mothers have been using for over 40 years.

Why should your baby get diaper rash? Diaper rash can happen to any baby—and usually does. Many cases develop when germs in the diaper area turn wetness to ammonia, which "burns" and irritates the skin. Your baby can get a rash even if you're extra-careful. That's why you should be ready with Desitin Ointment. In a recent survey of 400 pediatricians, three times as many said they recommend Desitin as any other diaper rash remedy. Here's why.

What makes Desitin so good? The ingredients in Desitin are excellent healing aids. Desitin has Norwegian cod liver oil, with Vitamin A and Vitamin D. It has petroleum jelly and lanolin and talcum. And *more* zinc oxide than zinc oxide ointment has. Together, they all work to heal diaper rash quickly.

How does Desitin work? Smooth, creamy Desitin soothes your baby right away—even before the rash is gone. It's so rich and thick that it stays on the skin for hours to help seal out wetness and germs. And the Desitin cod liver oil formula is one of the fastest ways known to help new and healthy skin tissue to grow. It works so quickly that in many cases diaper rash can actually disappear by the next morning.

How do you use Desitin? It's easy. Just apply three or more times daily, and especially at bedtime, when your baby may be in wet diapers for many hours.

What else does Desitin make for your baby? For extra protection every day, use soothing, fragrant Desitin Baby Powder.

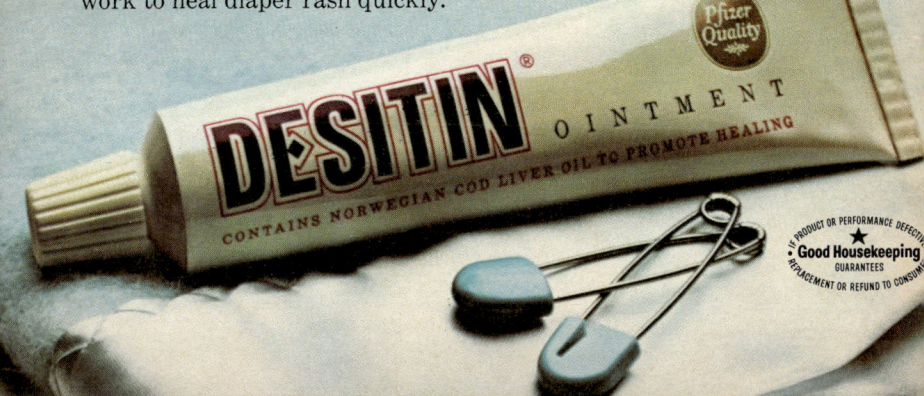

one of the best ways to cure "diaper rash" is to leave off the diaper for as much of the time as you can. If the baby is a few weeks old, you can give him a brief sunbath. Start with no longer than 5 minutes, and be sure the baby does not become overheated or chilled. He can be sunned indoors, if placed a few feet from an opened window through which the sunlight comes in.

CARE OF THE GENITALS

Be matter of fact about your handling the baby's genital area and about cleaning him when he soils himself. He will pick up your attitude toward his body. If you feel the products of his body to be shameful and disgusting, he may begin to feel the same. As often happens, your baby may touch or rub himself in the genital area as you bathe him or change his diaper. Try to treat this casually. The baby explores his mouth and ears, and toes and hair with interest, learning about himself and how he feels. In similar fashion, he's going to explore other sensitive areas of his body, too. The baby is not bad when he does so. As he grows, his interests will move beyond his own body to the world about him.

CLOTHING FOR THE BABY

When you get right down to it, the only clothing you really must have for the baby is a good-sized stack of diapers. All other adjustments for warmth can be made with an assortment of blankets. In parts of our country, even this item is dispensed with. The Eskimo mother tucks her little one inside her fur parka, absolutely naked.

Simple, easily washed garments are best. Babies grow so

fast it is better to have only a few things of any one size. Adjust the warmth of the garments to the weather. On very hot days, a shirt and diaper, or diaper alone, is enough. If you are cool, put a sweater on the baby. Overheated rooms are not needed for babies. A temperature around 70° suits them just as it does you. In most parts of our country, mothers find the following items useful:

3 to 6 dozen diapers: You'll probably use about 2 dozen a day on the baby. You'll also find yourself grabbing a diaper to throw over your shoulder when you bubble the baby. A diaper is also useful as extra sheeting, bib, towel, etc. The extra dozen or so is handy if you can't get diapers washed or dried daily. In many cities, it is possible to contract with a company to furnish and launder diapers. Such service is a great help, if you can afford it, especially at first. The diaper companies also rent certain items of equipment which you may like to have for only a short time. Even if you plan to use a diaper service, you may find it convenient to have a dozen or so diapers of your own.

Diapers are made of gauze, cotton flannel, bird's-eye, and other fabrics. There are squares, rectangles and shapes cut to fit the body and provided with snaps. Everybody has his own idea about which kind is best, and you'll just have to select the kind that appeals to you. Start out with the large sizes; they will last as long as you are needing diapers.

4 to 6 cotton shirts: Size 2 fits most babies in a few weeks. Sleeveless or short-sleeved shirts can be used in any weather. If it gets cold, you can add a sweater or the light jackets known as "sacks." Be sure to select a style of shirt that will go on the baby easily. Babies hate to have anything over their faces, and a mouthful of shirt sets them wild. Get armholes large enough and neck openings ample for the baby's head. Wraparound styles are available.

It's a wise mother who uses diaper liners.

Dennison Diaper Liners do away with the messiness of diaper changing. Try one. Change baby as usual, including a thorough cleansing and application of powder or lotion. Then simply add a liner between baby and his diaper — there's no pinning involved. Next time around your diaper changing chores are cut in half. Dennison Diaper Liners are as disposable as the nearness of your bathroom, saving you time, energy, and even aggravation at washtime because, with far less mess, staining is kept to a minimum.

Worried about diaper rash? Dennison Diaper Liners actually *help prevent* it. Each liner is saturated with Puracol, an effective anti-bacterial agent. With Dennison Diaper Liners baby gets the added protection he needs in between diaper changes — available at infants' departments everywhere — or mail in 25¢ for a week's sample. **Free booklet** *"Helpful Hints on Diaper Hygiene"*. Write to Dennison, Dept. A188 Framingham, Mass.

Dennison
Diaper Liners

2 to 3 sweaters and sacks: Size 2. It is easier to put on a style which opens down the front. Nylon and orlon fabrics take washing well and don't shrink. Some babies are sensitive to wool or nylon.

3 to 6 nightgowns: Avoid the type with string or cord at the neck. Cotton-knit or jersey doesn't need ironing. One of the advantages of a long nightgown is that the baby's windmill kicking doesn't send the covers off so readily. Some parents like to buy a sleeping garment which is long and roomy enough to enclose the baby's feet. It can be closed with buttons or a zipper. In it he should have ample room to kick and move about freely.

A cap for the baby. A warm one to cover the ears for cold weather. Knitted styles are good.

3 to 6 light cotton blankets about a yard square. Called "receiving blankets," these are useful for wrapping the new baby papoose style. Place the baby's head at one corner, bring up the point at his feet, and cross the side corners over his abdomen.

Nice, but not necessary, are dresses and slips, for special occasions.

A bunting, or garment for outdoors. In early months before he becomes so active, you can use a blanket.

Bibs of terry cloth or other absorbent material. A diaper will do.

Bootees and socks: Don't expect these to stay on those active feet, though. The baby's feet and hands may feel cold to your touch, but he may be quite warm enough. He still has relatively poor circulation in his extremities. Unless your house is very cold, covering for the feet is not necessary. When the baby begins to walk, shoes will protect him against splinters and pebbles.

HOW TO WASH AND FOLD DIAPERS

Caring for the baby's diapers is a seemingly endless chore. Between the daily washings, it is best to keep used diapers in a rustproof covered pail about half filled with water. Three-gallon size is ample. Plastic, enamel, or galvanized metal is often used. Some mothers like to add dissolved soap or a mild disinfectant to the water, especially if the baby tends to have a rash in the diaper region. Your doctor or druggist can tell you what kind to buy.

Before placing diapers which are soiled with bowel movements into the pail, empty the stool into the toilet. Remove with toilet paper any particles which cling. Rinse the diaper before adding it to the pail.

After the diapers have been washed, it is a good plan to fold the whole stack at once. Sit down by the baby's crib and chat with him as you smooth and stretch them back into shape, folding as you go. There's something very pleasing about a stack of fresh-smelling folded diapers. Like having the cooky jar all full.

As to the fold, this may change as the baby grows. For the new baby, a rectangle seems to create less bunching between the legs. Fold your diaper so that you make an oblong, three layers thick with an additional foldover at one end. The extra-thick end is placed on the front of a boy baby, to catch the urine; on the front of a girl if she sleeps on her stomach; at the back if she lies on her back. A pin over each hip secures the diaper. Always insert your fingers between the diaper and the baby's body when pushing a pin into the cloth. In this way you stick yourself, not the baby!

As the baby's stomach becomes rounder, you may wish to switch to the traditional triangle shape. Fold it so it can be fas-

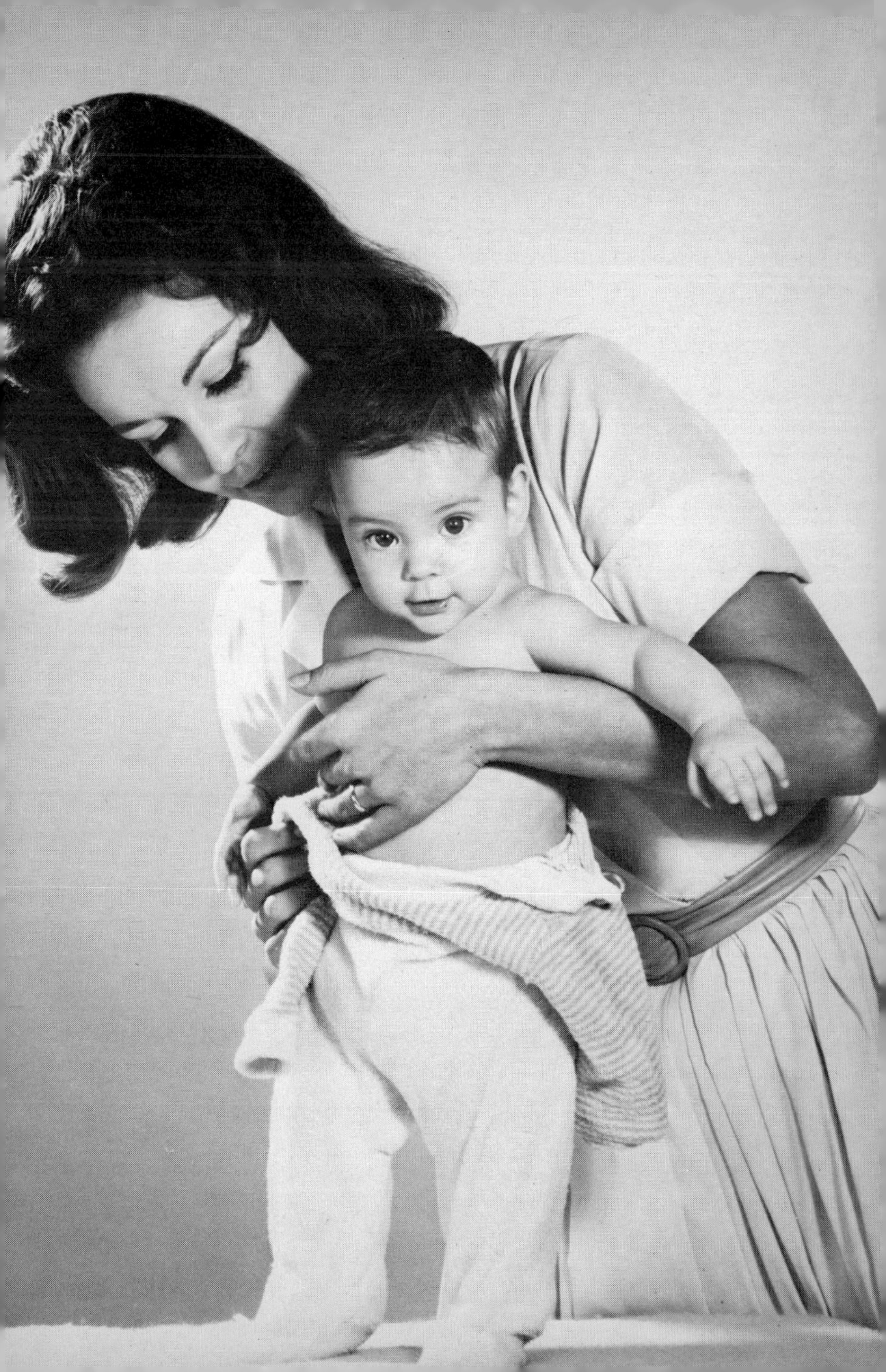

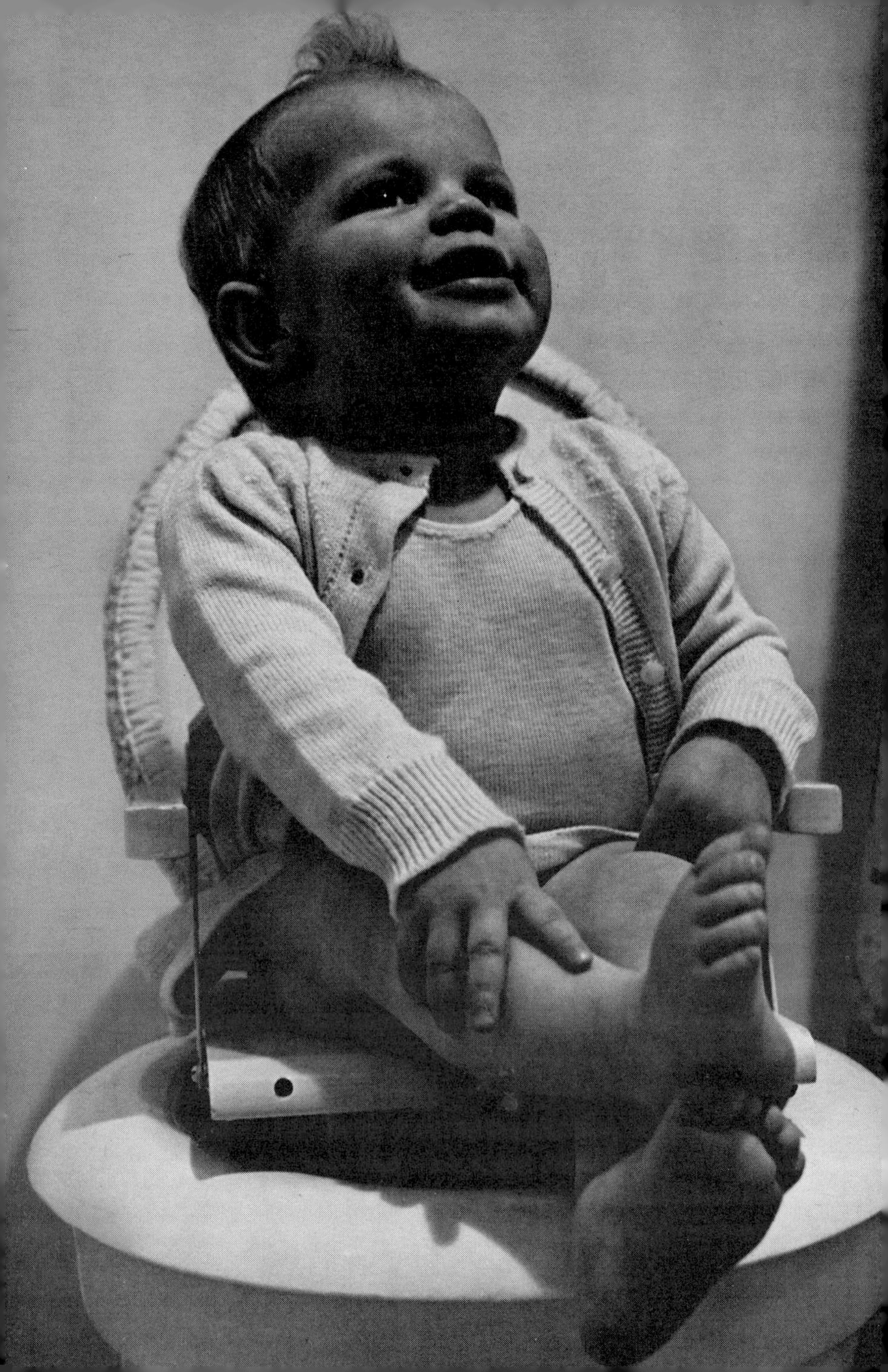

tened with either one pin (in the region of the navel) or two pins (one over each hip).

LAUNDERING HIS CLOTHES

You can wash all the baby's garments at the same time. Since everything the baby wears is apt to become soaked with urine, there's no reason to separate diapers from other things. Use hot water and a mild, low-sudsing detergent or mild laundry soap. Rinse the garments thoroughly. If you have a washing machine, the usual cycle is generally all right with one extra rinse. Until the baby is 5 or 6 months old, it is wise to keep his clothes separate from general family laundry. In a day, you'll collect enough for a full load anyhow.

6. Special problems of new mothers

Occasionally, parents are faced with special problems which threaten their ability to manage alone. The baby may have come prematurely or is born with some defect which will interfere with his normal growth and development. An older child must go to the hospital, and there will be no one at home to care for the baby. The husband may lose his job, or the mother becomes ill.

What seems overwhelming to one family may not appear so grave to another. Various situations affect each differently. Whatever the problem, if you find yourself with more than you can handle, feel comfortable about asking for help. There are persons in your locality trained to work with problems that affect families. It is not a sign of weakness to seek professional aid, but rather a sign of good sense.

Your doctor, minister, or public health nurse may be the one you can turn to most easily. If they cannot serve, they will know where to advise you to turn. If you live in a city where agencies serving families and children are organized into a council of social agencies, or a community chest, call that office for information. If you live in the country, or a town too small for such an organization, you may get information on resources by writing to your state or county department of health or welfare. They will know what services are available and will be glad to help you obtain what you need.

While each situation is different, and you will need the specialized guidance of someone who knows your circumstances well, some general points about a few of the problems which beset families are discussed in this section.

THE LOW-BIRTH-WEIGHT BABY

Babies weighing 5½ pounds or less at birth should have the special care and round-the-clock supervision of skilled nurses and doctors in a hospital. When such an infant is born at home, every effort should be made to get him to a hospital. Talk to the doctor before you set out, though. He can advise you about the best way to proceed. The health department may be able to furnish a special heated bed in which to transport the baby. Ambulance service may be available. Be sure to wrap the baby warmly.

Birth weight alone does not tell much about the baby's vigor and maturity. One near 5 pounds may be just as sturdy as another close to 6. A 5-pounder may or may not have had a full 9 months to develop before birth. He can be, in fact, a fullterm infant. But it is wise to give lightweights the benefit of all the help they can use in getting started.

Much has been learned in recent years about the care of small, weak, or premature babies, and many today live who would formerly have been unable to. In general, the risk increases as weight and length of pregnancy decreases.

The causes of premature birth are varied and, in some cases, cannot be determined. No one knows for sure what triggers the muscles of the uterus to begin labor contractions. The important thing, once the baby comes, is to provide the best care possible.

The premature loses weight after birth, just as full-term babies are apt to do. It may take him longer to regain the loss. Once he makes up the loss, however, the premature frequently grows by leaps and bounds, as if to make up for wasted time. When he weighs around 5 pounds, the baby usually can leave the hospital and will require the usual newborn care.

Meantime, his parents may have been having a difficult time. First, it was hard to leave the baby in the hospital, perhaps far from home. Explanations to friends and relatives were painful. They scarcely dared to hope the youngster would survive the first trying days. As the baby gains ounce by ounce, and the time to bring him home nears, they have all the usual worries of new parents plus the added doubts his premature birth creates. The hospital nurses seemed so expert, and as untrained parents, they feel inadequate.

Hospitals are naturally extremely cautious about admitting outsiders to the premature nursery. As the baby nears the time to go home, arrangements may be made so that his mother can begin to take care of him. She feels so much better if she knows him a little and learns to feed him with expert supervision. Once he's home, the visiting or public health nurse can be of great help. In many communities, the health department assigns one to visit each premature baby.

It may take the premature a while to catch up with babies who had a longer time to develop before birth; but in a year or two you won't know the difference. At first, you will need to make allowances for how young he really is. If a premature baby was born 2 months early, for example, by the time he is 3 or 4 months old he will probably be about the same size and do the same things as full-term babies born 2 months after him.

IF HE MUST GET CARE AT HOME

If it is absolutely necessary to take care of a premature baby at home, try to get regular help and advice from a public health nurse or someone experienced in the detailed and careful routine required. There are several points to keep in mind.

The baby should be kept warm. Instead of putting extra clothing or blankets on him, warm the air temperature around him. Your health department may be able to loan you an incubator. Eighty to 85 degrees seems to be about the right temperature for a very tiny baby. If he weighs 4 pounds or more, 75° to 80° is warm enough. If you cannot get an incubator, cover the crib in some way to retain heat produced from hot water bottles, hot pads, or some other source. Be sure not to cover the crib so completely that the baby's air supply is cut off and be careful that heated articles do not come in direct contact with his sensitive skin.

Keep a thermometer in the crib near the baby so you can be sure he is warm enough. The baby's body temperature will probably be below normal, but don't worry about taking it. There's not much you can do about raising it, and possibly a lower body temperature is good under the circumstances.

In the hospital, the premature baby stays in an incubator where temperature and humidity can be constantly controlled. If the baby has difficulty breathing, a measured amount of oxygen can be added to the air. At home, do the best you can to supply extra moisture. Pans of water or wet sheets on the radiator are not as effective as a humidifier or a vaporizer.

Do not disturb any more than necessary. The baby needs no bath or cleansing other than to remove soil from the diaper area with cotton swabs moistened with oil or water.

Avoid any chance of infection. One or two persons, at

most, should care for the premature baby. The caretakers should be extremely careful to keep their hands clean. Also they should have no infection.

Have a special feeding plan. Give the baby nothing by mouth the first day. Then, if things are going well, offer sweetened water. A strong baby may be able to suck from an ordinary nursing bottle. If the baby can swallow even though he is unable to suck, use a dropper which has been boiled. The infant too weak to swallow must be fed through a tube, which of course requires skilled nursing help.

You'll have time to get a doctor's advice on how to proceed. It would appear that the baby who lacks stored body fat is in dire need of nourishment, but it is better to wait for directions than to risk improper feeding or handling. He can go 2 or more days without food. By then, you can get medical help.

THE BABY WHO'S HANDICAPPED

If you have any question about the development of your baby, are worried if he sees or hears properly, are concerned about his bones or muscles or his mind, get help early. In some cases, early treatment will clear up the problem or minimize it. In others, it will prevent side effects or complications even though there is no cure for the condition.

Your doctor may suggest that you go to your local or state clinic for crippled children. While states vary in the conditions for which they can provide services, most will diagnose and treat children with orthopedic problems; with eye, ear, or heart defects; and with cerebral palsy and epilepsy. Since treating children who have crippling conditions is complex, the clinic staff may be composed of a team, including a doctor, social worker, psychologist, physical therapist, nurse, nutritionist, and others.

Only time will tell just how your handicapped baby will develop. Try to deal with each day as best you can, rather than attempt to settle the whole future at once. You may find it helpful to talk over your worries with the staff at a special clinic, or a crippled children's clinic, or a social worker or nurse in your area.

Parents of handicapped children have received much comfort as well as practical help from joining a group of parents whose children have similar problems. There are many national organizations, and new groups are being formed all the time. Your state or local health department can supply addresses for the various groups to which you can write for current information and pamphlets.

GET HELP EARLY

Whenever you are worried about the way your child behaves—about what he does or doesn't do—it is important to seek the best professional advice. Getting help early may make the problem much less serious than it would become if neglected. Treatment may mean fitting a child with corrective shoes or a brace, testing his hearing, taking him to a diagnostic or guidance clinic, arranging for him to have a physical examination, or whatever.

The handicap is but a part. Being handicapped or different is a hard blow for a child. But it is even harder if those important to him become so involved in the handicap they see only it. Some parents may feel they caused the problem. So they seek to make amends by indulging the child.

Occasionally, such words as "blind," "retarded," "divorced parents" or "emotional disturbance" become so large that parents forget a child is hidden behind them. They forget that, as a child, he needs all of the things we know are good for children. He needs good physical care, including his "shots" and going to the dentist. He needs fun and friends. He needs to be taught how to behave. He needs training and education. In other words, he needs normal experiences.

In the past, many handicapped children were placed in institutions in order to give them special care. As resources become available in the community, more children are able to stay with their families and still get the special training and therapy they need.

Rarely does a child who is handicapped need, or want, the center of the stage. All family life cannot revolve around his differences. From time to time, of course, any one of the children may need concentrated care and other things have to take a back seat temporarily. Long-range plans, however, must take into account the individual needs of all members of the family, including your own.

From the outset, frankly admitting the defect makes life easier for both you and the child. Other children in the family profit from being told honestly what the trouble is. This relieves them of doubts and fears that they or their parents may, in some vague way, be to blame for it. If they understand, they are in a better position to interpret the handicap to their friends.

MOVING TO A NEW HOME

Each year, one out of every five families packs up its possessions and moves. Sometimes this is only a few blocks, some-

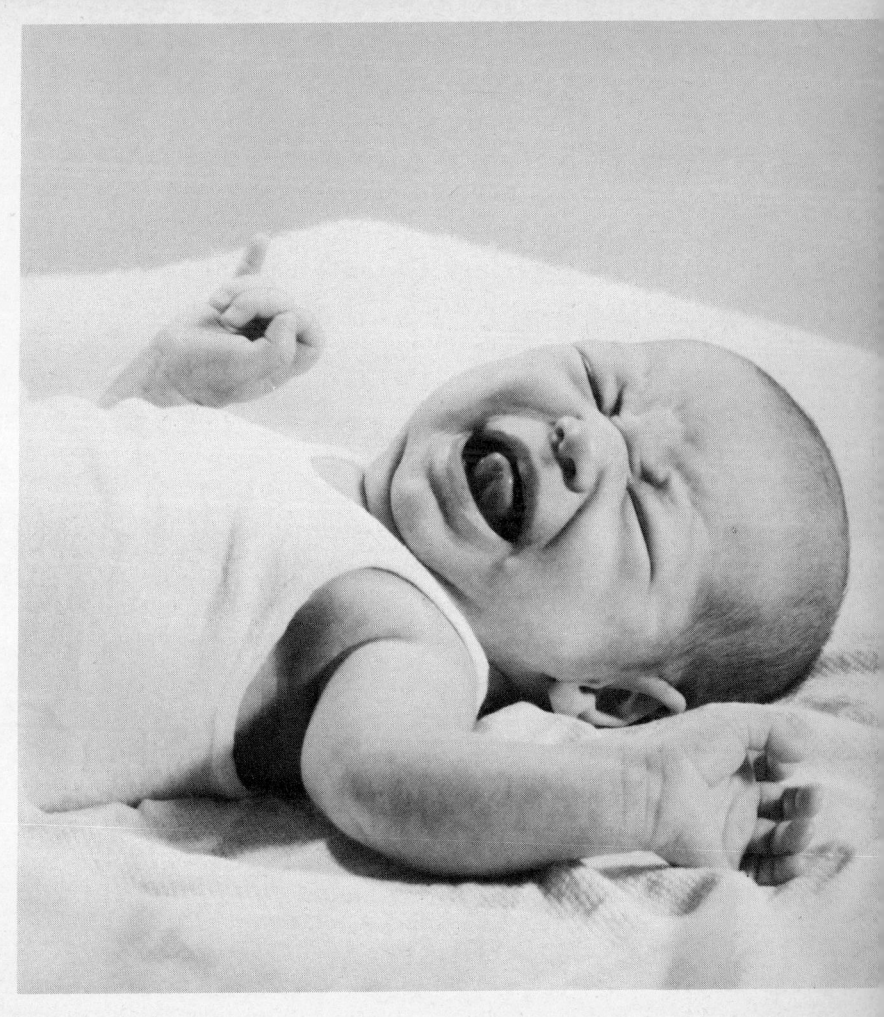

Don't expect the baby to follow a definite pattern of sleeping and wakefulness until he's about 2 months old. He may; but you can't count on it. For not until then will his 24-hour biological cycle (the so-called circadian rhythm) have become established so that he sleeps on a reasonably regular schedule.

times many miles away, leaving behind the familiar world.

For a young child, moving may not be as upsetting as it is to somewhat older youngsters who do mind terribly saying goodby to beloved teachers and friends. As long as the young child stays with his family, things right themselves rather quickly as a rule, especially when he sees his familiar bed and toys and chair again. For this reason, it is worthwhile to haul along shabby or outgrown objects important to him. Through these possessions the child recreates the familiar in his new setting. Seeing the objects he treasures thrown into the trash pile is not an easy thing to take at any time, but it is more upsetting when grownups are busy and preoccupied, or upset themselves in the process of upheaval.

Moving does threaten some children. Occasionally a child takes it in stride at first but shows balkiness or irritability some weeks later. Others are upset from the beginning and may show it in nightmares, bedwetting, timidness, or unusual clinging.

These signs of upset are particularly annoying at just the moment you have your hands full getting settled. You're eager to get out to buy new curtain rods, shelf paper, and the million and one things the new house needs. Nevertheless, you'll be rewarded if you try to devote as much time as possible to the reluctant transplant.

GOING TO THE HOSPITAL

Going to the hospital is typical of other unavoidable separations. Much of what follows applies generally to any situation when a child is taken away from his home, or his parents leave him.

Babies of a few months of age may not be particularly ruffled as long as they get a lot of individual attention and don't have to be away too long. As the child develops a strong attachment to his mother, however, it's not easy for anyone to take her place. Both parents are important, of course, but the child has usually developed a more intimate relationship with his mother, and at any time of stress turns more eagerly to her.

A child under 3 cannot really be prepared for the experience. Even though you tell him you'll have to leave, he cannot really imagine how it will be without you, day after day. For that matter, even an older child doesn't really know how lost he'll feel when the time comes.

For children over 3, you can do some things ahead of time. Talk about hospitals in a casual way when driving by one, or when some friend is having a baby, just as you point out any place of interest. Perhaps you can show your child the hospital where he was born.

Speak of the things that can be done in a hospital. Most 3- and 4-year-olds will be interested in hearing how an X-ray machine can take pictures of the bones inside a body, and about beds which have cranks to raise up your head or feet.

There are picture books which show life in a hospital in some detail—how to eat meals in bed, wear a funny nightgown, the friendly nurse who will help, the doctor who may wear a mask. Most books don't mention the unpleasant parts of going to a hospital, however, and emphasize the fun and the ice cream after the tonsils are out. The child should know he will have pain or feel bad sometimes.

If the hospital trip is planned in advance, tell your child a few days ahead of time. Give a little information at a time, and encourage him to ask questions. You'll want to be truthful without dwelling too long on the unpleasant parts. Don't go into detail about everything that might happen, such as injections or enemas. But let him know about bedpans and the special sleep from which he will wake up in a different room. Assure him that you'll know where he is, and can find him when you come. Tell him that other children will be there, too, and that some of them will be crying sometimes.

Together you can pack his things. Be sure to include any favorite going-to-sleep top or scrap of blanket he counts on. Let him see that things are being arranged for the time he'll be coming home again—his clean clothes in the drawer and his tricycle safe in the corner.

Your child should know why he is going to the hospital, and that anything which is taken "out"—tonsils, for instance—will leave him the same as before. Without this assurance, he may decide he's been naughty and is being punished. It is not unusual for a child to say "I'll be good now. I want to go home."

The more time you can spend with your child the better, even when it means that things do not go as smoothly at home without you. Some hospitals let mothers stay overnight and ask them to take over much of the child's routine care such as bathing, feeding, toileting, and dressing. More and more hospitals recognize how important mothers are to the well-being of their young patients, so they have flexible visiting hours.

Your patient may not always appear glad to see you, for he may want to hide from both you and himself how much he misses you. But your frequent visits assure him that he still has a mother and father. When you come he may be relieved of anxious feelings which otherwise can remain frozen within him too long, causing lasting disturbance. Let him tell you in actions and words how lonely he is, or how angry, and don't expect him to reassure you.

When it is time to go, leave something you value behind—a small purse or pair of gloves. These tell him you will return.

Take leave quickly. A goodby ritual may help. "I'll wave to you at the door. You make your teddy bear wave to me."

When the day to come home finally arrives, everybody expects the end of the matter. Hospital days are over, so all is well. It seldom works this way, however, for the child will frequently let down completely after his bravery throughout the separation. He may become extremely difficult to handle for weeks or even months. The best "soldier" may be the worst. This depends somewhat on how long a child has had to stay. But even after a brief period the difficulties may be all out of proportion to what you expect.

It requires a lot of patience to deal with a child who shows these effects of a hospital stay (or any other painful separation). It is very important to give him what he shows he needs—loving reassurance.

SHOULD NEW MOTHER TAKE JOB?

If you are well enough fixed financially that you can afford to ask the question "Should I take a job or not?" your answer probably should be "No," at least for the first few months. If you have any alternative to working outside your home, it is better for the baby if you do not go back right away.

Lots of times, women who have enjoyed working before and during pregnancy feel they will readily be able to return to the job they enjoy a few months after the baby's birth. When the time comes to go back, many find themselves quite reluctant, in a way which they had not expected. Of these, some return anyway, sure that their misgivings will melt away once they get a schedule worked out. It is unfortunate when mothers decide to leave their babies because they think the baby is too little to know the difference. What the mother can give to

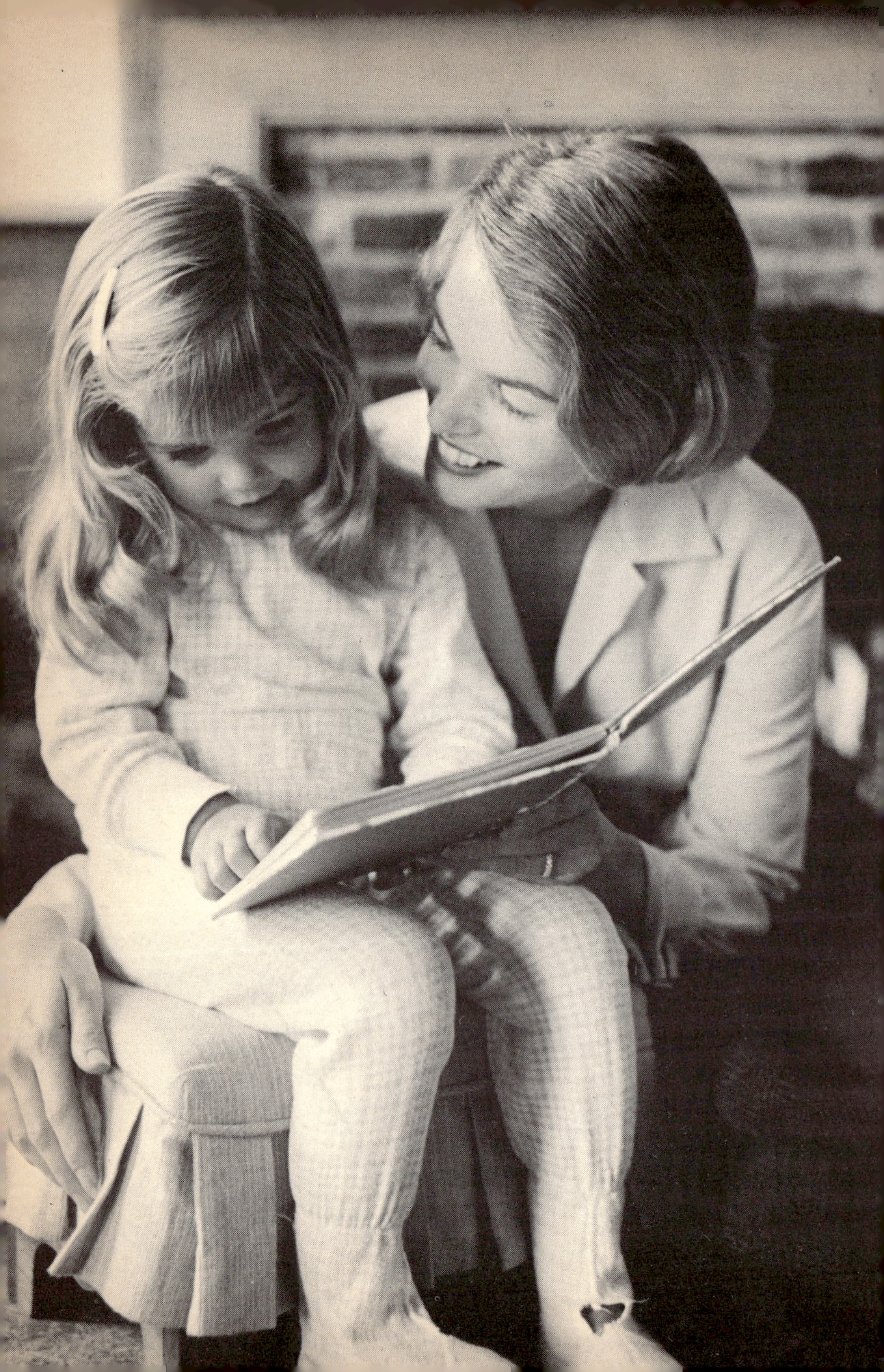

her baby—and gain from him in pleasure—is hard to replace. The months of infancy go so fast, and can never be recaptured.

If, however, you decide that you must go out to work, make the best plan for the baby that you can. Perhaps the baby's grandmother or some other relative in the home can take over without any particular stress or upset to him since, actually, he never leaves home. If such a person will give your baby the kind of care you want him to have, this is the best solution.

Finding someone outside the home to take care of a baby isn't easy at all. You not only want a warm, motherly caretaker (regardless of her age), but you want the arrangement you make to last, so the baby can develop a continuing relationship with one person. Babies don't do well, especially after the first few months of life, if they are constantly having to adjust to new people and new ways of doing things.

If you hire someone to come in, you will want to check references carefully and obtain proof that the one you employ is healthy. If you take your baby outside to someone's home, be sure that he will receive individual attention. A child under 3 years of age belongs in a family setting, not a group. There should be not more than a few (three or four at most) other children for whom the foster day mother is personally responsible. You not only want the caretaker to have time to feed, dress, and bathe your baby carefully, but you want her to have time (and inclination) to give him personal attention throughout the day.

In many communities, anyone who takes children into her home by the day is required to obtain a license certifying that she is fit to care for children and that the physical surroundings are suitable. In even more communities, licensing is required if care is given to children overnight or by the week. Be sure to ask your health or welfare department if such regulations exist in your locality.

Finding the right person to look after your baby isn't all that is involved, however. Unless you have a great deal of energy, you are apt to find the care of the baby at night and weekends, plus the care of the household, too much for one person. In some families, the husband is able and willing to pitch in. It is possible for two people to share the work so that each is carrying about a job and a half, one out of the home and about half a job in the home. If the father is not able to help, you may find that you, the baby, and he are getting the short end of things as your fatigue and irritation mount. Then the baby gets sick with a cold or something else, and you find yourself taking him outdoors when you know he should be kept in, or getting in trouble at work when you take leave. So many things seem to take precedence over the welfare of the baby, and you may begin to feel worn out and ineffective in every sphere of life. Furthermore, you may find that you have very little money left over, after you have paid for his care, your clothes, lunches, and transportation.

A somewhat subtle problem comes up now and then, too. The mother may find that she resents the baby's fondness for the caretaker she has employed. While the baby's affection for his substitute mother may be a sign that the substitute is doing a good job, the mother herself may feel a twinge of jealousy. She may begin to find fault with the care given to the child, become rivalrous with the substitute mother, or in other ways undermine the wholesome relationship which she may, in part, desire and, in other ways, deeply resent.

Despite all this, some mothers are going to work outside their homes, and in all fairness it should be noted that some are considerably happier at a job than having the unrelieved full-time care of a baby. A mother who finds this too confining may be better able to enjoy her baby if she has the satisfactions of her job.

It is best that you take care of your baby for as long as you feel that you can because it is in a baby's first months that he learns to feel love. It is this early love that sets the pattern for relationships with others throughout his life.

When you do return to work be sure to get as reliable and loving a substitute as you can find. And give your baby time to know his caretaker before you leave.

7. Keeping the child healthy

A healthy child is active, alert and interested in things. His color is good, eyes are bright, his hair shiny. According to his age, he plays vigorously, creeping, running, climbing, jumping. He is a strenuous companion, with his never-ending desire for activity. He is usually a bit noisy, chattering happily to himself and others, singing, banging. But when it is bedtime, he sleeps soundly. He needs no coaxing when mealtimes come. His teeth are clean and in good condition. He does not have aches and pains. As the months go by, he continues to gain steadily in weight and height.

Parents used to feel that a big child was a healthy child. They would check the tables of average height and weight for children. If their child was above average, they were satisfied. If not, they worried and tried to find ways to make him eat a little more to grow "big and tall." Nowadays they are more apt to see that comparing a child to an average is not really useful because so many factors determine size.

Standards for height and weight are now expressed as a range or curve which allows for normal differences. A perfectly healthy 3-year-old may be 34 inches in height. Another, unusually tall for his age, may measure as much as 43 inches. In weight, the normal range extends from 25 to 42 pounds. As the years increase, the normal range widens.

Even so, inches and pounds are merely measures of quantity. The preceding description of a healthy child mentions more basic indications of well-being. The proportion of fat to bone and muscle, and the ability of the tissues to resist disease are also important in determining the healthiness of a child.

WHAT DETERMINES SIZE?

Children tend to have the same body build and stature as their ancestors: slender, stocky, tall, short. What they inherit, of course, comes from two sets of families, so already the outcome is unpredictable. From generation to generation, children are getting somewhat larger. Their growth is affected, just as their parents' was, by diet, climate, health or sickness, and general atmosphere of contentment or tension. Since some unfavorable conditions have been removed over the years, young bodies are more apt to reach their maximum growth possibility without interference.

There are fast and slow growers. Although exceptions occur, a child will tend to keep the same tempo. The toddler who is heavier and taller than other 1- or 2-year-olds will tend to retain his head-start throughout childhood.

Even though the individual has his own rate of growth, all children follow much the same overall pattern. Babies grow very rapidly their first year, and slow down in the second. At 2, the child is about half as tall as he will be when fully grown, although he weighs only a fifth as much. If his growth continued at the same rate as the first year, he would wind up about half a mile tall. The total gain in height and weight for the next 3 years will be less than the amount added during the first year.

103

Preschool children usually grow about 3 inches and add from 4 to 5 pounds yearly.

All through the first years, boys tend to be somewhat taller and heavier than girls. But girls, from birth onward, possess a somewhat larger percentage of their mature height and weight. Their bone structure, although lighter, is more mature. At the start, a girl baby is about a month ahead of a boy baby in physical development. By the age of 6, she may be a whole year ahead of a boy her age. By 12, she may be 2 years ahead. This gives girls an advantage in learning how to dress themselves, to write, and to do other things that depend upon muscular control.

CARING FOR HIS TEETH

The child gets two sets of teeth. While only the baby or "milk" teeth are visible during the first 5 years of life, the permanent teeth begin to form in the jaw soon after birth, and are nearly completed by the time a child reaches school age. Whatever nourishment is in the child's body during these 5 years has to be the building material for adult teeth. It is no wonder that dentists emphasize a diet adequate in minerals and vitamins for young children.

Brothers and sisters are apt to be like each other in the time it takes their teeth to erupt. Most children cut a tooth by 8 months of age. They will have anywhere from 2 to 10 teeth a year, with 4 to 6 as average. If a 1-year-old has no teeth at all, see the doctor.

Teeth continue to come in — usually in pairs — until the age of 2½ or 3, when all 20 of the first set are in and the child can handle an adult diet. When a tooth is coming in, the child may be irritable or fretful, and may not eat well for a few days. But

Don't place too much importance on how much weight your
baby gains between visits to the doctor. He wants a healthy
youngster, not a roly-poly. Beware especially of fond but
misguided grandparents and others who equate health with
heft. Each baby has his own growth pattern. He knows best how
much food he needs and will let you know when he needs more.

teething alone rarely accounts for an illness. Because teething goes on for such a long time, it is easy to blame all childhood upsets on cutting a tooth, but it is safer to rule out other causes first.

The first 4 permanent teeth to come through are the 6-year molars which appear sometime between the fifth and seventh birthdays. They come in behind the last baby teeth on both sides of upper and lower jaws, and are sometimes mistaken for temporary teeth. Take good care of the 6-year molars, for they must last a lifetime.

All of the child's teeth are important, however. They enable him to chew his food properly as an aid to digestion. The presence of baby teeth helps to form a proper jaw line. The child's bite, or occlusion of the teeth, is determined largely by his heredity; but premature loss of baby teeth can alter it. Therefore, baby teeth need to be examined regularly by a dentist and checked between times if decay appears or a tooth is chipped or broken by a fall. Before age 3, a child can begin to brush his teeth. He'll need reminding and supervision for many years, though.

To be sure their children have the lifetime benefits of good teeth and sound jaw structure, all parents will want their children to have:

A diet which emphasizes milk, vegetables, and fruits and minimizes sugars and sweets. Too many sweet foods and soft drinks make the child neglect other more essential foods.

Regular checkups by the dentist beginning at age 2 or 3. With an early start, the child will be able to make friends with his dentist through the examination and cleaning. Cavities will be found early and easily treated. If the first visit is postponed until a later age, the child's introduction to the dentist is apt to be less pleasant.

A water supply which contains sufficient fluorine to help prevent cavities. Many communities vote to add appropriate amounts of fluorine to their water if it does not naturally contain enough. There is no doubt that a proper amount of fluorine in the drinking water is harmless and can reduce by two-thirds the number of cavities in the teeth of its growing citizens. If your water supply does not contain sufficient fluorine, a dentist or dental hygienist can apply a fluorine solution to your child's teeth at regular intervals.

PROPER FOOD FOR CHILDREN

Little children need food that will help them grow—that builds muscle, bones, blood, and sound teeth. They need food which helps them to stay well most of the time and to get over colds and other sicknesses. Children use tremendous amounts of energy—running, climbing, and pushing play equipment around. Good food for children means food which gives plenty of building material, regulating material, and energy.

A child will get the substances that do these things if he eats regularly some foods from each of the groups shown in the accompanying table. All these foods are available at the grocery store.

Vitamin D is the sunshine vitamin which does not occur naturally in sufficient amount in food, but which sunshine helps the body manufacture. Most children in the United States do not get enough sunshine because of the weather, the clothing they wear, and the amount of time they spend indoors. Therefore, doctors prescribe 400 units of vitamin D per day the year round, through the preschool years.

This may be in the form of drops, capsules, tablets, or milk to which vitamin D has been added. If your child does not take a quart of milk a day, it is wise to give him additional vitamin D to make up the 400 units per day. An excessive amount is dangerous. Don't give more than the doctor prescribes.

Planning the meals. Mothers have always wanted their children to eat a lot, and probably always will be worried when they don't. That's natural. When you see important foods listed, as in the accompanying table, you probably feel you have a big job to get it all in. Divided into a day's meals, it becomes easier to see how to manage it. By choosing different kinds of meats, vegetables, fruits, and cereals, you can provide variety, match your pocketbook, and cater to your family's tastes. The following sample meal plan for a child shows how little adjustment, if any, needs to be made in the pattern you use for the whole family.

Breakfast	Lunch	Dinner
Fruit or juice	Main dish—mainly meat, eggs, fish, poultry, dried beans or peas, cheese, peanut butter	Meat, poultry, or fish
Cereal with milk		Vegetable
Toast		Relish or salad
Butter or margarine		Bread
Milk	Vegetable or salad	Butter or margarine
	Bread	Fruit or pudding
	Butter or margarine	Milk
	Dessert or fruit	
	Milk	

Snacks between meals. Because a small child frequently cannot eat a great deal at one time, you may wish to plan for a snack once or more during the day. This gives him renewed energy at a time when he needs it—mid-morning, mid-afternoon, or before bed. At this time, give him food which is a part of the whole day's plan, food which will make a real contribution to his nourishment. Nibbling on cookies, crackers, bread, potato chips and the like, with soft drinks to wash them down,

A DAILY FOOD GUIDE FOR CHILDREN

Type of food	Amount each day
MILK GROUP	2 to 3 cups
Milk (fluid whole, evaporated, skim, dry, buttermilk).	
Dairy products such as cheddar cheese, cottage cheese, and ice cream.	May be used sometimes in place of milk.
VEGETABLE-FRUIT GROUP	Choose 4 or more servings including:
A citrus or other fruit or vegetable high in vitamin C, such as grapefruit, orange, tomato (whole or in juice), raw cabbage, broccoli, fresh strawberries, guava, mango, papaya, cantaloupe.	1 serving each day—usually ½ cup or a portion as ordinarily served, such as a medium orange, half grapefruit.
A dark green or deep yellow fruit or vegetable for vitamin A, such as apricots, broccoli, cantaloupe, carrots, greens, pumpkin, sweet potato, winter squash.	1 serving at least every other day, usually ½ cup of vegetable.
Other fruits and vegetables including potato.	2 servings (count as 1 serving ½ cup of fruit or vegetable).
MEAT GROUP	Choose 2 or more servings.
Meat, fish, poultry, egg. Or, as alternate, dry beans, dry peas, lentils, nuts and peanut butter.	Count as 1 serving 2 or 3 ounces of lean cooked meat, poultry, or fish (without bone); or 2 eggs; or 1 cup cooked dry beans, peas, etc.; or 4 tablespoonfuls of peanut butter.
BREAD AND CEREAL GROUP	Choose 4 or more servings.
Whole grain; enriched or restored bread and cereals; and other grain products, such as cornmeal, grits, macaroni, spaghetti, and rice.	Count as a serving 1 slice of bread; 1 ounce ready-to-eat cereal; ½ cup to ¾ cup cooked cereal, cornmeal, grits, macaroni, noodles, rice, or spaghetti.

PLUS OTHER FOODS

Sugars, oils, margarine, butter and other fats may be used in many ways to complete meals and to satisfy appetites. Serving sizes may differ: small for young children, extra large (or seconds) for very active teenagers.

spoils the appetite for the well-balanced meals. Frequent nibbling is also conducive to tooth decay.

Good snacks may be selected from one or both of the following groups:

Dry cereal, with or without milk	Fruit juice
Simple cookie or cracker	Milk
Raw vegetable	Fruit drinks made with milk and juice
Canned, fresh, or dried fruit	
Toast, plain or cinnamon	
Cheese wedge	
Fruit sherbet or ice cream	

If a child has a small appetite, use fruit or fruit juice, skim milk rather than whole milk, or milk rather than ice cream between meals. Because these contain less fat, the child is less likely to feel full when he comes to the next meal.

Other aspects of planning. There are other things to consider along with the food values. Children appreciate foods which are easy to handle. While they are learning to feed themselves, they tire easily and are apt to give up. Soups may be offered in a mug, to be drunk. Many foods can be handled with fingers.

A variety of texture appeals to children. Foods can be soft, chewy, or crisp; and at one meal, not all should be the same. Children prefer moist meats and vegetables rather than dry, hard, or gummy ones. Liver loaf, for instance, is more popular than broiled liver.

Color appeals to young eaters. They enjoy sparkling gelatin desserts, colorful vegetables, or a bit of parsley or lettuce on the plate.

Temperature extremes are unpleasant to most children; they like their food, like the Baby Bear in the story, "just right." Milk and other beverages are often more pleasing to a child when served at room temperature rather than iced. Usually a child does not object to his food being lukewarm.

Strong flavored cooked vegetables are not very popular. Children accept cabbage, broccoli, or kale better when served raw, or with mild foods.

Most children object to having foods mixed together. They get suspicious of what the next bite of a casserole mixture will contain.

Comfort and convenience in the way the meal is served add to mealtime zest. A child's feet should touch a support or the floor. The chair should be of a height appropriate to the surface on which his utensils rest. Small cups or glasses don't tip over so readily; and if spilled, the loss is less. Plastic dishes and cups can be attractive and give child and mother peace of mind. Plan a washable floor covering and washable walls for the beginner.

If a child is too tired to eat, help from an older child or adult may tide him over. Avoid overfatigue by planning a short rest before meals. Let him lie down, play quietly, or sprawl over a picture book. Call to lunch is welcome when the child is about to become bored with resting.

During the meal, a child can often be allowed to get up for a stretch. He can carry his empty dish to the kitchen counter, and come back for fruit or dessert. Discourage playing at mealtimes, of course, but still find ways to let the child move around a little. When he has finished eating, excuse him, for he finds it agonizing to sit while others linger to talk.

The amount will vary. Give your child reasonable portions. Base the amount on what you know he will manage, not what you wish he would consume. If you're feeding him, place a small amount on a spoon. This is enough to start on, for a

Don't expect too much of a small child. For instance: Don't leave breakables where he can reach them. Don't drag him through the temptations of a supermarket. Don't roughhouse with him and then expect him to go right to sleep. Don't expect him not to pick up trash without substituting something more interesting. Don't think he's "bad" when he drops his food from his high chair. Think of something better to say than "No."

trial taste. If he likes it, he can have more. If he doesn't, he may accept it the next time it is offered. If you give him a reasonable serving, he's likely to eat it all. Often children will clean the plate, but are distracted by other things and will refuse to bother with the second helpings you are counting on them to ask for.

Children have spells of wanting the same things over and over, then suddenly declining these favorites altogether. A mother is understandably annoyed when her child refuses to eat the things she has prepared for him. But if she knows that likes and dislikes will change from time to time, she can take whims more calmly.

Sometimes children go on food "jags." If a child wants two or three eggs at a meal for a while, let him have them. In time he will settle down and eat normally.

Unsuitable foods. Children soon discover soft drinks, candy, and other items of little food value. You have every right to place foods you do not consider good for your children on a forbidden list. Some hesitate lest they be considered fussy or old-fashioned, or because they mistakenly feel they are depriving their child. Your child has no way of knowing what is good for him unless you help him select. He is governed by taste alone. Actually, children sense their parents love them as much from what they are not permitted as from what they are. "My mother won't let me have that" can be said in pride.

Nuts aren't good for children under 2. If the child chokes, hard fragments can easily be drawn into his lungs. Popcorn should not be given to children under 2 either.

Variations in appetite. You may feel your child is a problem because he eats so little or is so fussy about what he eats. Before you coax or wheedle, force, or punish, take stock. Perhaps you haven't counted up everything your youngster is eating or maybe you have an unreasonable idea of the amount he needs. This is often the case when the child is around a year and a half, at which time his growth slows down and he needs less food than before.

You may be upset also because you feel that you—and the food you prepare—are being turned down. You're a bit angry at your rebellious eater. You can't help your feelings, but you'll be wise to keep them under control.

There are times—around age 2 and again at 4 or so—when a child wants to be independent. He may well want to be independent about what he eats—and how and where—as well as whether he will come when you call him or go to bed at the proper time. Since this is a normal stage of trying "his wings," go along with him, within reason, and avoid head-on clashes.

What is "within reason"? Families vary a great deal in how flexible they can be about meal practices. However, no one member of the family should be allowed to spoil the meal for everyone else. Perhaps a child in a rebellious frame of mind will do better to eat alone, ahead of the others. His mother can keep an eye on him, but there won't be such an audience for dawdling or naughty behavior. The effectiveness of an interested but casual attitude toward the child's eating is often seen in nursery schools or day-care centers. "Problem eaters" disappear in the relaxed atmosphere where everybody eats.

Children who feed themselves, despite their initial messiness, often retain a zest for eating lost by those who are fed too long. A child may refuse food if he feels neglected or lonely, or wants to get even with people. He finds it very satisfying to discover this way of getting a lot of extra attention—Mother pleads, Daddy stands on his head, and Auntie plays his favorite records. At the other extreme is the child who eats all the time. He, too, may be substituting food for love. It is better to show an interest in the child himself all through the day, and not center only on what he eats.

The child who has a small appetite may find himself lured into eating or drinking more if he is permitted to serve himself, and to pour his own milk from a syrup pitcher or small teapot. Give him a small glass, for if the glass is too large, he gets to pour less often, and is discouraged by the amount.

Birthday parties are best planned to coincide with a regular mealtime. Otherwise, the refreshments served are bound to spoil the succeeding meal. Sharing the lunch, or an early supper, with 2 or 3 friends makes the occasion one to be looked forward to eagerly and long remembered.

Party fare need not be elaborate. Children like foods which are familiar to them and easy to eat.

YOU AND YOUR CHILD'S DOCTOR

Modern parents believe in going to a doctor to keep their children well, instead of waiting to call him when sickness comes. They select a doctor before or soon after the baby comes. Through regular visits, the doctor keeps track of the child's progress, can advise the parents about his health care and needs, and sees that he is protected against certain diseases by inoculation or vaccination.

When you take your child to the doctor regularly, you make sure that defects or unusual conditions are found early, and you can start appropriate treatment before further damage is done. These preschool years are the best time to detect problems such as with hearing, vision, speech, or feet.

This doctor may be a pediatrician—a doctor who specializes in the care of children—or a family doctor (general practitioner). Or you may take your child to a well-baby clinic to obtain medical supervision until he is of school age.

The doctor will want to see the young child at least twice a year up to 6 years of age. This is in addition to visits for immunizations.

Children show some doubt about a physical examination during the years of 1 to 6. Around 1 year of age, a child may be very suspicious of strangers, and resist having his ears, eyes, or mouth looked at. Some of this wariness will disappear by the age of 2½ or 3, especially if a child knows his mother will stay with him. At age 4 or 5, a child may once again be upset by shots, despite his increased age.

Parents help children most when they are calm and firm about the importance of anything the doctor does. By the age of 3, a child profits from knowing ahead of time what the doctor is going to do. Even so, there may be tears. Never tease a child about his fears or call him "sissy."

Sometimes, without thinking, a parent will try to make a child mind by threatening to take him to the doctor—or policeman, dentist, schoolteacher, or other authoritarian person—thus attempting to bolster his own failing authority. The result is that these people, who can be real friends to the child, are made to appear as enemies.

8. Preventing disease and accidents

The everyday care you give the baby will go a long way toward keeping him healthy. You are preventing disease when you give him nourishing food and see that he gets all the sleep he wants. You prevent disease when you make sure that the water supply is pure and that he gets clean milk which is kept clean and cold until used. You prevent disease when you see that he gets regular checkups by the doctor, and when you keep the baby away from any person who is sick.

In addition, all babies should be immunized to protect them against certain serious diseases. These preventive measures can be started in the first months of life.

While it is true that the baby is born with some resistance to disease, you really can't count on it. It is properly called "temporary passive immunity." He'll be able to resist only certain diseases—those to which his mother has developed antibodies which have passed through the placenta. Antibodies to measles and diphtheria can be transmitted; resistance against tuberculosis, whooping cough, and chickenpox can't. Furthermore, what resistance or immunity the baby does have lasts a short time, probably about 3 months. Some experts believe that breast-feeding prolongs this immunity, but it is risky to count on this. For these reasons, it is important that every baby get protection against all the common diseases which can be controlled. The list includes polio (infantile paralysis), smallpox, diphtheria, whooping cough (pertussis), tetanus (lockjaw), and measles.

POLIO

Also called poliomyelitis and infantile paralysis, this can be a crippling disease. Not much can be done after it is caught, but it can be prevented. Two vaccines have been developed. Whichever one your doctor normally gives his patients will be effective. Just be sure to have all your children protected with one or the other.

Salk injections have been used successfully for some years. The vaccine is given in a series of three shots, with continued boosters spaced at intervals throughout childhood.

Sabin vaccine is given by mouth. Different kinds of virus which cause polio are given separately, spaced 4 to 6 weeks apart.

SMALLPOX

For vaccination against *smallpox*, the doctor scratches a small amount of vaccine into the skin of the child's arm or leg. This usually causes a red spot to appear in 3 to 5 days. It becomes a blister with pus surrounded by a red area which grows larger and seems tender. The blister may or may not ooze or break. The baby may have a slight fever or be fussy around the 8th to 12th day. For these 4 or 5 days, sponge the baby off instead of giving a tub bath because the blister should be kept dry. A covering of gauze is needed only if the baby tends to

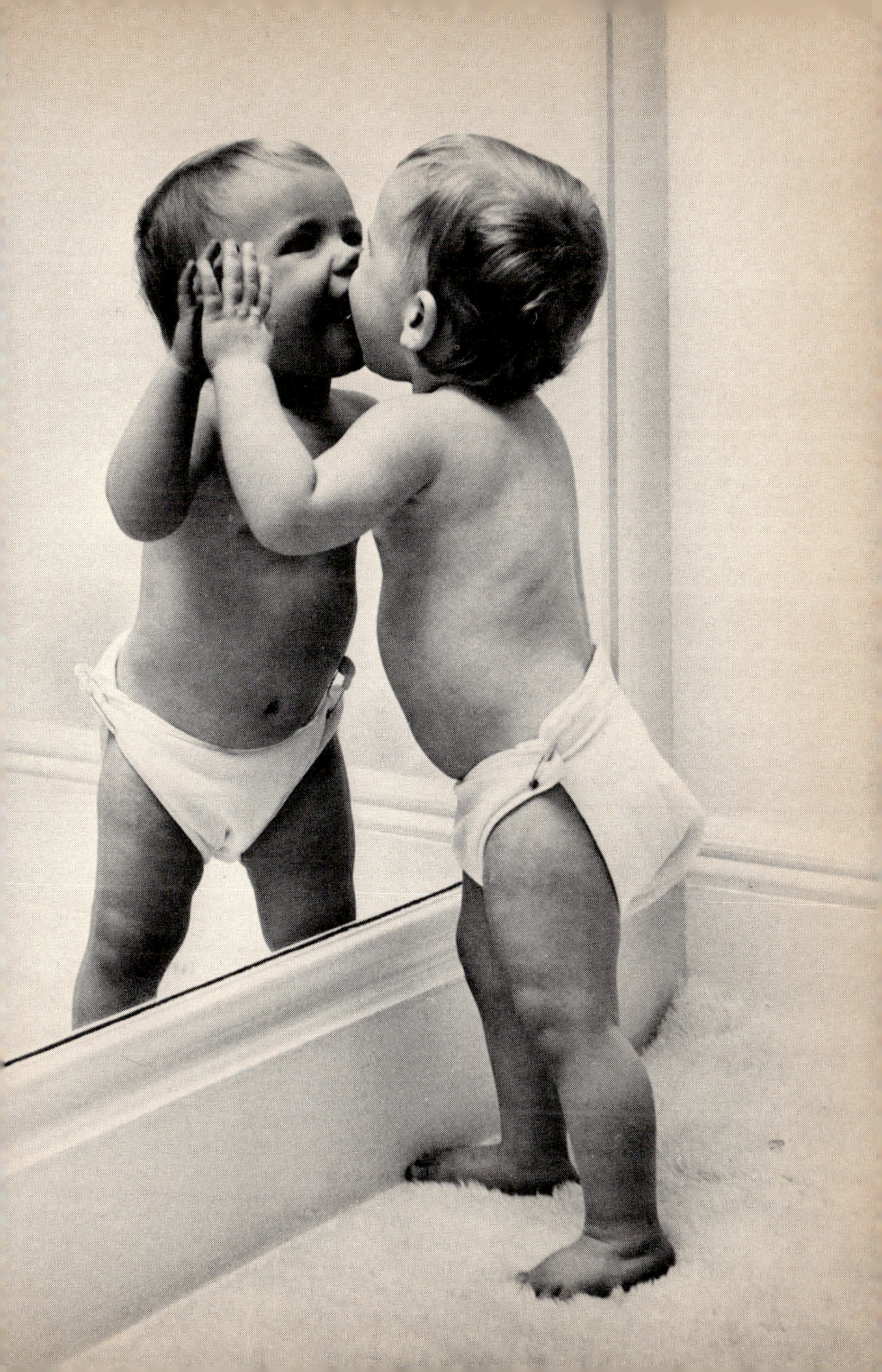

scratch or pick at it. A bandage that keeps air away should never be used. Keep a short-sleeved undershirt on the baby while the vaccination is "taking." If the blister oozes, wipe it lightly with cotton moistened with alcohol.

In about 14 days after the vaccination, a scab will form and you can bathe the baby again. The scab will drop off in about 4 weeks. Vaccination should be repeated before the child goes to school. Sometimes the first vaccination does not "take." Let the doctor know, for he'll want to try again.

DPT INJECTIONS

To prevent *diphtheria*, *pertussis* (*whooping cough*), and *tetanus* (*lockjaw*), a single mixture is given in three injections, about a month apart. They are called *DPT shots*, named for the first initial of the three diseases. Booster doses, to keep the immunity high, are also needed. A baby may get whooping cough in spite of the shot, but it will be a much lighter case. DPT shots produce a slight reaction in some children, but it is a small price to pay for the protection they give and the peace of mind you have. Slight fever, fussiness, tenderness, or swelling around the shot may occur, lasting for a few hours or a day or two.

If the baby is very uncomfortable, your doctor may advise a small dose of aspirin. Give one-fourth of an adult tablet or one baby aspirin to a child from 6 to 12 months of age. You can repeat once after 4 hours.

MEASLES

Measles and the complications which can result may be very serious to a child. Among these complications are pneumonia, middle ear infection, and inflammation of the brain, which sometimes causes mental retardation. Therefore it is important that all children be given measles vaccine.

A vaccine is now available which can provide an immunity as good as if the child had the disease itself. The measles vaccine is usually given the infant at 12 months of age or as soon thereafter as possible. Unlike the smallpox vaccination and the DPT injections, which should be given early, the measles vaccination should not be given much before the end of the first year.

If a child is not vaccinated against measles, control measures depend on knowing when he is exposed to the disease. Gamma globulin, if injected promptly after exposure, may prevent measles or make the disease, if contracted anyhow, quite mild. The effect is temporary, however, lasting but a month or so. Unless the injection is given soon after exposure, it may not prevent an attack. If measles has been prevented by this method, the doctor should be consulted about when to give a measles vaccination so it will be prevented permanently.

KEEP RECORD OF IMMUNIZATIONS

Keep a record of the inoculations your baby is given. This information is needed if you change doctors, if you move to a new locality, and when the child enters school or goes to camp.

Getting an injection is not pleasant for either you or the baby. Chances are, however, at first you suffer more than he does. When he is a few months older, he may remember about those injections he got at the last visit to the doctor's office and be upset just at the sight of the place. Along with this, he's now learning to sit or pull up, and the idea of being held down or laid flat is an outrage. Even painless probing such as looking at eyes, mouth, or ears makes him ready to fight back.

You can help most by holding the baby on your lap and reassuring him with your voice. He can take almost anything if you are there. It may help if you anticipate the struggle by putting a favorite toy in his hand. As the child grows, be sure you picture the doctor as a friendly, helpful person. Never threaten him with "a shot" as a way to make him behave, or with medicine as a punishment.

Through the years of childhood, most youngsters go through different phases of behavior toward doctors and shots. At one time, they'll be brave and unflinching, and later, be fearful and worried. Don't be dismayed about the changes. If you remain calm and firm about the importance of anything the doctor does, the child will gain strength from your continued support. If you, yourself, fear injections, he may learn to fear them from you.

OTHER PREVENTIVE MEASURES

Tests for tuberculosis: In addition to the inoculations to prevent disease, every baby should be checked for tuberculosis (TB) during his first year. Throughout childhood, and up to age 18 or 21, the doctor will want to repeat the test at intervals. Any time you think the baby may have been exposed, get a test immediately.

Detecting TB in its early stages gives the best chance for successful treatment. There are several simple tests. If the baby shows a positive reaction, the doctor will do further testing to see if the disease is active, or if it has already healed. He will also try to find from whom the baby caught the disease.

Babies and young children are particularly susceptible to

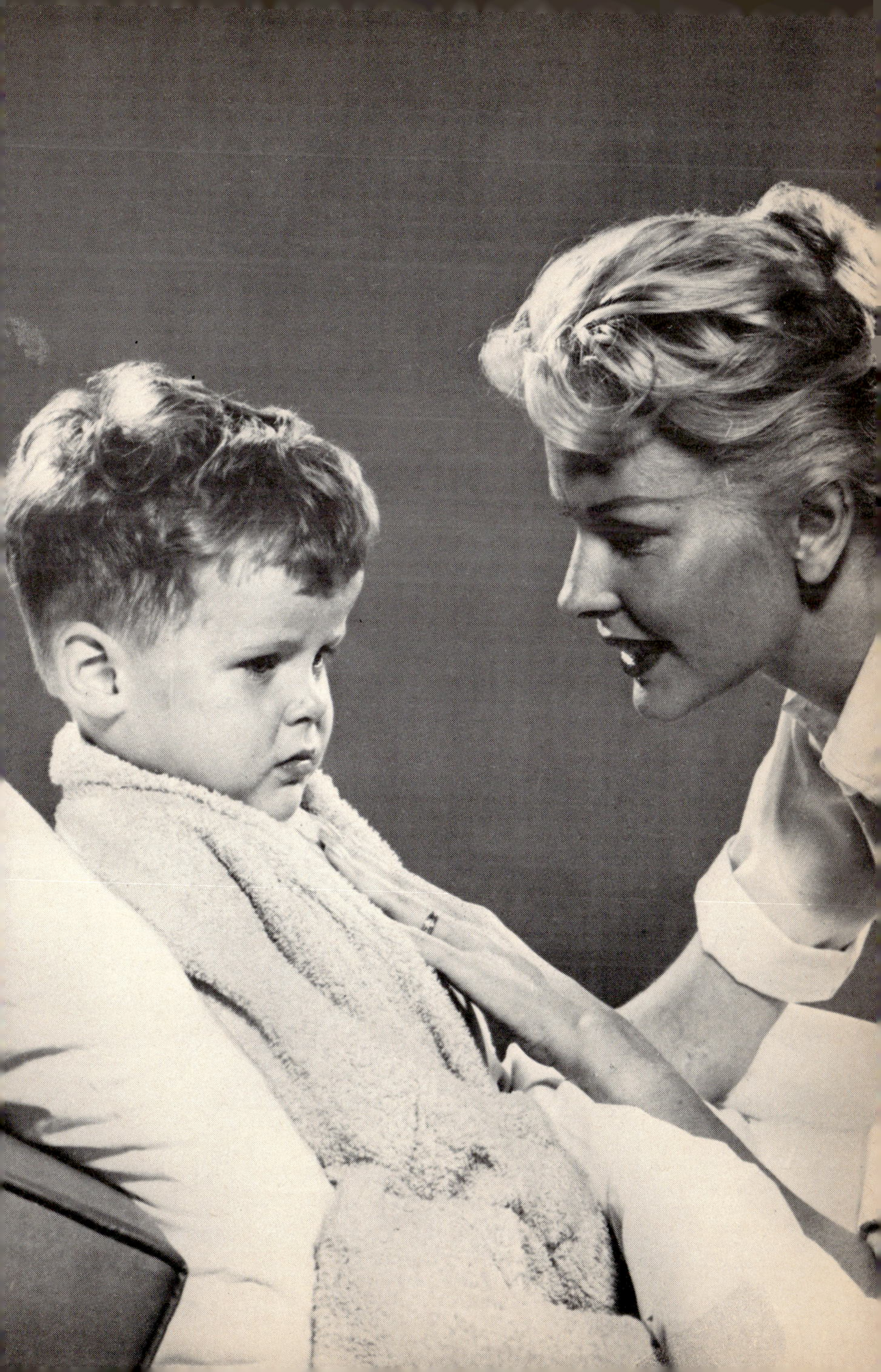

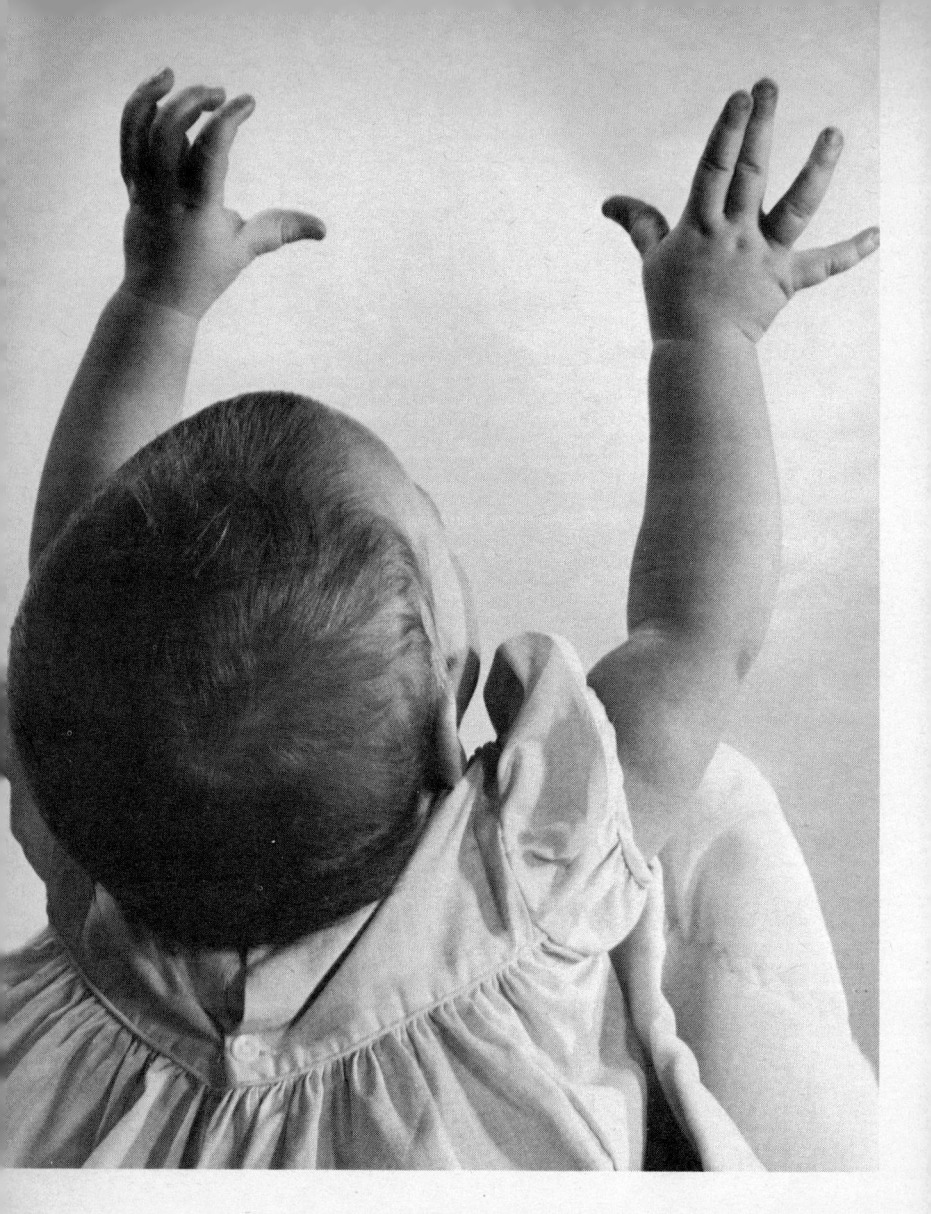

Any baby may be tempted to stick his fingers or some other object into an electrical outlet. So get a few plastic covers of the type that fit over outlets and use them in all the rooms he plays in.

tuberculosis. Take special pains to keep yours away from anyone who has the disease or who has a cough of unknown origin. Ask a new maid or nurse or anyone coming into continuing close contact with your family to prove that she (or he) is free from the disease.

Test for phenylketonuria (PKU): It is becoming common in this country for all babies to have a simple test to detect the presence of PKU. This test is frequently given before the baby leaves the hospital. PKU is rare, but is worth checking for, because early treatment is important. If there is a known case of PKU among relatives, it is particularly important that this be brought to the attention of your doctor.

Typhoid fever inoculations are not used routinely because this disease is not common in the United States today. If typhoid fever is known to exist in your locality, or if you plan to travel to a place where it is common, check with your doctor or health department about the steps to take.

Animal hazards: A baby bitten or scratched deeply by an animal (cat, dog, rat, squirrel, bat, or other), even if it is a family pet, should be seen promptly by a doctor. If you can't reach yours, check with the health department or hospital. Meanwhile, try to capture the animal, alive if possible. In many areas, the police will help.

The animal should be kept under observation for a week or 10 days. If it has, or develops, rabies, the person bitten must be given a series of injections. Because tetanus may also result from the wound, an injection for tetanus, or a booster shot, may be needed. Other infections, and parasites, can be transmitted from an animal to a baby who eats or crawls about in soil contaminated by an infected animal.

Household pets are often remarkably patient about the mistreatment they get from babies—babies who have no sense at all about how to treat live things. Even so, it isn't wise to get an animal for the sake of a baby, especially a young pet. Stuffed animals make much better companions until the child is at least 3 years of age, when he can be taught to be reasonable about poking, yanking, and exploring the waving tail, the sensitive eye, the soft fur.

SAFETY AT HOME

As more diseases can be prevented and effectively treated, accidents loom as the largest cause of death and a large cause of permanently crippling conditions in babies and young children. Yet the majority of these accidents can be prevented.

Expect the baby to be able to do more things and get more places than you think he can. He'll always be one step ahead of you, crowing with glee over his accomplishment as he teeters on the brink of some cliff or another, even if it is only the edge of a bed. Almost every mother has had the horrible experience of scooping her fallen infant off the floor. She may rush to the doctor's office in a state of shock even if the baby is calm and undamaged.

Babies need a certain amount of freedom, though. The baby has to be put down on the floor to learn how to creep or crawl. He's got to inch up stairs again and again with you standing by holding your breath, in order to learn how to navigate them himself. He needs wide-open spaces to challenge him to walk, with an occasional safety island like a chair he can grab.

To make his explorations safe, before he takes his first step, look over your home for hazards which will soon be within his reach. Since he'll become such an accurate mimic of what he sees you doing, learn to check your actions and habits for safety. Put away unnecessary objects and breakables so you can keep your "no, no" to a minimum. Never leave a baby alone in a house.

A toddler doesn't understand safety, or the lack of it. So keep all nooks and crannies free of hazards. Since he will taste and test things, don't leave poisons within reach. He is a great imitator, so he'll do the things he sees you doing. Show him how to do things safely.

As children grow older, they cover more territory, indoors and out. But if you've been teaching them to do things correctly all along, you can begin to rely on their judgment by the age of 4. Don't make temptation too great, though, by leaving dangerous objects around for curious hands.

Explain why you think a thing is dangerous. Instead of forbidding an act, show him how to accomplish it safely — to cross a street, handle a saw, climb a tree. You want to encourage the child to reach out into the world, and you prize his confidence and courage. Above all, while you want him to live to tell the tale, you do want him to have some tales to tell.

Listed below are steps you can take to protect your child.

BURNS AND FIRE

Keep a fire extinguisher readily accessible. Have it checked annually.

Be cautious if you smoke near a baby. He's apt to grab the lighted tip or hot ashes can fall on him.

Screen the fireplace. Never leave a baby alone in a room with an open fire unless he's safe in a playpen.

Turn handles of cooking utensils away from front of stove.

Avoid tablecloths that hang over the table edge. The baby is sure to grasp the dangling corner to pull up by, and can pull off hot foods or a pot of scalding coffee along with the tablecloth.

Use safety covers on electric outlets to keep out the baby's fingers and toys or other objects.

Replace electric cords and equipment when they show wear.

Keep steam kettle or vaporizer and portable heater out of the baby's reach.

Keep the electric coffee pot and the iron (and its cord) well out of the baby's reach.

Guard against overexposure to sun. A few minutes a day, at first, is enough. Keep the baby's head covered and eyes shaded against any continued exposure.

FALLS

Keep the stairs free of objects which can cause you to fall while carrying the baby. Keep one hand free to grasp the handrail.

Place a guard across stairs. A folding gate is useful at doorways to confine the baby to a safe part of the house.

Keep a harness or safety strap on an active baby in the carriage or stroller, and never leave a baby alone in a carriage.

Never leave a baby alone on a bed, couch, or dressing table for even a moment without a barrier to keep him from rolling off. The baby who cannot roll over one day may be able to do so the next. Babies sometimes can hitch backwards before they can creep forward.

Buy a high chair with broad space between the legs so it will not tip over, or select a low, table-type variety.

Keep scissors, knives, and other pointed objects out of reach.

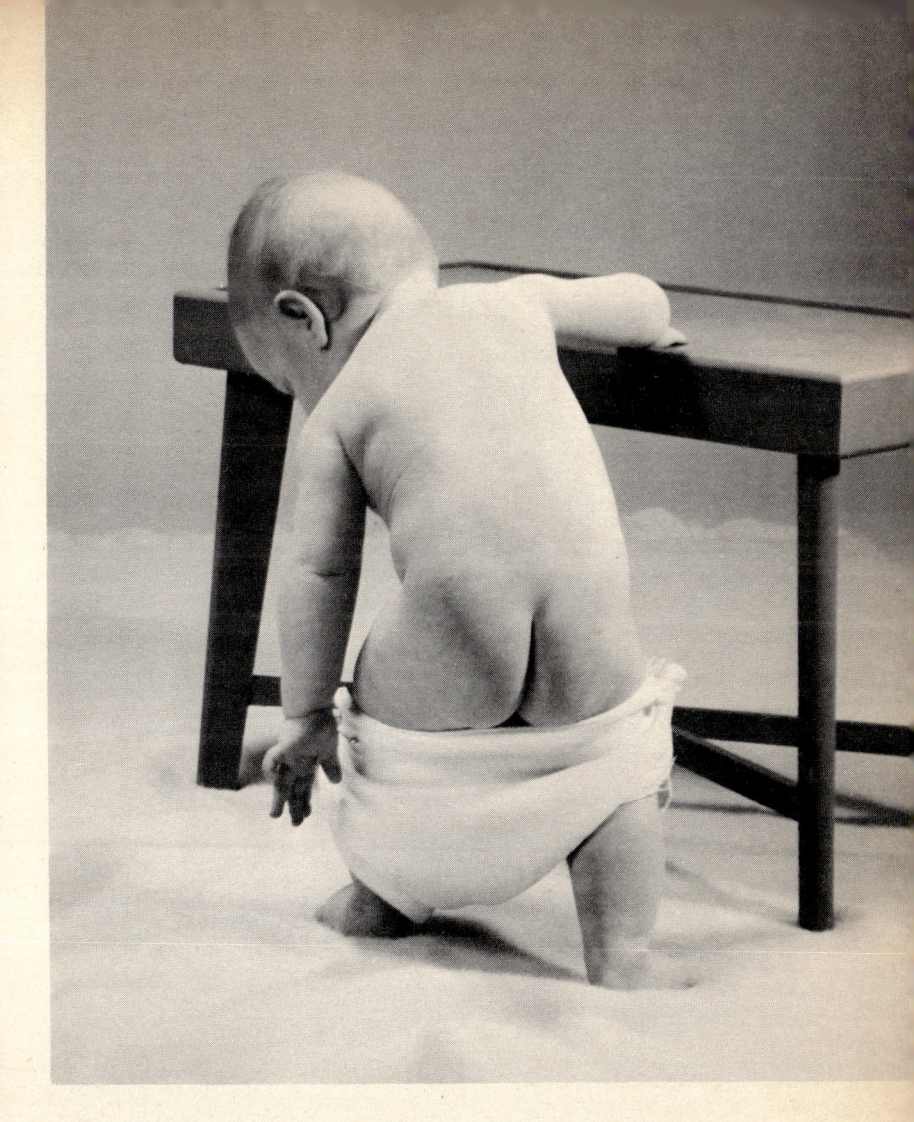

Many children have been poisoned—some of them fatally—by sucking or chewing on toys, furniture, or woodwork painted with toxic paint. It is highly important, therefore, that only nontoxic paint be used on such surfaces. Look on the paint can for some such notice as "Conforms to American Standard Z66.1-1955. For use on surfaces which might be chewed by children."

POISONS

Follow the doctor's directions exactly in giving medicine. Be sure that all products are properly labeled. Read the label twice before giving medicine. Measure the dosage carefully. Never refer to medicine as candy. Do not permit another child to give medicine to the baby unless under strict supervision.

Never store liquids which are not meant to be swallowed in food or soft drink containers, or leave them in unmarked jars about the kitchen. Cleaning materials, paint thinner, hair waving lotions, boric acid solution, and other clear liquids may be mistaken for water or sampled by the baby as he's learning to drink without a nipple.

Keep medicines and cleaning materials in a locked cabinet or closet. Put them away immediately after use even if they have a safety cap. Fasten lids tightly, taping shut if necessary.

Destroy old medicines by flushing them down the toilet. Be sure the baby cannot get at an empty bottle.

Let your doctor or dentist use X-ray on your child when he thinks it is needed, but do not urge him to use X-ray if he thinks it unnecessary. Do not let salesmen use X-ray shoe fitting devices. Many states no longer permit shoestores to use these. There has been much publicity about fallout from atomic bomb tests, but the chief source of radiation to which people in this country are exposed is X-ray used for medical and dental purposes. X-ray can do more harm than good if not used correctly.

SUFFOCATION AND CHOKING

Keep plastic bags, such as those placed on drycleaning, away from babies and children. One plan is to tear them into small pieces before throwing them away. It is not safe to use thin plastic to cover a mattress. It clings to the nostrils and can cause smothering.

Be sure that gas fixtures don't leak. Use rigid metal connections instead of rubber tubing which may wear and crack.

Remove small bones from fish and chicken for children under 3.

Blow up balloons before giving them to the baby to play with. And do not let him play with a collapsed balloon. The child too young to know how to blow may suck the balloon into his throat and choke on it.

Keep small objects such as beads, coins, pins, and buttons picked up and out of reach. The baby is sure to put anything he finds into his mouth, and is apt to swallow or choke on small items.

No toy should be smaller than the baby's mouth or have small removable parts.

In cold weather, when the furnace is on, leave a window open a bit at top and bottom to provide ventilation.

Remove the catches or doors on old ice-boxes or chests. Children love to hide in these. Suffocation easily results.

Don't force the baby to take any oily medicine. Oily particles, if inhaled from choking, can cause damage to the lungs.

Let the baby sleep alone. Don't tie him into his bed.

Place his crib away from venetian blind cords.

Do not feed the baby nuts, popcorn, or small candies, or leave them within his reach.

Avoid clothing with a drawstring about the neck.

If the baby vomits, lift his hips slightly to permit the liquid to flow out of his mouth. Do not pick him up at such a time.

Be sure the wringer of your washing machine has a safety release. Unplug the washing machine when it is not in use.

WATER HAZARDS

Do not leave a child under 2 alone in the bathtub even for an instant. Empty or securely cover wading pools when not in use. It takes only enough water to cover nose and mouth to cause drowning.

Keep your eye on a child who can crawl or walk every minute you are at the beach, or near a pool or lake.

Be sure all cesspools and wells are securely covered.

Do not leave bathtub filled or tubs of water around.

Expect a child to seek out interesting water in the neighborhood—the swimming pool, storm sewer, excavation, or whatever. Make sure such areas are fenced off or supervised.

SAFETY IN AUTOMOBILES

From the outset, teach the baby safe practices for riding in a car. Never let him move about as you drive. Be sure the car bed is provided with a safety strap and can be fastened securely.

When the baby can sit up, he needs a car seat which permits him to look out the window. Avoid those with plastic steering wheels attached. In a sudden stop, the wheel can shatter the baby's face or cause internal injuries.

Never leave a baby alone in a car, locked or unlocked. Know where your child is before you back out of the driveway. Never drive over a carton or a pile of leaves in the street. Children love to crawl into these to hide.

Never let a child stand in a moving automobile or put his head or arms out the window. Provide safety locks for rear doors. If children misbehave while you are driving, pull to the curb and stop. Don't start again until you have them settled.

9. When your child is sick

In spite of the good everyday care you give your child, he's going to get sick. Many of his illnesses will be minor, but some will be serious. All take your patience, ingenuity, and nursing skill. Here are some of the signs which indicate that a child is not-well:

Flushed face and hot dry skin; or paleness and coldness.
Unexpected profuse sweating.
Drowsiness, especially at times he's usually wide awake.
Watery or glassy appearance of the eyes.
Runny nose, sneezing, coughing.
Sore throat, hoarse or husky voice, swollen glands.
Nausea, vomiting, diarrhea.
Stiff back or neck.
Pain in ear, head, chest, stomach, abdomen, or joints.
Rash, bumps, or breaking out on the skin.
Convulsions, "fits," or spells of stiffening and twitching.
Unusual irritability, fussiness, or crying.
Loss of appetite.
Urine or bowel movements tinged with blood.

Any of these may signify a slight or serious illness. Only time will tell. Meanwhile, keep the child quiet, in bed if he has fever. Keep him away from others as many illnesses are most

Bring down fever fast with St. Joseph Liquid **A**

Relieve your baby's fever with fast acting, safe St. Joseph Liquid **A** Acetaminophen Drops. Made especially to reduce fever in young children, help relieve the ache of innoculation and teething.*

St. Joseph Liquid **A** is easy to give, too. The precise dosage is clearly marked on the plastic dropper.

Dependable St. Joseph Liquid **A** Acetaminophen Drops are made to the same high standards of quality and purity as St. Joseph Aspirin For Children.

Ask for St. Joseph Liquid **A**.

*Consult your doctor for correct dosage for children under three.

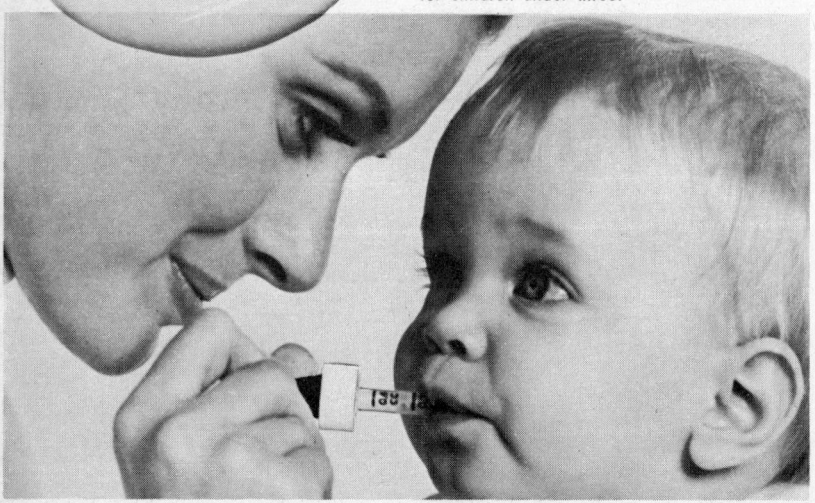

St. Joseph Liquid A, effective as our aspirin.
A Product of Plough, Inc.

contagious in the early stages. And keep a close watch. He may not eat as much as usual, but this is no cause for alarm. Offer him liquids frequently—water, fruit juice, milk or broth.

As soon as you can tell somewhat the nature of the illness, check with your doctor on what to do next. He'll want to know if the child has fever, as well as any other symptoms. Do not give any kind of medicine until directed by the doctor.

Children who are moderately ill may be kept at home rather than placed in the hospital. Today doctors are more aware of the unfavorable psychological results of taking a child away from home. They consider this as well as the illness in deciding whether to admit the child to a hospital.

New medicines have changed the course of many diseases. However, not all diseases respond to antibiotics or drugs, so do not insist that the doctor prescribe medicine if he thinks it is not indicated.

If you need help in knowing how to take care of a sick child at home, call your health department. A visiting or public health nurse may be available to talk with you. Such help will enable you to carry out the doctor's orders more effectively. Taking a home nursing class through your local adult education program or the Red Cross will also be worth your while.

If you have any choice, place the child in a room convenient to the bathroom. Remove extra furniture. It is pleasant for the child to be near a window he can look out of, but place the bed so that no draft will cross it if the window is open. Many children enjoy having a bell to call you when they need company or help.

A makeshift bedside table may save many steps. Use a snap clothespin to fasten cloth or brown paper bags to the bed to keep playthings, tissues, and other items convenient to the patient.

HOME NURSING TECHNIQUES

A child who has had fever should be kept quiet (preferably in bed) at least 24 hours after his temperature has returned to normal. If he had fever more than 2 or 3 days, the doctor may advise another day or two in bed. With this precaution, many serious after-effects of an illness can be avoided.

A sick child needs a daily sponge bath in bed, or a tub bath when he is getting better. Take care that he is not chilled during or after the bath.

Offer the sick child a drink every hour or so when he is awake, especially if he has fever. If he has not had a bowel movement for 48 hours, or has pain in his abdomen, check with your doctor. Never give either a laxative or an enema without a doctor's advice. They may be very dangerous, especially if there is pain or swelling of the abdomen.

Taking the temperature. You can usually tell if a child has fever by the way he looks and acts—listless or drowsy, flushed, eyes bright, face and neck hot. At these signs, put him to bed. You may want to measure the actual body temperature by a thermometer. Your doctor may want you to keep a record of this. Therefore, you'll want to buy a thermometer and learn how to use it.

To read a thermometer, grasp the end opposite the bulb in one hand and rotate the glass rod until the mercury column comes into view. Before you use it, shake the mercury down below 95° or so. Hold it tightly as you shake!

Normal body temperature fluctuates between 98° and 100°. On most thermometers, the bar above 98.6° is red, but a reading somewhat above or below this so-called normal may indicate individual variations, activity, time, or other influences.

Take a temperature in one of three ways. Any thermome-

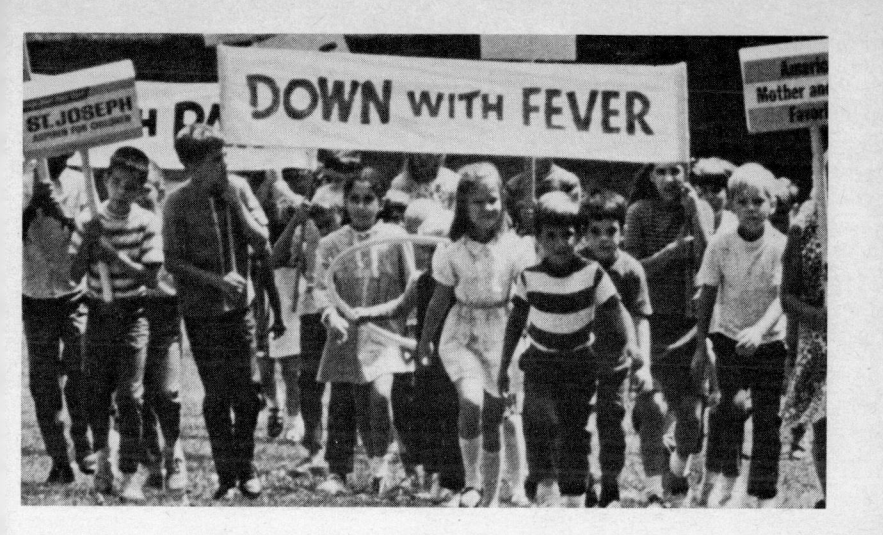

Down with fever!
Down with pain!

Win the victory over colds and flu:
Give your child St. Joseph Aspirin For Children. It quickly relieves the fever and pain of colds and flu that strike without warning.

More children's doctors recommend it than any other brand.

More mothers trust it.

More children prefer its pure orange flavor.

St. Joseph Aspirin For Children is pure aspirin in the exact measured dosage doctors prescribe.

So, down with fever!
Down with pain!
Win the victory.

Especially during the colds and flu season, help your child feel better fast with St. Joseph Aspirin For Children.

NEW DUAL-GUARD CAP!

ST. JOSEPH®
ASPIRIN FOR CHILDREN
PURE ORANGE FLAVOR

A Product of Plough, Inc.

Good Housekeeping GUARANTEES
PRODUCT OR PERFORMANCE DEFECTIVE REPLACEMENT OR REFUND TO CONSUMER

Recommended by children's doctors 4 to 1*
*Among those replying to a nationwide survey and naming a specific brand.

ter will do for any method you select. After use, wash the thermometer in warm water and soap. Hot water will break it.

Taking the temperature by mouth: For a child over 3 or 4, place the thermometer under the tongue and tell the child to keep his mouth closed. Caution him not to bite the slender glass rod or the bulb. Keep it in place for about 3 minutes.

By rectum: Used for younger children, or a child who is very sick. Hold him on your lap, face down, or place him on his side. Grease the bulb of the thermometer with cold cream or petroleum jelly. Gently insert the thermometer for an inch, and hold it in about 3 minutes. Watch against sudden movements which might cause injury. A rectal thermometer has a round stubby bulb which makes painless insertion easier. In other ways, it is identical to the mouth thermometer.

By armpit (axillary temperature): Remove enough clothing so that you can slip the thermometer into the child's armpit. Hold the child closely to you, in order to press his arm against his side. Allow the thermometer to stay in position 4 or 5 minutes. The temperature may be slightly lower than when taken by other methods, but it will be satisfactory for most purposes.

Tell your doctor the method you used.

Usually taking the temperature morning and evening is sufficient. An evening recording is apt to be higher, although this will vary with both the child and the illness. You can't be sure that the fever has disappeared until the temperature is normal at the time of day when the reading has been the highest.

The amount of fever is not a true indication of how serious an illness is. A sudden high temperature may mark the onset of a simple cold, while a more serious condition may never send the temperature up more than a degree or two. In general, children run temperatures more readily and to a higher degree than adults.

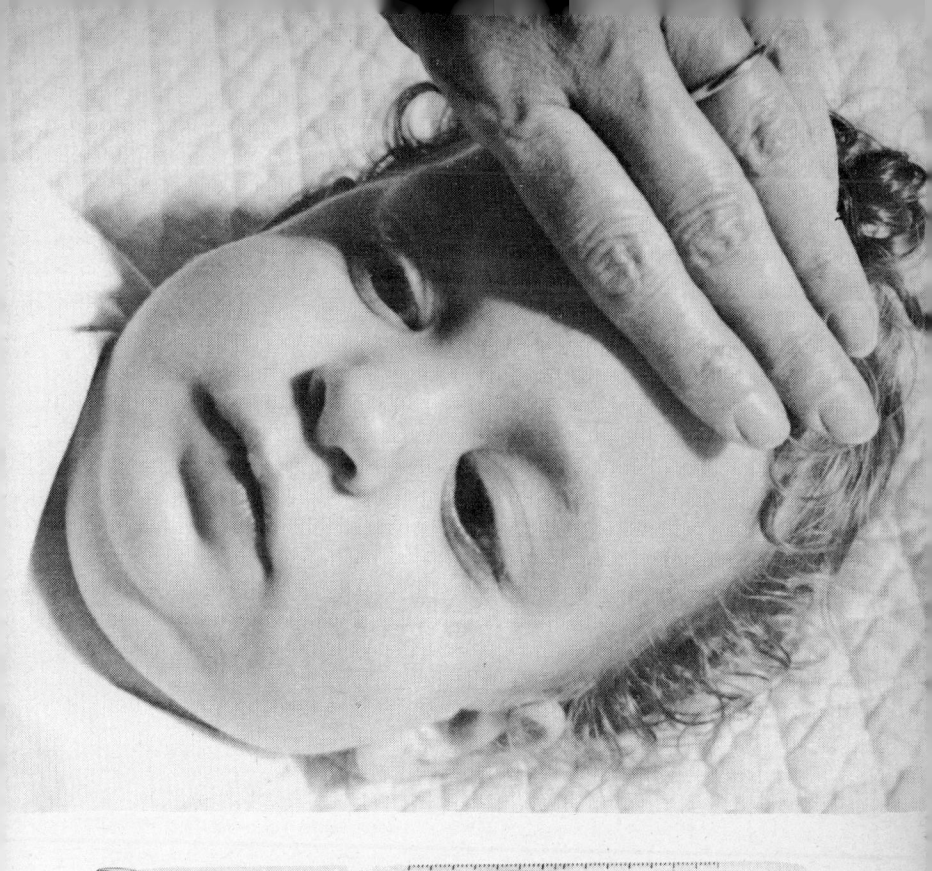

A B-D Baby Thermometer – next to your most precious possession.

When baby feels hot, you'll appreciate the guaranteed accuracy and reliability of a B-D Thermometer. To check if baby has fever. To follow its course and report exactly to the doctor.

You'll appreciate the smaller, stronger SECURITY bulb that provides greater safety and comfort. The clear, permanent scale that makes reading as simple as it is accurate.

You'll always be glad you insisted on the very best.

BECTON B·D
DICKINSON

Consumer Products Division
Becton, Dickinson & Company
Rutherford, New Jersey 07070

If a child's fever shoots up to 104° or more, temporarily ease him by sponging him with cold water. Guard against chilling. If he begins to have convulsions, watch him closely. Send somebody else to phone for the doctor. Keep him from injuring himself. You can't stop the convulsions themselves.

Steam inhalation and vaporizers. Young children who have bronchitis, laryngitis, colds, croup, or asthma are often helped by breathing warm air which is heavily laden with moisture. Let the child breathe steamy air for 10 or 15 minutes three or four times a day to make him more comfortable.

There are several simple ways to provide extra moisture. All of them require great care to prevent burning or scalding. Stay with a child under 3 whenever live steam is being used.

Place the child in the bathroom, with hot water running, or in a small room where a kettle is boiling. Keep the kettle or vaporizer out of reach of the child.

A steam tent is any arrangement to guide steam toward the child and keep it there. This may be done by draping a sheet around the sides of the crib. An umbrella behind the child can serve as a shield.

FEEDING THE SICK BABY

If the baby should begin to vomit, stop giving all food. You can offer him 1 or 2 teaspoons of plain boiled water every half hour or so. Add a little sugar to the water if he'll take it better (2 teaspoons in 5 ounces water). If vomiting should continue, stop giving even water until you can check with the doctor. Severe vomiting and diarrhea can lead to a serious loss of fluid from the child's body. This is a condition known as dehydration, which may require hospital care.

When feeding can be resumed, start slowly with diluted

milk. If you are breast-feeding, give all the cooled, boiled water the baby will take first, and then let him nurse. With a formula, dilute it half with boiled water. Gradually increase the strength of the milk if things go well. If vomiting should start again, stop giving anything to eat or drink for a few hours. Then begin again with a few sips of sweetened water or diluted tea. If this stays down and no vomiting occurs, try diluted milk.

A baby who has been sick for any reason, even though his stomach is not upset, may not eat well. But if there is no vomiting or diarrhea, you can continue to offer the customary diet in smaller amounts. Do not force the baby to eat.

Use simple foods and those the baby ordinarily likes best, but beyond that let his appetite guide you on the amount. Don't introduce anything new at this time, and be prepared to go back a few steps if need be. The baby may, for instance, want to have his bottle again even though he's been taking most of his milk from a cup. He may need to be fed, even though he's been starting to feed himself. He may want soup, gruel, or purée even though he ordinarily likes to bite and chew. Follow the clues he gives you.

Fluids are more important than solid food when there is a fever. You can often get additional liquid into the baby by offering water flavored with fruit juice, sips of cola, ginger ale, sweetened diluted tea, or flavored gelatin in liquid form. Liquids in a form that can be sucked or eaten rather than drunk appeal to the older baby — ice cubes, homemade frozen fruit sticks, colored gelatin cubes.

GENERAL CARE

The sick, fretful baby will take a lot of your time, night and day perhaps. He may need to be soothed, sponged off, given fluids to drink, talked to, or just held and rocked. Give him all the comfort and attention you can, without fear that it will spoil him. When he begins to get well, his eager, normal interest in his surroundings will return. If he ordinarily gets a full fair share of your interest at intervals throughout the day, he is not apt to seek more attention.

Until you talk to the doctor, do not give any medicine. Even though you have some left over from a previous illness of the baby or somebody else in the house, it may not be safe to use for this case.

Don't give a laxative or enema just to clear out the baby's system. Use them only when the doctor specifically says to.

Avoid abrupt changes of temperature, or a shift from steamy warm air to cool dry air. Keep the baby's room comfortably warm, but do not overheat. A temperature of 70° to 72° is warm enough for the sick baby.

AMUSING THE CONVALESCENT

Usually a child is very good about staying in bed when he is acutely ill. But a child who is getting well is another matter. Children have such remarkable come-back powers that, once an acute illness is over, they soon feel fine and begin to clamor to get up. Instead of nagging a child to stay in bed, a wise mother will try to find ways to keep him contented there. But if restriction is upsetting, it may do more harm than letting him get up. Sometimes the child will lie quietly on the sofa or on his parents' bed, nearer the base of family activity. A steady diet of television is to be avoided.

For young children, a new cuddly animal or doll, or an old and loved one, large beads to string, coloring books, or a toy telephone are entertaining. Fish, a tiny turtle, or a bird will provide company and amusement. A homemade mobile is fun—both to make and to watch after it is suspended.

Older children enjoy pegboards, weaving sets, and jigsaw puzzles (make your own by pasting picture to cardboard and cutting it up). Magazines or mail order catalogs provide an unending source of interest. Old greeting cards can be cut apart and pasted into a scrapbook made of paper bags or colored paper tied together to form a book.

You may feel that paint, clay and water play are too messy for the child in bed. If you can stand it, though, they are prize activities for keeping a child amused and quiet. Try the watercolor sticks which have the paint inside. A 10-cent-store jar of soap bubble liquid is fine for a child of 4 or more. Most can handle it without spilling.

Sick children usually prefer less complicated activities than those which appeal to them when they are well.

10. Common diseases and disorders

Of course, you'll want to take any question about your baby's health to your doctor. The following brief descriptions will give you background information on some diseases and disorders which affect babies. They will not take the place of a doctor's diagnosis and treatment.

Brought together in this way, the number may seem alarming, but no baby will get more than a few. They are grouped more or less according to the part of the body affected. We'll lead with the mouth, as the baby does.

THE BABY'S MOUTH

While generally speaking the baby's mouth needs no special attention, there is one fairly common mild infection called *thrush*. Thrush causes white spots, rather like milk curds that will not rub off, to appear on the baby's tongue. Occasionally, it will spread to the inside of cheeks and roof of the mouth or inner lips. Thrush usually clears up without causing trouble. Give the baby a drink of cool boiled water to rinse out his mouth after feeding. This is enough to do. Swabs or gauze are too rough. Thrush seems to grow more readily when there is a residue of milk left in the mouth.

Thrush can be caused by the use of unclean bottles or nipples. It may result if older children in the family play with the baby's bottle. Their hands may carry the infection, though they no longer are susceptible to it. To avoid thrush, keep bottles, nipples, and equipment used in preparing formula clean by washing them thoroughly and boiling them.

Check with the doctor if the baby's mouth becomes sore, bleeds, or is generally inflamed.

DON'T ALWAYS BLAME TEETHING

Occasionally, babies have some discomfort when they are cutting teeth, but teething by itself rarely accounts for actual illness. If the baby has fever, is coughing, does not eat well, or has other signs of illness, he should be checked to see if there are other causes. Some mothers blame everything from crankiness to rashes on teething, which tends to make them overlook the real trouble.

If the baby's gums are sore, it may help to give him toast or a hard rubber ring to chew on. Keep him from gnawing on wood surfaces or on toys painted with paint which is not safe for children. A fretful, teething baby may need extra patience and attention for a few days.

TONGUE-TIE

Every now and then parents worry because the little cord under the tongue appears to be too short. They wonder if their baby is tongue-tied. If the baby can move his tongue out to his lip and from side to side, there's no cause for concern. The little cord seldom has anything to do with speech problems, and never causes a baby to be late in talking.

DEFECTIVE VISION

If your baby seems uninterested in lights and movement of objects (not held closer than 2 feet), his vision may be defective. Report this to your doctor at once. A baby does not see clearly before 4 to 6 months of age, but should be aware of and alert to his surroundings. As he grows older, his vision matures and should be approximately 20/20 by school age.

CROSSED EYES

During the first few months, not only is the baby's vision blurred, but the eye muscles are poorly coordinated and frequently the eyes are out of line. If your child seems to have crossed eyes after the age of 4 months, that may mean one of two things. The false appearance of crossing may be because of the broad flat bridge of the nose and the close-set eyes; or there may be true tendency to crossed eyes. It is hard to know, and often only the medical eye specialist can decide. If appearance of crossed eyes is due solely to the features, time will correct it. If true crossed eyes (strabismus) is present, treatment is important and the earlier the better. Crossed eyes do not cure themselves.

Treatment may consist of patching (or covering) the "good" eye to improve the vision in the crossed eye; medication; glasses (at any age after 1 year); or surgery. If the cross is due to muscle difficulty, surgery is important. If the cross is due to eye strain (usually not before the age of 18 months), the treatment is medication or glasses.

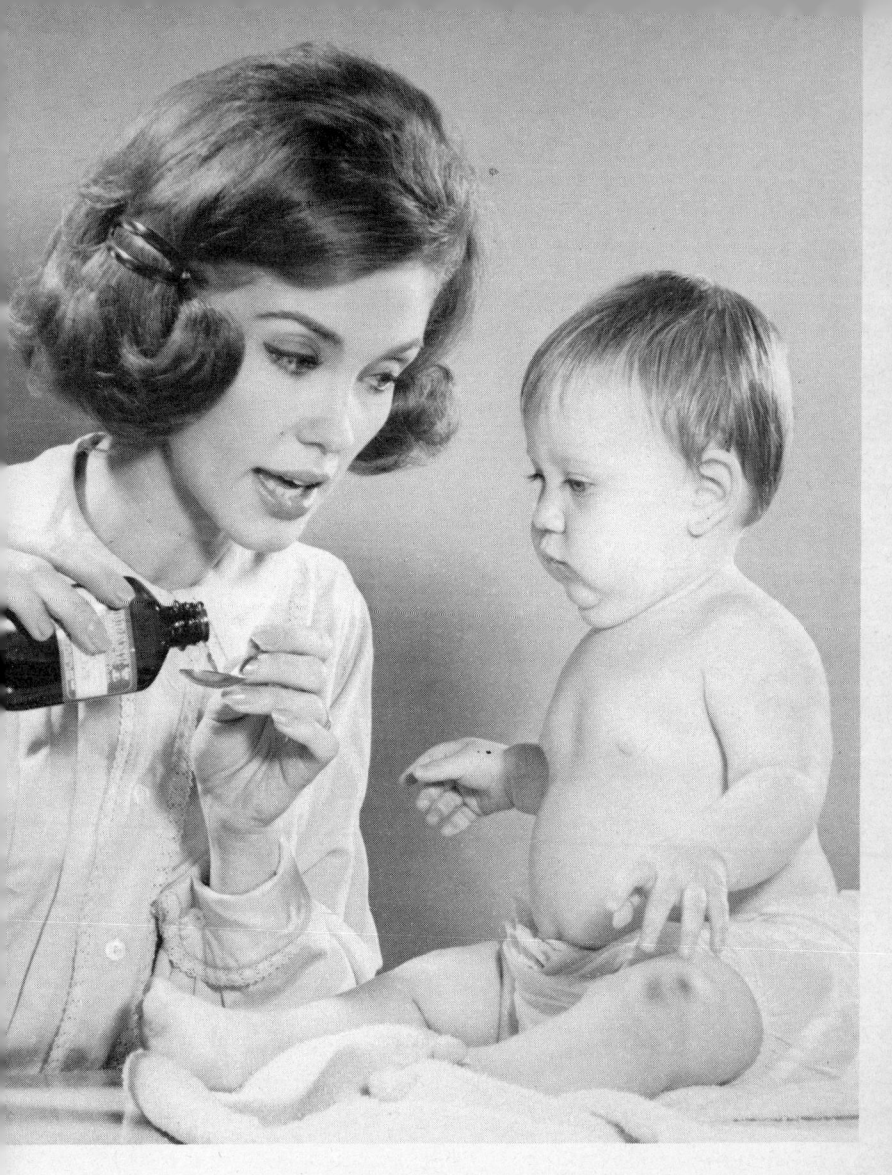

Since poisoning is an ever-present danger among children, many physicians provide the new mother with a small bottle of ipecac, to be used as instructed to induce vomiting. If your doctor has not done this, ask him about it.

INFLAMED, TEARING EYES

Watery, irritated eyes are not unusual for a few days after birth. If, however, thick pus forms or inflammation continues more than 4 or 5 days, this is *not* due to the drops that were put in the baby's eyes at birth but rather to infection. Report this condition to your doctor. Continued infection may cause serious damage to vision.

A small number of babies will have watery eyes with some discharge due to blocked tear ducts. When tears begin to form at 10 to 14 days of age, they are not able to drain off through the blocked tear ducts. Tears will stand in the eyes, run down the cheek, and some pus discharge may be present, especially in the morning. If blocked tear ducts have not cleared by the age of 3 to 4 months, your doctor may want to open them, a relatively easy and innocuous process. The real danger in blocked tear ducts is that secondary infection may take place and cause real damage to the eye.

RESPIRATORY INFECTIONS

By far the most frequent and troublesome problems are those of the upper and lower respiratory tract—the nose, ears, throat, lungs, and bronchial tubes. A first baby may escape with few infections of this type. But the second and third child picks up everything the older brothers and sisters bring home, and lots of times, it's a cold. The baby has not had time to develop defenses against infection, and what may be a mild cold for an older child hits the baby much harder.

You can't afford to treat signs of a cold lightly. At the outset, it is impossible to tell what will develop. Keep the baby quiet, give him extra fluids, keep him indoors if the weather is

149

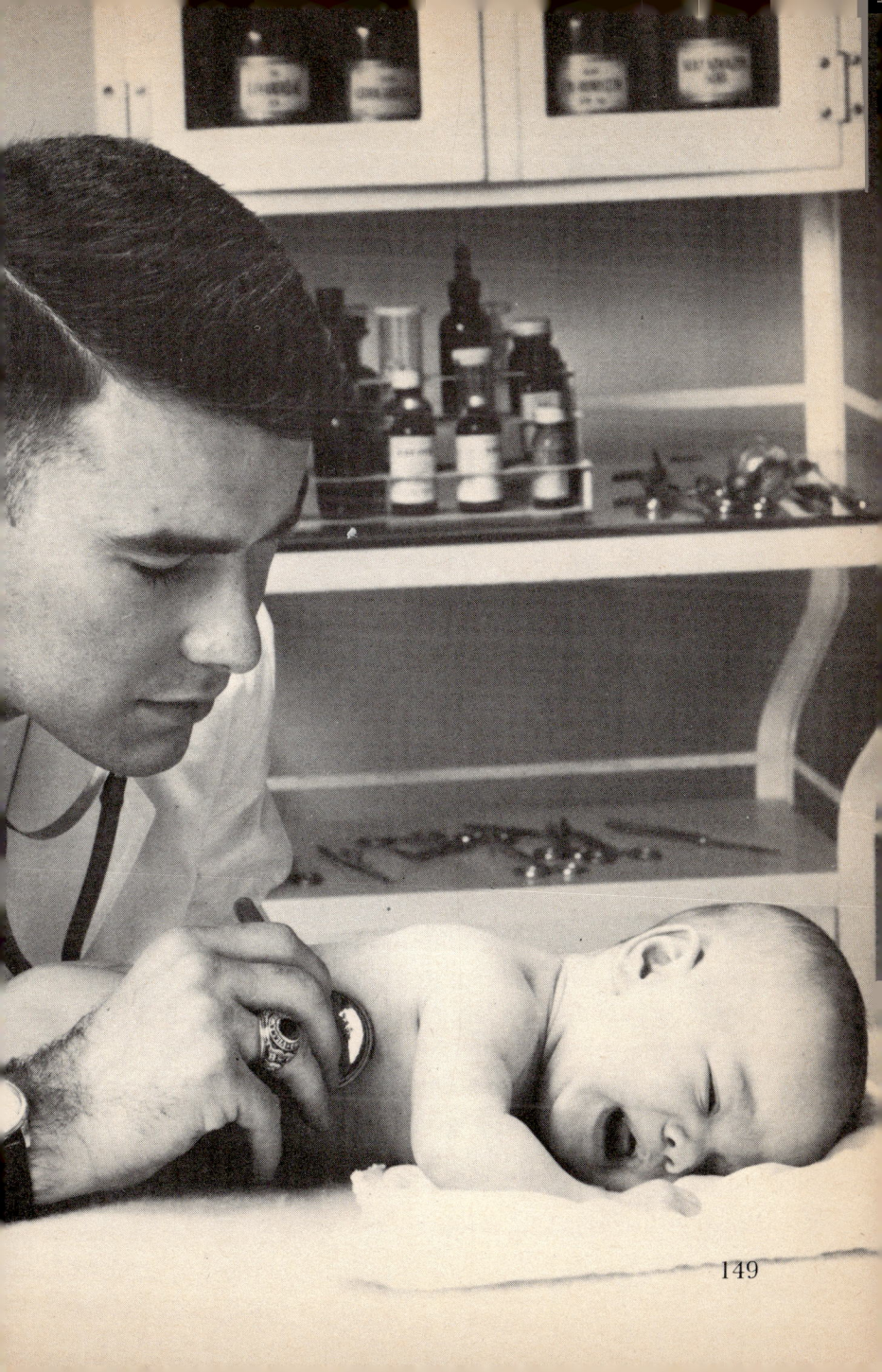

at all chilly or unpleasant. Check with the doctor for further steps to take, and keep in touch with him if symptoms change.

If the baby's nose is so stuffed up he can scarcely nurse or sleep, check with the doctor about nose drops. Find out when to stop using them, too. Some types shrink the swollen membranes and bring relief of a temporary nature—long enough for you to feed the child, or get him to sleep. Never use oily nose drops. Steam or added moisture in the air may be helpful.

Sometimes there is fever at the onset of a cold which will gradually disappear in a few days. A sudden rise in temperature around the fifth day or later may signify a new infection on top of the old one. A cold lasts longer with a baby than an older person. Ten to fourteen days is about average. If there is discharge from the nose or a cough after 2 weeks, something more than a cold may be causing it. Always investigate if such symptoms hang on.

Tonsils and adenoids are spongy masses of tissue at the back of the throat and nose. In function, they are similar to other glands in the body such as those of the groin, under the jaw, and in the armpit. Tonsils and adenoids tend to increase in size through early years of childhood and then to shrink by age 8 to 10. Diseased tonsils and adenoids are sometimes removed if there is chronic trouble with them, but this is done less frequently now than in the past. It isn't necessary to take them out simply because they are large. Removal of tonsils and adenoids is something you don't have to worry about in infancy.

When the larynx (the upper part of the air passage to the lungs containing the vocal cords) becomes inflamed, the resulting congestion can cause the typical barking cough of *croup*. Breathing becomes rapid, noisy, and difficult. Because the air passages are small in diameter, the congestion may lead to more serious difficulty with a baby than with an older child. Call the doctor if croup occurs.

If you are caring for a baby with croup at home, stay with him, holding and reassuring him, for his fright and struggle for air may increase his problems. It is a good idea to sleep in the same room with a croupy baby in order to keep close check on the situation.

A baby who is congested with croup may get a lot of relief from breathing warm air heavily laden with moisture. You can add moisture to the air in many different ways. Buy a vaporizer or steam kettle if you can. It will be useful often. Get a large size which will send out lots of moisture and the type which shuts off when empty. Follow the manufacturer's directions for use and care of the equipment.

You can make steam in other ways, too. If your water supply is hot enough to make steam in a closed room, take the baby into the bathroom, close the door, and let the water run. Or place a kettle or open pan on a hotplate in the child's room. Whenever you use steam or heat near the baby, take great care to keep him from getting burned or scalded. Always stay with an active baby under 3 years of age when steam or a vaporizer is being used. Even then, place it well beyond his reach. If the doctor tells you to use a steam tent, you can make one by draping a sheet over the side of the crib, or placing an opened umbrella behind the child. Or you can sit near steam, holding the child in your lap, and an umbrella over both of you.

Pneumonia is a general term for infection of the lungs. It can be caused by different kinds of bacteria or virus, or the presence of foreign matter such as fatty droplets of liquids which have been inhaled.

Frequently pneumonia begins with high fever, chills, vomiting, and cough. The baby may appear to be recovering from a cold or common childhood disease, when a sudden change in condition indicates the fresh infection. Modern drugs bring about prompt recovery in most instances when treatment is begun early.

Ear infection: Any infection of the respiratory tract can spread to the ear through the Eustachian tube which connects the back of the throat with the middle ear. In a baby, it is very short in length, so infection does not have far to travel. An ear infection may flare up suddenly with fever and sharp pain which causes the baby to fight and scream. Infection can be present, however, without these vivid warnings, and you may not know of its existence until pus appears in the outer ear.

In either case, take the baby to the doctor. Treatment should be given to clear all traces of infection. A lingering ear infection can permanently damage the child's hearing. To give relief to a baby in pain, apply either warmth or cold if you can make him hold still long enough. Use a hot water bottle, partially filled with ice or warm water and wrapped in a towel. Just picking him up seems to relieve some of the pressure on the ear, and reassures him besides.

ASTHMA

Asthma is an allergic response to some substance, usually something in the air or in food. In an asthmatic attack, the air passages of the lower respiratory tract become narrowed and produce mucus so the baby has trouble breathing and he wheezes and coughs.

A first asthma attack is very frightening, and usually comes at night, when anything seems worse. It may relieve the baby if you pick him up so he can breathe more easily. Let him breathe air to which moisture is added.

As with other allergies, treatment depends on finding and eliminating the offending substance. You'll need the doctor's help. In some cases, asthma is caused by allergy to certain germs, including those of a cold. Because of their tiny tubes, babies frequently simulate the wheezes of asthma, but this response is not always an allergic one.

COMMUNICABLE DISEASES

Information about common, and a few less common, communicable diseases is summarized in the accompanying charts.

If your baby is exposed to any of the diseases listed and has not been given protective injections, check with your doctor. Some of the diseases can be modified by protective serum if given in time.

Communicable diseases spread from one person to another, usually one child to another. It is worth going to a lot of trouble to avoid letting your baby get exposed to one of them. While contracting the childhood diseases is probably inevitable, and with some is a good thing before adulthood, infancy is not the time. Whenever a baby contracts an illness, even if you think you know exactly what it is, get in touch with the doctor for diagnosis and help with treatment.

Meningitis is a serious disease which requires prompt medical attention. The most usual form begins abruptly, and the infant becomes obviously ill, with high temperature, stiff neck, vomiting, and often convulsions or a stupor. A fine, purplish-red rash may appear that hemorrhages into the skin. Take a

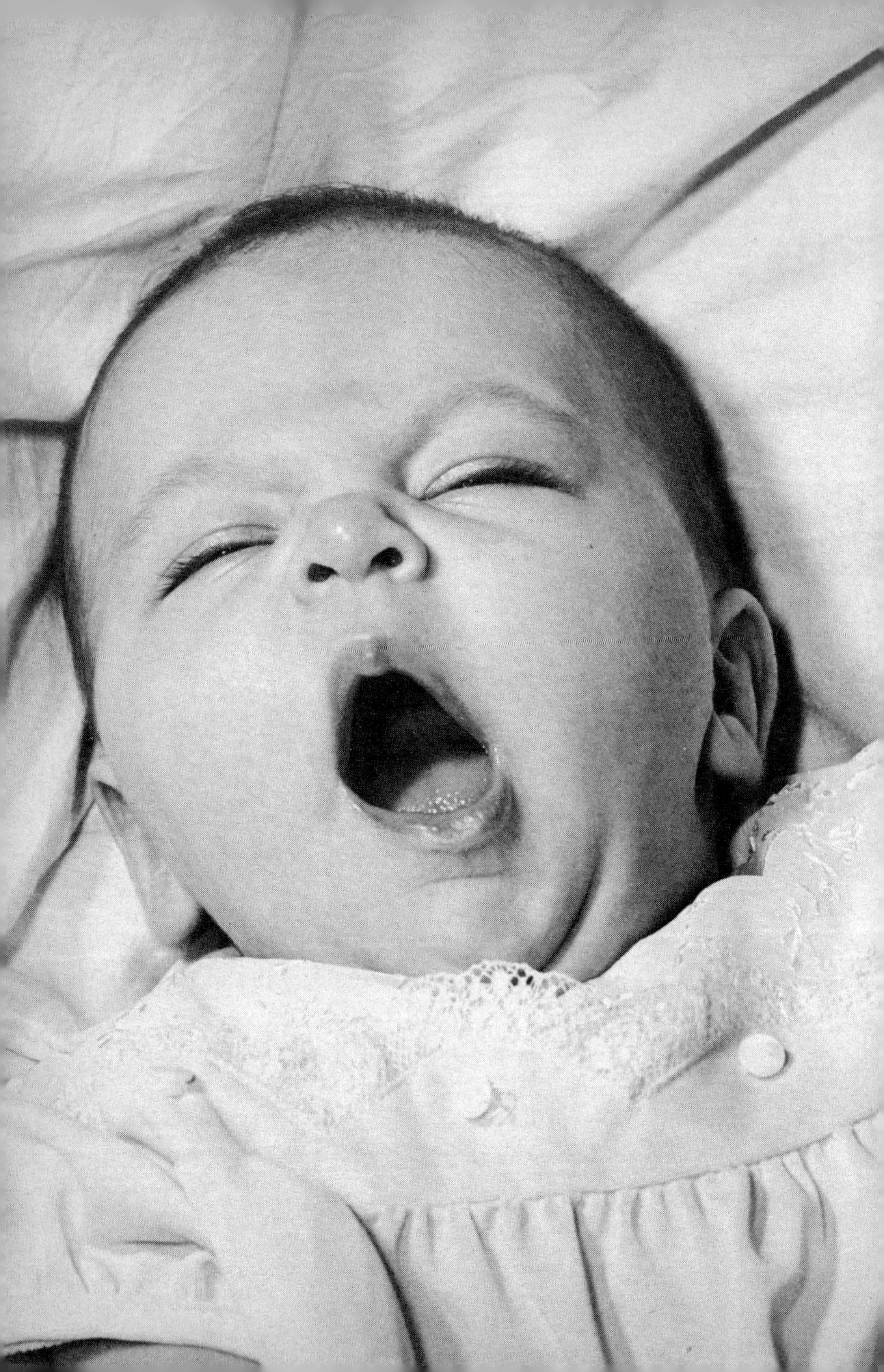

baby with such signs to the hospital if you can't reach the doctor quickly.

HEART TROUBLE

A small number of babies are born with a heart defect. In some cases, because of poor circulation through the lungs, insufficient oxygen is absorbed by the blood, which makes the baby's skin look blue. The baby may appear blue most of the time, or only occasionally after the exercise of hard crying or some other activity.

When the doctor hears a "murmur" through his stethoscope, it may mean unusual functioning of the heart. A "murmur" may or may not reveal a condition significant to the baby's health. By far, the largest number make no difference at all, and many disappear. Modern improvements in surgical techniques make it possible to operate successfully on many kinds of imperfect hearts.

SKIN AILMENTS

The baby's tender skin is readily irritated and, if broken, permits infection to enter. Keep any irritation or break in the skin scrupulously clean. Further treatment will depend upon the cause. Get a doctor's advice. The use of patent medicines may waste time or make the situation worse. Keep the baby's nails trimmed so he won't cause irritation by scratching himself.

The skin becomes involved with many contagious diseases, of course. The eruptions of chickenpox, measles, scarlet fever, and other rashes accompanied by fever and illness need no

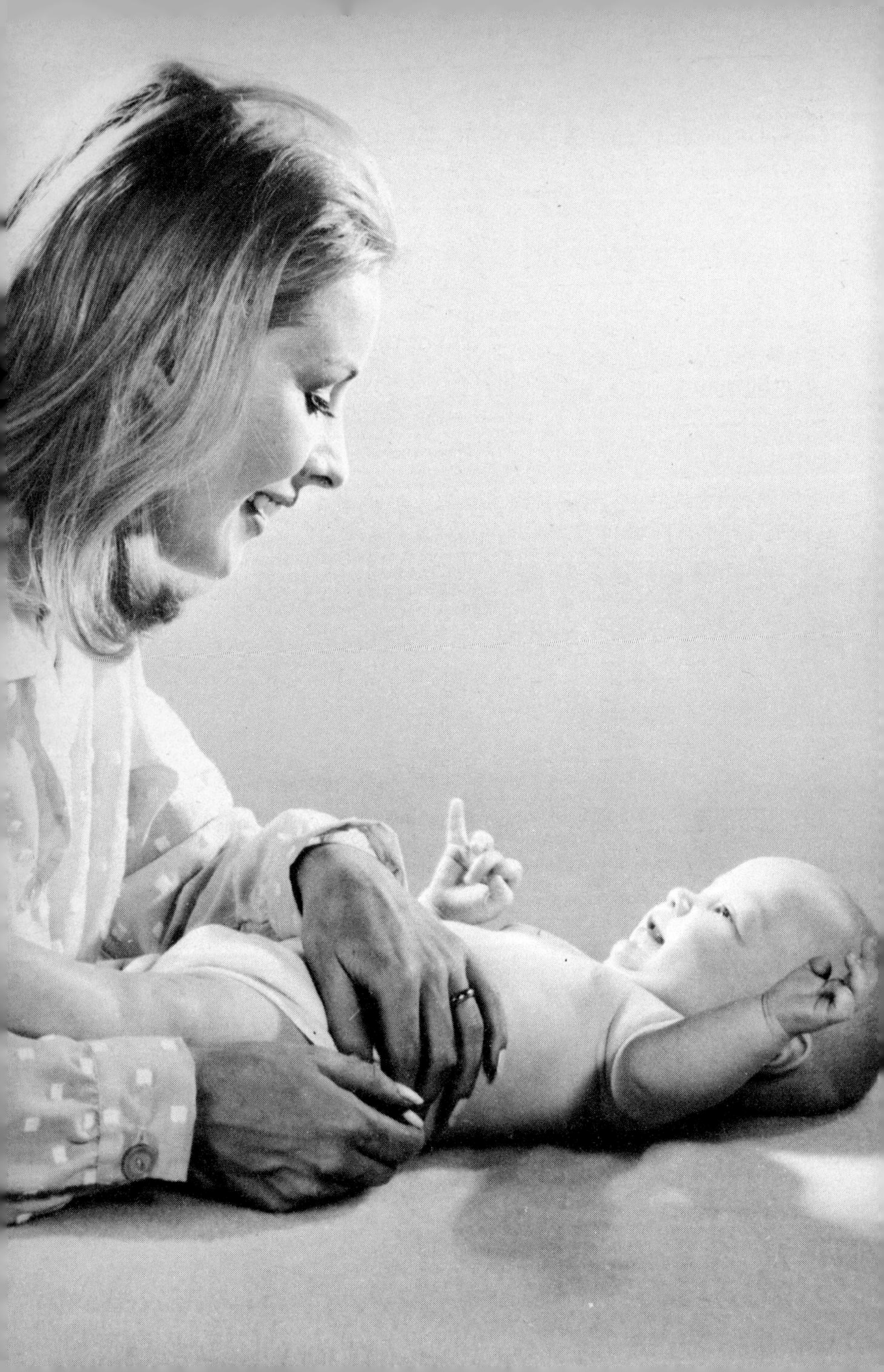

treatment other than to keep the baby as comfortable as you can. Sponge him off frequently, dust him with powder or cornstarch, or pat his body with cotton dipped in a solution of water and alcohol.

By far, the most frequent skin problems are diaper rash and prickly heat. In many parts of our country, prickly heat is a more or less constant nuisance in the summer. If the baby is overheated, though, it can occur at any season. Commonly, the rash looks like little pimples, first appearing in the folds of the neck and shoulders; but it may spread downward and into the creases of the legs. Try to keep the baby cool. Give frequent sponge baths. You can let him wear just a diaper on really hot days. Some mothers feel that the baby is really more comfortable in a thin upper garment that protects him from direct contact with their hands when they lift or handle him.

Allergic skin conditions: Sometimes a more or less chronic skin irritation is caused by allergy. When a baby (or older person) is unable to accept some substance which is harmless to others, he is said to be allergic to it. Allergy can cause skin eruptions, can look like a cold, cause digestive or intestinal upsets, such as nausea and diarrhea, or a number of other things. Ordinarily, a baby has the same response whenever he comes in contact with a certain irritant, but it can change over time and he may outgrow it eventually. It may be easy to find the cause, as when the baby breaks out in a rash after trying a new food, or his skin becomes irritated every time you put on a certain sweater. In other cases, the doctor has to do patient detective work to locate what the child is sensitive to. Occasionally, a baby will be allergic to so many things, or to substances so widely present or so obscure that you can't hope to eliminate the particular offenders.

In order not to set off an allergic response, doctors prefer to start slowly with egg and other foods that may cause allergic reactions. Once you begin, if you observe any reaction, omit the food and check with the doctor before trying it again.

Treatment for the allergic response—skin rash, digestive upset, or whatever—won't be necessary, of course, if the irritating substance can be eliminated. For instance, *hives*—raised itching welts scattered over large portions of the body—will quickly disappear when the irritant is gone. Relief can be given for hives by applying ice to the welts, or giving the baby a warm cornstarch bath (¼ cup cornstarch to a small baby tub). The doctor may be able to prescribe medicine that has the effect of counteracting the allergic reaction.

Eczema is more resistant. If the skin has become reddened in rough scaly patches which are dry and thickened, or moist and oozing, the irritation may last a long time. Eczema often begins on the cheeks, or in the fold of the elbow or knees, but it may spread over a large portion of the body. Eczema itches and makes the baby miserable, but it is an additional problem because the raw areas are so prone to further infection. Get a doctor's help, both to locate the cause of irritation, if possible, and to supervise the treatment of the eczema itself.

Cradle cap, which occurs in the first months of infancy, is an accumulation of a thick greasy crust, usually on the scalp, but it may occur behind the ears, on eyebrows or eyelashes, corners of the nose, on the cheeks, or even on the trunk. Sometimes mild eczema or a dermatitis resembles cradle cap. If the treatment suggested in Chapter 5 under "The Skin and Scalp" does not clear it up, the baby should be checked by a doctor, since it is not easy to tell what is causing the problem.

Impetigo is a very contagious skin disease which has open sores that look like a collection of blisters. It may start on the face or in the region of the diaper. Impetigo spreads readily from one person to another and from one part of the body elsewhere. In an older child, the sore tends to crust over, but in a baby it may not. See the doctor promptly if sores appear on the skin of your baby. Some of the new treatments will clear up impetigo in a few days.

Usually a baby gets impetigo from someone else in the family who has the infection. If the baby, or anyone in the household, has any contagious skin disease, his clothing and bedding should be laundered separately. Boil the garments, let them dry in hot sun, or press with a hot iron to kill the germs which cause impetigo.

INTESTINAL AND GENITAL ILLS

Many different things are quickly reflected in the digestive system, bowels, or urine. A mild cold may depress the appetite, cause diarrhea or more frequent urination. A more serious illness can do the same. Check with the doctor when anything unusual appears. Treatment will vary with the cause, not the symptoms.

Diarrhea in a small child is of great concern because it can so quickly lead to loss of water and imbalance of salts in the body. Diarrhea may be a symptom of enteritis or dysentery caused by specific organisms which are usually spread by careless handling of the baby's milk or lack of cleanliness by the one preparing it. However, diarrhea is more often the result of irritation from food, allergy, or other illness. Give the baby with diarrhea as much fluid as he will take. Care for diarrhea lasting more than 24 hours should be supervised by a doctor.

Constipation is seldom serious. Parents mean different things by the word "constipation." Some mean that the baby

The small one is for grown-ups.

The very small one is for children.

No reason anymore for the old-fashioned enemas people sometimes use. The tiny Fleet ones are cleaner, neater, more sanitary...and *effective*. Hospitals use them. Physicians recommend them. You ought to have one of each in your home, ready for emergencies: the 2¼ fluidounce Fleet® Pediatric Enema for infants and children; the 4½ fluidounce regular Fleet® Enema for adults. **Warning:** Frequent or prolonged use of enemas may result in dependence. Take only when needed or when prescribed by a physician. Do not use when nausea, vomiting or abdominal pain is present. **Caution:** Do not administer to children under two years of age unless directed by a physician.

C. B. FLEET CO., INC.
Lynchburg, Va. 24505

1869-1969

fleet
pharmaceuticals

A century of service to medicine

does not have a daily bowel movement. This is normal for some babies. Some mean that the baby strains at producing a stool. All babies strain during the first 2 or 3 months of life as they gradually stretch the anal opening. They look uncomfortable, but they are all right. They do not need a laxative. Some seem to like the parent to hold a hand under their feet so they can flex their knees and shove their feet against the hand.

Some parents use the word to describe hard, dry stools. Usually this type can be controlled by increasing fluids or by minor changes in the baby's diet. It may help to change to dark corn sirup or brown sugar in making the baby's formula. See that he gets foods which aid in keeping the bowels soft, such as fruits and vegetables. Prunes and prune juice are good unless they give the baby cramps.

The doctor can prescribe a safe regime for stubborn cases of constipation. While you wish to avoid subjecting a baby to painful bowel movements, the routine use of laxatives or enemas is never wise unless specially prescribed.

A baby who is sick probably eats less and, as a result, may have fewer bowel movements than usual. There's no magic in emptying the bowels to make him get well.

If the baby struggles and strains to move his bowels, yet nothing much but a thin, ribbonlike movement appears in drops or dribbles, it may be a sign of an obstruction at the lower end of the rectum. Report such a condition to the doctor.

Foamy, frothy, foul-smelling bowel movements usually result from poor absorption of food—an inability to digest and absorb food properly. For *malabsorptive disease*, often called *celiac disease*, you'll need the doctor's help in planning a diet which will eliminate foods containing the elements the baby cannot tolerate.

Occasionally there will be an obstruction somewhere in the

baby's digestive tract. One of these is *pyloric stenosis*, which is characterized by frequent vomiting so forceful that the regurgitated milk lands some distance from the baby's body. Vomiting results because the opening leading from the stomach to the intestine is narrowed unnaturally by a thick, tight wall which fails to permit the food to pass through. Almost every baby will, on some occasion, lose a whole feeding. But forceful vomiting, increasing in frequency, should be investigated. If the baby's vomit contains green bile, another type of obstruction may be involved. Get immediate medical help.

Once in a while, in a baby from 3 to 6 months of age or older, a segment of the bowel will fold in on itself, cutting off the passageway. The baby will scream in pain and pull up his legs. When the pain goes away, though, he seems well or possibly pale or listless. Pain may return, next time with vomiting. The bowel movement, when it occurs, may be dark with blood. This condition, known as *intussusception*, requires immediate medical attention.

Any unusual appearance of the baby's urine should be investigated. A kidney infection, called *pyelitis*, may cause the baby to have fever and appear quite sick. He's cross as can be and is quite miserable. There may, or may not be, vomiting. Loss of appetite is characteristic. The doctor will make the diagnosis from examination of the child's urine. Pyelitis is more common in girls than boys perhaps because the urethral tract is shorter and infection can reach the kidney more readily.

A discharge from the vagina of a little girl is normal in the first few weeks of life, but thereafter a discharge of any kind may indicate a mild or serious infection. Consult the doctor.

In the circumcised boy the tip of the penis occasionally will become raw and irritated, somewhat the same as diaper rash. If it progresses to become a sore, with scabs forming, it may cause pain on urination or block the opening. It will probably help if you keep the scab soft by using an ointment containing lanolin, petroleum jelly, or Lassar's paste. If it does not clear up within a few days, consult the doctor.

The boy who is not circumcised occasionally gets an *infection under the foreskin.* Painful swelling may occur. The doctor may need to open the foreskin to treat the infection and allow the swelling to go down.

EMERGENCIES

The slightest wheeze or a case of hiccups may set off a panic in the household of a new baby, but in time parents learn to remain calm and see what happens next before they run to the phone. Every now and then, though, something really serious occurs and you know that every second counts. At such times, it is a help if you have taken a class in first aid such as one given by the Red Cross or an adult education center. If you can't take a class, buy a handbook and familiarize yourself with its contents. Keep it handy in bathroom or kitchen, and always check it before you use any treatment. Even if you can handle the immediate emergency yourself, have your child seen by a doctor afterward for followup treatment.

Uncontrolled bleeding, choking, deep burns, and poisoning are usually the only real emergencies that occur with a baby. Other situations may be urgent, but you can take time to try first aid or to get in touch with a doctor. With these four emergencies, waste no time. If you can't reach your doctor immediately, set out for a hospital. If no hospital is within reach, ask the telephone operator to find you a doctor, and stay off the phone yourself until one calls. Or call the fire department. Many maintain emergency service.

Cuts and bleeding: For a small cut, wash out well with soap and water and apply a clean bandage or freshly ironed piece of cloth and adhesive tape. If the cut is deep and large, cover with sterile gauze, press firmly over the wound to stop bleeding, and hold in place until you can get to a doctor or emergency room of the hospital. If the bleeding doesn't stop, take more towels, diapers, or clean cloths as needed, and continue pressing but don't remove the first pads.

Bleeding—bright red and spurting—can sometimes be stopped by pressing the side of the wound toward the center of the body. Blood flowing into the hand, for instance, can be slowed down by gradual firm pressing on the inner surface of the upper arm.

If a puncture wound does not bleed, encourage bleeding by gentle pressure near the hole. Cover lightly but don't try to close the puncture with bandage or adhesive. Be sure to check with a doctor about a tetanus shot or booster. The germs causing tetanus thrive in wounds which cannot be reached by air.

A deep prick from a safety pin (in yourself or the baby) can often be effectively treated by applying water (hot for you, quite warm for a baby) to the site. The purpose is to bring more blood and the body defenses to the area to combat immediately a germ that might have been introduced.

Choking: Pick up the baby by his feet and slap his back sharply. If he keeps on choking, seek emergency treatment at a hospital without delay. It rarely pays to try to dislodge the object with your finger. You risk sending it farther down.

If the baby should swallow something small and smooth such as a fruit seed, button, or coin, check his bowel movements for a few days to be sure it has passed through his body. If he swallows a sharp object, such as a pin or needle, call a doctor immediately.

MOUTH-TO-MOUTH RESUSCITATION

1. Place the baby on his back.

2. With your finger, quickly clear mouth and throat of mucus, food, or other obstruction if you can.

3. Tilt his head back, with chin up. Bring his lower jaw forward.

4. Pinch his nose shut.

5. Put your lips to his and blow gently.

6. Release his nostrils and listen for the return of breath.

7. Take a breath yourself.

8. Repeat the process. Close the baby's nostrils, breathe into his mouth, release the nostrils. Count to 3, slowly, and repeat again. Continue at this rate, about 15 to 20 times per minute until the baby breathes again. Don't give up too soon. Keep your movements slow and gentle.

With a small infant, you may be able to seal both mouth and nose with your mouth instead of pinching the nostrils shut.

If the baby should stop breathing and you cannot get medical help, try artificial respiration. The mouth-to-mouth breathing method is easiest and safest with a baby.

Study the instructions above so that you will be familiar with this simple method should an emergency arise.

Poisons: If possible, get the baby to a hospital. Take along the container of poison so the doctor will know what the child has swallowed. Depending on the type of poison, you may or

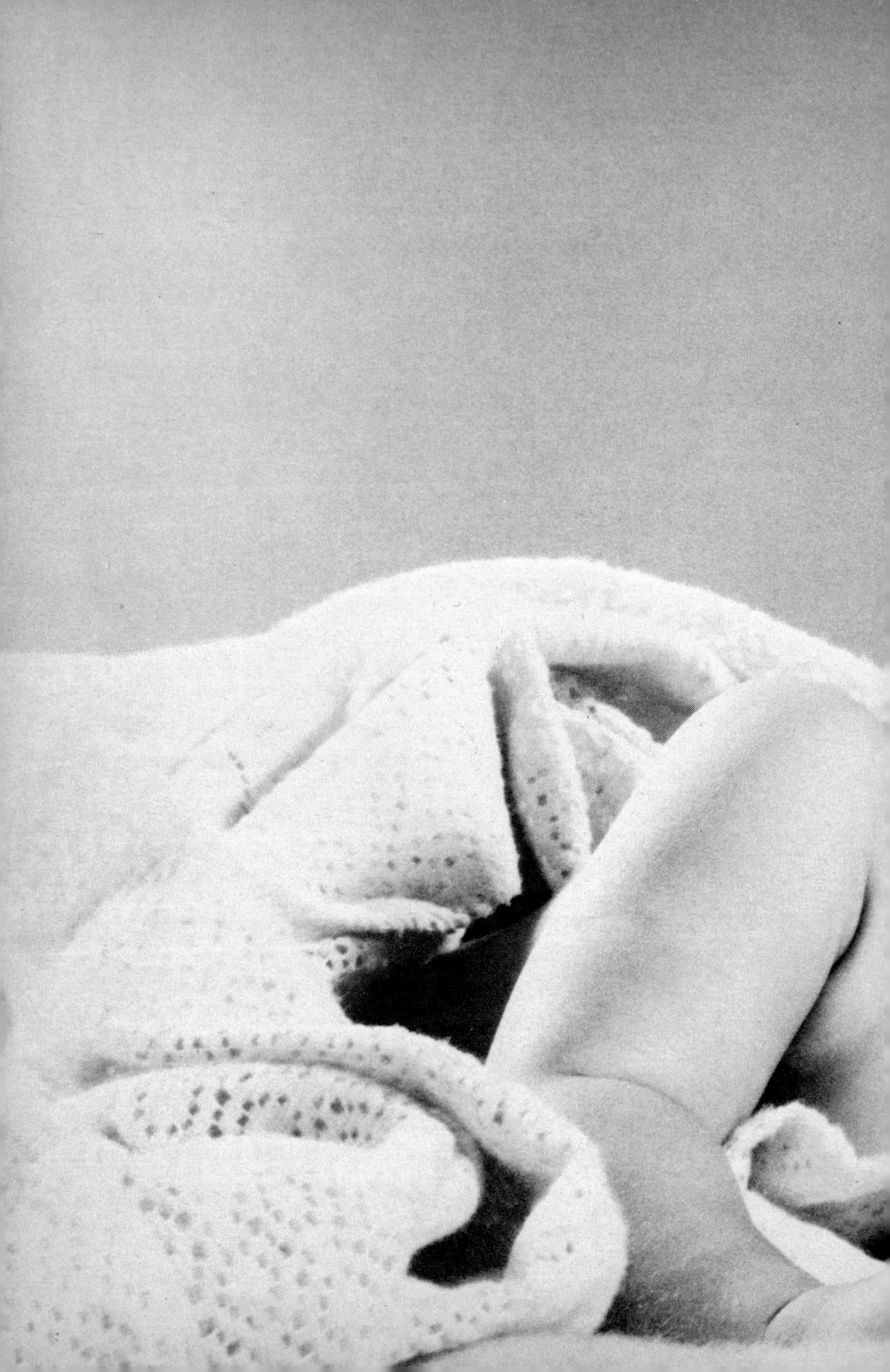

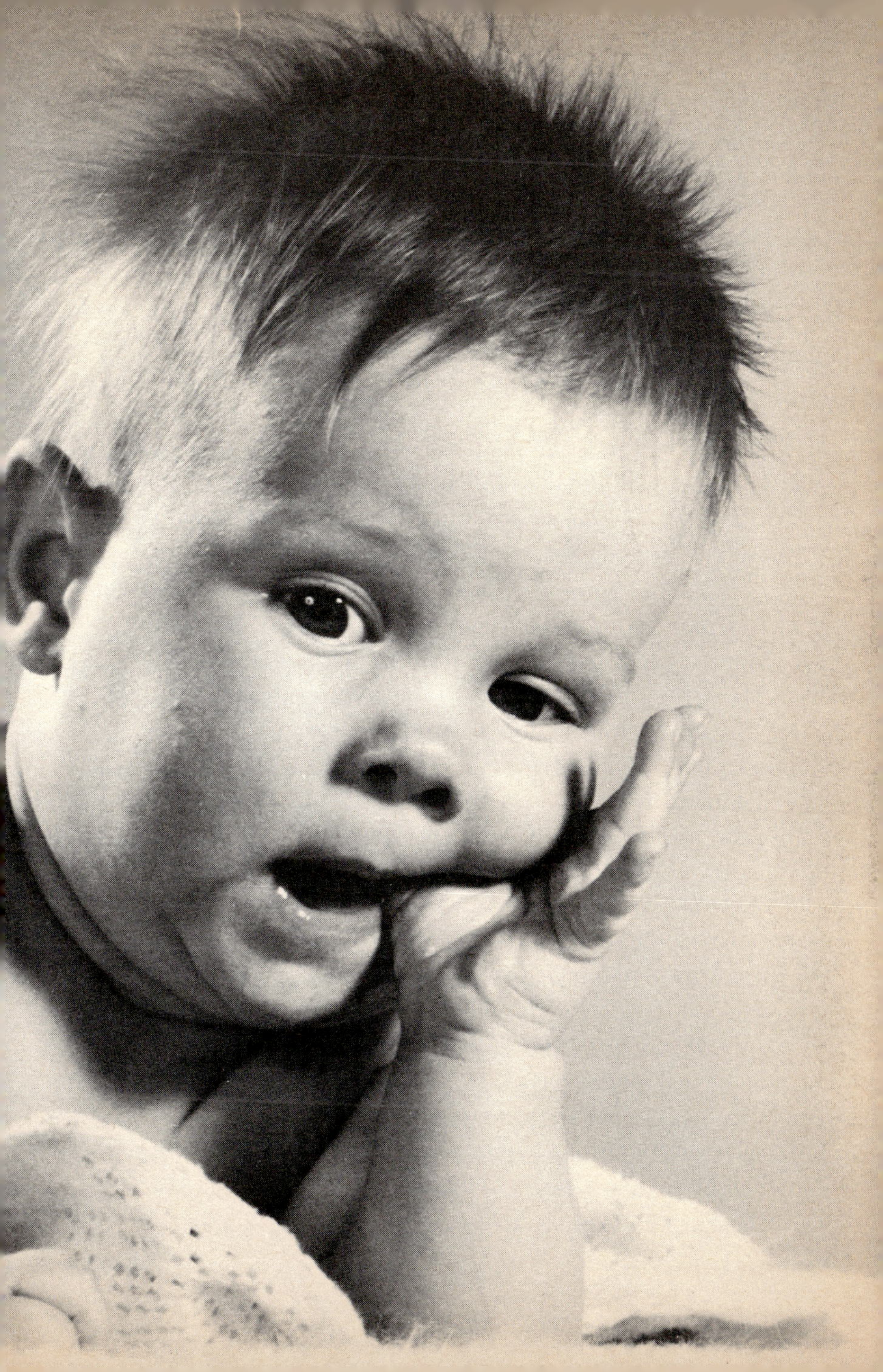

may not want him to vomit. If you cannot take the baby to a doctor or an emergency ward immediately, proceed as follows:

DO NOT make the baby vomit if he has taken: **Oily substances,** such as kerosene, gasoline, benzene (lighter fluid), cleaning fluids, insect spray, furniture polish, turpentine;

Strong alkali, such as lye, ammonia, caustic soda, carbon tetrachloride (fire extinguisher fluid);

Strong acids, such as hydrochloric acid, nitric acid, sulfuric acid (battery acid).

DO try to make the baby vomit if he has taken: **Most other poisons,** including arsenic, antifreeze solution, aspirin, atropine, barbiturates (sleeping tablets), bichloride of mercury, boric acid, camphorated oil, cathartics such as those containing strychnine, cigarettes, codeine tablets or cough sirup containing codeine, fly poisons, heart medicine (with digitalis), ink (if much has been taken), iron tablets, mothballs, paregoric, nicotine garden sprays, rat poison, roach powder, sedatives, sleeping medicines, weed killer, wintergreen oil.

To make a baby vomit, put him in your lap in the spanking position, then slip your finger down his throat to make him gag. Don't be afraid to leave your finger there for a few seconds, wiggling it, to make him gag thoroughly. It may help to give him a drink of water or milk first. If he just won't vomit, try giving him all the liquids he can drink and try again.

Don't try to make a baby vomit or force liquids if he is unconscious.

If the baby has breathed poisonous fumes, take him to fresh air immediately.

Burns: All burns should be immediately doused in cold water to prevent further destruction of tissue. A burn which simply reddens the skin can be left open to the air. A burn which blisters may be covered with a clean gauze square.

All extensive burns should be seen by a doctor. The second-degree burn (such as a steam burn) and deep burns (third degree) in which the skin is burned off and which penetrate deeply into the body need immediate medical attention. Put the child in a tub of cold water for a few minutes. Then wrap him in a clean sheet and blanket if necessary and take him to the hospital emergency room.

Sunburn can be serious. Try to avoid it if possible. Use preventive lotions if the baby has fair skin, and watch the time of exposure carefully. If there are fever, chills, vomiting, or the baby's skin blisters, check with the doctor.

CONVULSIONS

A high fever may send a baby into convulsions (seizures, fits, spells). The convulsion itself needs no treatment. Place the baby on the floor or bed on his stomach, with chin raised. In this position, he can breathe easily, is less likely to choke on saliva or swallow his tongue. If his teeth aren't clenched together, you may wish to place a small pad of cloth between his teeth so he won't bite his tongue.

When the convulsion is over, place the baby in his crib where he can sleep. Then check with the doctor. Convulsions which occur at intervals may be a sign of epilepsy. For many types of epilepsy, medicine can be given regularly to prevent the recurring seizures.

BITES AND STINGS

If the baby is bitten by an insect (bee, wasp, hornet, yellow jacket, ant, mosquito), remove the stinger, if any, with tweezers. Apply ammonia, diluted with equal parts of water or a solution of baking soda and water, to neutralize the acid causing the pain. Very rarely an infant will be allergic to the sting. Get medical help if the baby becomes unusually pale, has difficulty in breathing, vomits, loses consciousness, is drowsy, or convulses.

Ticks attach themselves to warm-blooded animals, including humans. Ordinarily, a baby is handled so frequently that a tick does not go long undiscovered. Check the scalp for ticks if you live in a tick-infested area. Always remove a tick with tweezers. Be sure to get the head as well as the body. If it clings, loosen its hold by smearing it with grease, oil, or turpentine. Crush the tick (but not with your bare fingers), flush it down the toilet, burn it, or drop it into turpentine or kerosene. Clean the wound with soap and water or mild antiseptic.

Most ticks are harmless, but a few carry the germs of tick fever which may be passed on to a human if the tick remains attached long enough to become swollen with blood. Fever, headache, nosebleed, or rash, about a week after a baby has been bitten by a tick, may be signs of tick fever. Modern treatment methods are effective.

Injections to prevent tick fever can be given to children who live in heavily infested areas, but such a course is probably not necessary for babies.

BROKEN BONES

Although babies bounce pretty well if they fall, a broken bone can occur. Keep the baby from moving the part of his body where you suspect a fracture, and don't move it yourself. Get him to a hospital.

Perhaps the best way to immobilize an arm or leg is to tie it loosely with strips of gauze or cloth in several places to a small pillow, a rolled up bath towel, or a smooth board. A long-handled wooden kitchen spoon would do. If you suspect a back or neck injury, don't try to move the baby unless absolutely necessary. If you must carry him, use a flat surface (breadboard, tray, firm mattress).

PARTICLE IN EYE

Wash your hands before working around the baby's eye. Try to keep him from rubbing it. To dislodge the speck, bring the upper lid down over the lower for a moment or two. This causes tears which may wash the speck out.

Washing out the eye may also help. Use cooled boiled water to which a quarter teaspoon of salt is added per cup. Drop this fluid into the baby's eye with a clean medicine dropper or a clean teaspoon.

If the irritation continues, get a doctor's help.

SOME OF THE MORE COMMON

Disease	First signs	Incubation period*
Chickenpox	Mild fever followed in 36 hours by small raised pimples which become filled with clear fluid. Scabs form later. Successive crops of pox appear	Usually 13–17 days
German measles (3-day measles)	Mild fever, sore throat or cold symptoms may precede tiny, rose-colored rash. Enlarged glands at back of neck and behind ears	Usually 18 days
Measles	Mounting fever; hard, dry cough; running nose and red eyes for 3 or 4 days before rash starts at hair line and spreads down in blotches. Small red spots with white centers in mouth (Koplik's spots) appear before the rash	Usually 10 or 11 days
Mumps	Fever, headache, vomiting; glands near ear and toward chin at jaw line ache and develop painful swelling. Other parts of body may be affected also	11–26 days (usually around 18)

*The usual amount of time which elapses between exposure to the disease and onset of the first symptoms. For example, if a child is exposed to chickenpox, he can safely play with other children until 12 or 13 days afterwards. The following week, he

COMMUNICABLE DISEASES

Prevention	How long contagious	What you can do
None. Immune after one attack	6 days after appearance of rash	Not a serious disease; trim fingernails to prevent scratching; a paste of baking soda and water, or alcohol, may ease itching
None. Immune after one attack. Girls are often exposed intentionally, since contracting the disease later in early months of pregnancy may harm the unborn baby	Until rash fades. About 5 days	Generally not a serious disease in childhood; complications rare; give general good care and rest
All children should receive measles vaccine at 12 months of age. If an unvaccinated child is exposed to measles, gamma globulin given shortly after exposure may lighten or prevent the disease	Usually for 5 to 9 days, from 4 days before to 5 days after the rash appears	May be mild or severe with complications; follow doctor's advice in caring for a child with measles, as it is a most treacherous disease
Is apt to be milder in childhood than later. Some doctors like little boys to get mumps over with before school age	Until all swelling disappears	Keep child in bed until fever subsides and indoors unless weather is warm

should be kept away from other children since he may be in the early stages of the disease and it will be contagious before you note any symptoms.

[Table continued on next page]

SOME OF THE MORE COMMON

Disease	First signs	Incubation period*
Roseola	High fever which drops before rash or large pink blotches covering whole body appear. Child may not seem very ill despite the high fever (103°–105°) but he may convulse	About 2 weeks
Strep throat (septic sore throat) and scarlet fever (scarlatina)	Sometimes vomiting and fever before sudden and severe sore throat. If followed by fine rash on body and limbs, it is called scarlet fever	1–7 days (usually 2–5)
Whooping cough	At first seems like a cold with low fever and cough. Changes at end of second week to spells of coughing accompanied by a noisy gasp for air which creates the "whoop"	5–21 days (usually around 10 days)

*The usual amount of time which elapses between exposure to the disease and onset of the first symptoms. For example, if a child is exposed to chickenpox, he can safely play with other children until 12 or 13 days afterwards. The following

COMMUNICABLE DISEASES [*Continued*]

Prevention	How long contagious	What you can do
None. Usually affects children from 6 months to 3 years of age	Until he seems well	No special measures except rest and quiet
If doctor feels it wise to prescribe antibiotics, they may prevent or lighten an attack	7-10 days (when all the abnormal discharge from nose, eyes, and throat has ceased)	Frequently less severe than formerly; responds to antibiotics, which should be continued for full course to prevent serious complications
Give injections of vaccine to all children in infancy; if an unvaccinated child has been exposed, the doctor may want to give a protective serum promptly	Usually not after 4th week	Child needs careful supervision of doctor throughout this taxing illness

week, he should be kept away from other children since he may be in the early stages of the disease and it will be contagious before you note any symptoms.

SOME OF THE LESS COMMON

Disease	First signs	Incubation period
Infectious hepatitis (catarrhal jaundice)	May be mild with few symptoms or accompanied by fever, headache, abdominal pain, nausea, diarrhea, general weariness. Later, yellowed skin and whites of eyes (jaundice), dark urine, and chalklike bowel movements	2–6 weeks (commonly 25 days)
Infectious mononucleosis (glandular fever)	Sore throat, swollen glands of neck and elsewhere, sometimes a rash over whole body and jaundiced appearance, low persistent fever	Probably 4–14 days or longer
Meningitis	May be preceded by a cold; headache, stiff neck, vomiting, high temperature with convulsions or drowsy stupor; fine rash with tiny hemorrhages into the skin	2–10 days
Polio (infantile paralysis or poliomyelitis)	Slight fever, general discomfort, headache, stiff neck, stiff back	1–4 weeks (commonly 1–2 weeks)
Rocky Mountain spotted fever	Muscle pains, nosebleed occasionally, headache, rash on 3d or 4th day	About a week after bite of infected tick
Smallpox	Sudden fever, chills, head- and backache. Rash which becomes raised and hard; later, blisters and scabs	6–18 days (commonly 12)

INFECTIOUS DISEASES

Prevention	How long contagious	What you can do
Injection of gamma globulin gives temporary immunity if child has been exposed	Perhaps 2 months or more	May be mild or may require hospital care
None	Probably 2–4 weeks, but mode of transmission is not clear	Keep in bed while feverish, restrict activity thereafter
None	Until recovery	Immediate treatment is necessary. Take child to hospital if doctor is unavailable. Continue treatment with antibiotics as long as doctor advises
Be sure to complete the series of the Sabin vaccine	1 week from onset or as long as fever persists	Hospital care is usually advised
Injections can be given to a child who lives in heavily infested area	Spread only by infected ticks	New drugs have improved treatment
Vaccination practically perfect protection	Until all scabs disappear	Doctor's care necessary

177

11. One to four months

By a month of age the wobbly head becomes more steady, and the baby can hold it erect for a few minutes as he studies the nursery curtains flapping in the breeze. The wobbly hand that supported that new head becomes steadier also, as the two of you approach the end of the first month together. The newness has gone, and you may be surprised as you look back at how well you have learned to read the baby's signals.

He's now entering a stage of rapid growth. Once he has regained his initial birth weight, he may put on as much as an ounce a day, which adds up to about 2 pounds a month. You can almost see him grow. Of course there are individual variations, and perfectly healthy babies may gain less. The important thing is that the gain be steady from month to month.

Fortunately, this rapid gain begins to taper off soon. Toward 6 months of age an increase of a pound a month is about average. Through the second year, it will level off to about half a pound a month. If the baby didn't stop gaining so fast, you'd never be able to lift him in the months before he starts to walk.

HOW HE WILL DEVELOP

All babies follow a predictable pattern in learning to use their bodies. First the world is explored with mouth, then eyes;

Partly used bottles should never be put away and then given to the baby again; for once he has sucked from a bottle it will tend to become contaminated.

after that, the baby learns to control his head. In downward and outward direction, from head to toe and from center out to fingertip, the rest of the body follows. He gains control of his trunk and can turn over, first from stomach to back and then in either direction. Later he can push up to sit, hunched over. Finally, mastery of feet and legs allows him to stand. Use of the arms has made it possible for him to sit up and to bat at toys hung over the crib. At first the arm moved as a unit, pivoting from the shoulder. It takes most of the first year to learn to move the wrist, then the fingers, and last of all, to place the fingers against the thumb. He can then pick up tiny objects precisely. With more practice, he will be able to release an object accurately, too. He'll be tossing things off his high chair or out of the playpen for some time until he gets the aim and timing right.

At first, arms and legs wave all at once. Steady practice makes it possible for him to control each limb separately. By 10 or 12 months, he can raise one foot, poke the toes into his mouth, explore the crib bars with the toes on the other foot, perhaps waving his bottle with one hand at the same time. Describing such circus tricks carries us far ahead of the baby at one month, however. It makes it more fun to take care of a baby when you can anticipate how he'll be developing but right now, you're still interested in the way he uses his mouth, sucking, feeling, puckering in endless variations.

TO SCHEDULE THE DAY

Your baby has probably put himself on some kind of a schedule. With a little firmness, you can adjust his rhythm to yours. If you want the day to begin, say, at 7 o'clock, feed the baby then and let the rest of the day follow almost automatically. Feedings 4 hours apart would fall around 11, 3, 7, and so on.

It's a help to both you and the baby to work around some kind of a plan. On the other hand, don't let a schedule dominate. You get flustered if you can't maintain it; he becomes irritable at being prodded or forced to wait when for some reason his stomach is on a different timetable.

After a while, the baby omits one night feeding. Let him sleep as long as he will after the 6 o'clock (or evening) feeding. Nine out of ten babies will skip one night feeding at about 3 or 4 weeks of age. If you are using bottles, redistribute the formula into the number of bottles you will now be using. Sometime thereafter, by 2 or 3 months of age, most babies will go through the whole night without taking food, from about 6 p.m. to 5 a.m. When yours is content with four bottles, divide the entire formula into these four parts. For awhile, the baby may waken earlier than you'd like, but you can shift him to a more convenient hour as time goes by.

Some parents like to waken the baby for a night feeding before they retire. There is no objection to this practice, but there comes a point when the baby will make an adjustment naturally to a long sleep at night if left to waken himself.

Even after the baby goes on to four regular feedings a day, he may waken during the night now and then demanding food. Feel free to give it to him. Just as you occasionally seek a midnight snack, you can indulge him in this extra meal without fear that it will become a lasting thing.

INTRODUCING SOLID FOODS

The best way to acquaint the baby with new foods is to do it so gradually he scarcely knows he's being asked to do anything unusual at all. This is the system, actually, to use with changes you want to make in feeding, weaning, toilet training, or anything else. "Civilizing" the baby goes faster with less upset for both you *and* him if you wait until he's ready for it and take small steps at a time. If you go too fast too soon, you run the risk of making the baby balk at the whole idea.

At first, mix the new food so thin it still resembles milk in consistency. Give him a taste or two. Don't worry if he acts as if you are trying to poison him. He is equipped with a reflex which makes his tongue automatically reject a foreign object put into his mouth. The technique of sucking also tends to propel solid food forward and out. So don't be surprised if much of what you put in reappears and dribbles down his chin. It doesn't mean that he doesn't like the food. All you're interested in, really, is getting him used to the idea of taking food from a spoon. That's more important than what he eats, or how much, at the beginning.

Cereal is commonly given first, but fruit such as applesauce and mashed banana are also good to start with. Use prepared baby cereal or thoroughly cook a finely milled cereal such as farina or rice. Oatmeal is good, but strain it after cooking. Mix a teaspoon or two of cereal with an ounce of milk (2 tablespoons) blending it into a smooth cream. Use formula if you have it to spare. If not, boil pasteurized whole milk for 2 minutes; or use evaporated milk diluted with equal parts of boiled water. No need to add sugar. He is developing his own sense of taste. Mothers often oversweeten things to their own taste.

Some babies regard the spoon as a bother, an interruption to their familiar method of sucking milk. They accept solids more gracefully if they have a chance first to dull their keen eagerness for food with the breast or bottle. Let such a baby take about half his regular milk, then offer some tastes of the cereal. Afterwards, complete the milk feeding. Cereal can be given twice a day. Mid-morning and late afternoon or evening is customary.

If the baby seems to dislike cereal, just wait. Offer it again a few days later. Expect him to spit it out. This is part of learning how to manage the process. In due time, you can begin to offer fruits. Mash a small portion of completely ripe banana (speckled skin, tan fruit) and mix with milk as suggested for the cereal. Stewed strained fruit, or canned fruit puree, is accepted by most babies. As you start fruit, thin with milk as before. Apricots, apples, peaches, pears, and prunes are all popular.

Vegetables can be added, one at a time, also. Carrots and squash often appeal to the baby because they are naturally sweeter. Spinach, stringbeans, beets, asparagus, and others are good too. No single one is essential. If one or two of these seem to be disliked by the child, don't worry about it. Later on, when the baby seems to be in a hungry and tolerant frame of mind, try them again.

You can give the baby some of the vegetables cooked for the family if you use only a little salt and no added fat in the preparation. Thoroughly mash or strain the baby's portion. A blender or food mill can be used. Strained vegetables canned for babies may be bought in cans or jars. Both types of containers are perfectly safe for storing unused portions in the refrigerator. Discard any leftover after 2 or 3 days.

If you buy baby foods in screw-top glass jars, inspect each jar before purchase to be sure the lid is tightly sealed. Once the vacuum is broken by unscrewing the lid, the contents of the jar are no longer safe for use unless the food is refrigerated.

In introducing new foods, always begin with small amounts of only one new kind at a time. It is probably better to avoid mixtures of foods at first, such as combinations of fruits, vegetables, or meats and vegetables. If you have given a single new item, you will be able to tell if the baby is taking it without upset to his digestion. If the baby cries as if in pain, if he vomits, develops a rash, or shows any other sign of being upset after getting a new food, omit it for several days to see if it is causing the problem. When more than one new food is introduced at a time, you don't know which to blame.

As the baby takes to the spoon, you can thicken the mixture somewhat more each day. You may have noticed that he is beginning to have saliva in his mouth which helps him to swallow thicker mixtures. Increase the amount as needed; but, remember, there is no hurry. Eventually, he may be taking half a cup of cereal twice a day and possibly one-third cup of fruits and vegetables at other meals.

Cereals, fruits, and vegetables are important in the baby's diet. They provide vitamin C and minerals, including iron, which are needed in larger quantities than milk alone can provide.

If the baby is already taking fruit juice, such as orange, the amount should be increased, a teaspoon at a time, until he is getting 4 tablespoons (2 ounces) of undiluted juice and by 8 to 10 months is getting 6 tablespoons (3 ounces). The juice can be cool or warmed, but don't really heat the juice because high temperatures destroy vitamin C, which is the reason you are giving it.

GOING PLACES WITH THE BABY

When your baby is about a month old, he will enjoy getting out of doors for some time each pleasant day. It is convenient to have a stroller or carriage for this purpose. Before you buy either, check for safety. Select one which will not tip over easily, which has a handle suited to your height, is equipped with safety harness or strap, and has a strong brake. Some styles fold up, which may be helpful if you are short on storage space. A stroller which adjusts to become a flat bed has many uses.

Many mothers put an older baby outdoors for one of his naps. Park the carriage (brake on) in a secluded spot in the yard or on a porch, out of direct sun and wind. The motion of the stroller or carriage is soothing and most babies enjoy a walk, just as you do. In freezing weather when there's no sun, or on wet or windy days, the baby is better off indoors. In hot weather, put him in the coolest spot you can find, but not under the direct draft of a fan or air conditioner.

With the first baby, you may find it easy to take him out with you in the evenings as you visit friends. It gets more complicated with more than one child. An older one becomes more dependent on familiar surroundings and may not drop off to sleep so readily in a strange bed.

The young baby is quite adaptable, though, and will settle down comfortably in a portable bed or folding playpen. It is not wise to pin or tie the baby to the mattress of an adult bed. He hates the restriction, and may fight against sleep. There is also some danger he might become tangled in the straps or pinned blankets.

Most babies enjoy riding in a car. They will sleep for hours, lulled by the motion and hum of the engine. A car bed provided with safety strap is ideal for the young baby. Be sure to hook it securely to the seat so that turns or sudden stops do not dislodge it. Place it parallel with the car's length, hooked securely over the backs of both front and back seats. Use the safety strap on the baby. Keep his eyes shaded from direct sun, and be sure he is not in a blast of air. As the baby grows older, get a car seat equipped with a safety strap or some other device to keep him safe and able to look out the window. Buckle the strap each time you set out. The baby should learn from the beginning that he cannot roam about in a moving car.

Never leave a baby alone in an automobile. You can't be sure that you'll get back in half a minute, as you plan. Serious accidents can occur to an untended child. Furthermore, a car quickly becomes hot as an oven when parked in the sun. Many babies have suffered heat prostration from such a practice.

It is good for both of you to get out. There is one caution, however. It is not wise to take the baby into crowds, to visit anyone — child or adult — who is not well, or to expose him to groups of children. You never can tell when another person's youngster is about to come down with something; whooping cough, for instance. Even a mild cold caught from an older person can become a serious illness to the baby. The younger the baby, the more careful you should be. You might find it embarrassing to shoo away interested bystanders, or think yourself old fashioned to be so particular, but your caution will, in the long run, pay off.

THE BABYSITTER OR MAID

There are many occasions when it is better to leave the baby at home. Sometimes you are fortunate enough to have a good neighbor with whom you can trade baby care. Some families have a loving grandmother nearby who is delighted to be needed. Often nowadays parents must hire somebody to look after the baby in their absence. It's important for them to get out now and then to resume outside interests and enjoy an evening together.

You'll feel better if you know the sitter well and have

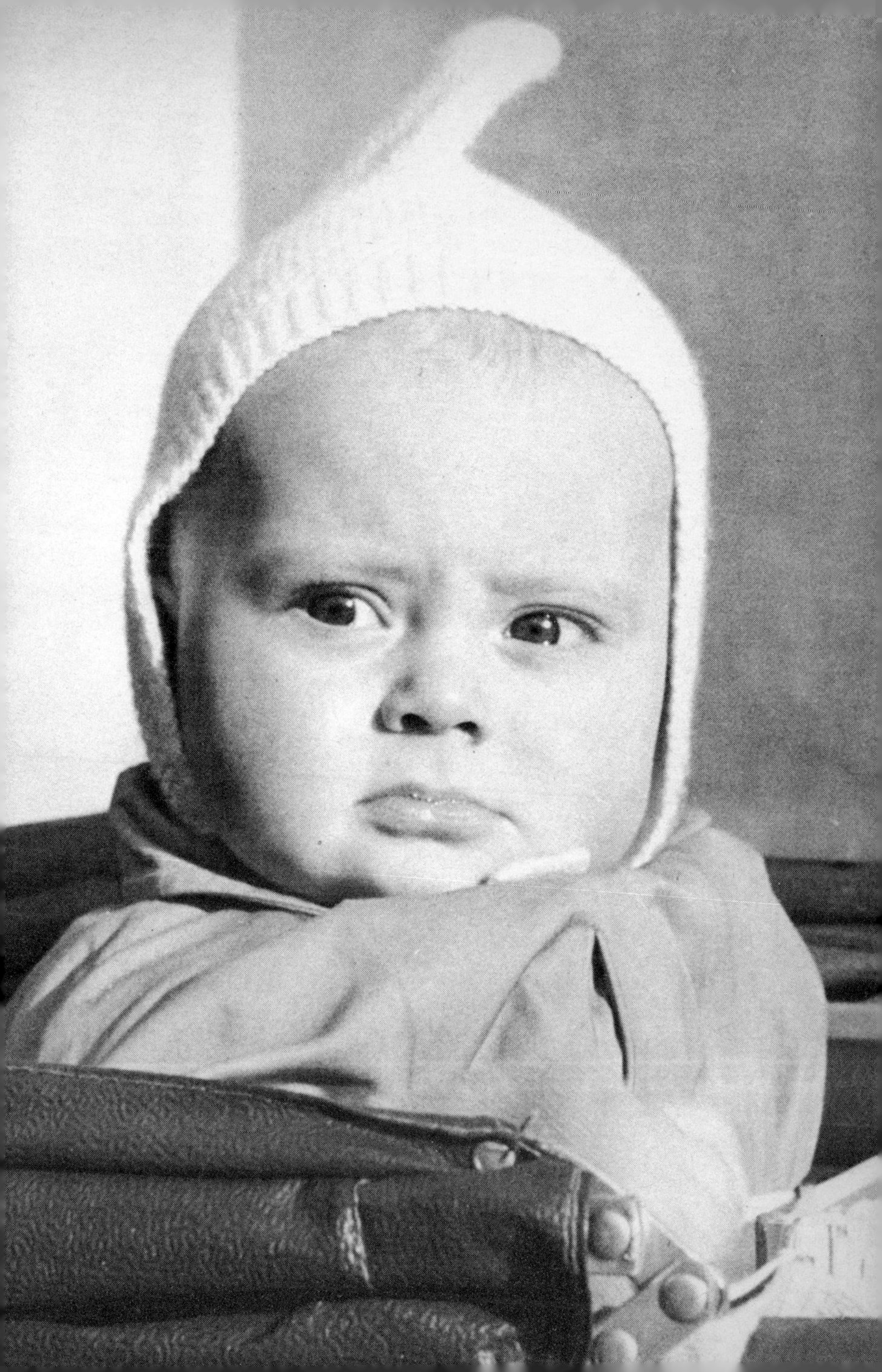

confidence that she is a loving and dependable person who believes in taking care of the baby as you do. Regardless of how long or how frequently you use a sitter, she must be someone who can be trusted. It is best to use the same one or two consistently. When you hire anyone who will have more or less regular contact with your baby, ask for references and the report of a current physical examination, including a test for tuberculosis.

Both you and the sitter will feel better if you take time to acquaint her with your ways of doing things. Show her where you keep the baby's clothes, diapers, towels, extra blankets. Let her watch you give a bottle if she's to feed the baby. You have many little tricks which you and the baby have worked out, and it's hard to remember even what they are. Up to the age of 6 or 8 months, most babies will readily accept care from a strange person. From then on they may need a little time to get used to a stranger.

Anyone left to care for your baby, even for a brief time, needs to know such information as: where you can be reached; the telephone number of your doctor and fire department; the name of another responsible person (neighbor, relative); details about your house, such as how to regulate the heat; what and when and how to feed the baby; and when you will return. A sitter will appreciate knowing exactly what you expect from her: what she can eat or drink; if she can have visitors, use the TV or radio; and what, if any, extra jobs you have in mind.

12. Four to eight months

The middle months of the first year—from 4 to 8 months—are relatively restful. The baby is more fun, he learns something new nearly every day, and he's less trouble all the time. Later on he's into things—creeping, walking, and exploring—and has to be looked after almost every minute. But now he stays put, more or less, and doesn't demand much.

Sometime in these months you're apt to be struck with how busy your baby is. As each part of his body matures and is ready to be used, he uses it. Head up first, then trunk propped up in sitting. Maybe a detour to creep or crawl or roll. Then finally your baby pulls up to stand. You just can't keep him down.

In the first year of life, increase in ability to handle the body is the best indication that the baby's brain is developing well. An alert baby, interested in everything about him, is using his mind. You can tell. He shows you that he knows what is going to happen next, by adjusting his posture when you lower him into the bathtub, for instance. Or by looking toward the door Daddy always uses as he hears the car approach in the evening.

Through daily experiences, he learns. He'll learn the most

if he has a change of scenery now and then, some interesting things to do, and people interested in what he does. Go to him frequently for a pat or a chat, a kiss or a laugh. It takes but a minute, and keeps him contented, sure that all is well. The baby who is left alone for long periods of time gets bored and fretful, and learns that he has to whine or cry to get attention. That is a lesson no thoughtful parent wants to teach a child.

Some parents argue, "But he has to learn to play by himself. He'll be spoiled by all that attention." But the neglected or ignored baby, the one always hungry for a bit of attention which he never seems to get until he's desperate, is the unfortunate one. A baby sure of those who care for him is free to branch out and away when he's older. If unsure, he keeps one foot on base, so to speak, for a longer time.

LEARNING TO TALK

Talk to the baby as you go about your work — talk about anything. Echo the sounds he makes. He'll repeat, delighted with the conversation. First he uses vowel sounds, many of which are used as he cries; later he makes consonants. M-m-m-m-m-m when he's contented; poo, boo, when he's full and pushes the bottle away. From the beginning, he uses his voice to tell you something. Finally, he gets fancy with bubbles and "razzberry" sounds as he learns to blow with lips closed. He'll try it with a mouthful of cereal, and find the results interesting indeed.

By 6 months of age, he can repeat at will some of the sounds he has hit upon. You'll notice that he uses a certain one to call you in the morning. If it doesn't work, after several tries, he'll give up on it and cry instead, but these sounds, different for each baby, are in truth his first words. Later, as he uses a sound which you believe is a word, your enthusiastic response makes him use it again. Sooner or later, it becomes a word with meaning — mama, dada, bye-bye — because you've given it meaning by your actions.

Some babies have half a dozen words, or more, by their first birthday. Others carry on lengthy conversations in their own words, aptly imitating the flow and rhythm of the language they hear, whether it's English, Spanish, or Chinese. Still others say nothing much, but clearly show they understand much of what you say. Keep on talking. Use gestures to show what your words mean. In time, the silent types will speak up and you may, instead, wish for a little silence.

HE BEGINS TO PLAY

Playing with sounds is the basis for learning to talk, playing with people is the basis for learning to get along with them, playing with things helps the baby to master his body, and eventually, to master his environment. From now on he'll enjoy a small collection of playthings. He really doesn't need much, and only a few at any one time. He'll concentrate for increasing lengths of time on a rattle, and begin to look for it when he drops it. He'll enjoy the movement and color of bright toys hung across his crib or a mobile suspended from the ceiling. A spoon and cup, spools strung together, a small pan and lid, clothespins, a cereal box, or measuring spoons fastened together all make good toys. And don't forget some floating items for the bath.

Around 4 months of age, he may begin to use his fingers separately. He then wants to practice this new skill by scratching on surfaces which give interesting results. Keep the baby's fingernails short so they won't splinter in the process, and give

ALL SIGNS ARE HAPPY SIGNS...

including yours(!) when you start your child early in protected-play habit patterns. Baby is always safe and busily playing while you get the home chores completed. Double drop sides eliminate bending backaches. Folds compactly for traveling. All signs are definitely "GO!" with a Pride Trimble Play Yard.

Pride Trimble
A VIRCO COMPANY

SOUTHERN PINES, NO. CAROLINA · GLENDALE, CALIFORNIA

him a variety of surfaces on which he can practice. You'll notice him scratching the high-chair tray, or the mattress pad. Give him a pie tin, bits of smooth ribbon, a piece of corduroy, or any harmless object around the house on which he can scratch, have fun, learn, and widen his experience and skill.

Any toy you give to the baby should (1) be sturdy enough that it will not splinter or break, (2) be large enough so he can't swallow it, (3) have no sharp points or rough edges, (4) have no parts that can come loose to be swallowed, such as whistles on rubber toys or buttons or eyes on stuffed animals, (5) be painted with lead-free paint.

Give him a squeaky toy he can work himself, and he thinks he's great. With any encouragement at all, most babies become real clowns. Drop a ball, and make a funny sound. The baby chuckles with delight. Bang the spoon on the high-chair tray and make it march toward him. He giggles right out loud.

One of the games all babies like to play is peekaboo. You hide behind a diaper, then you reappear. You hide his bottle, then suddenly produce it. The now-you-see-it-now-you-don't game is a sure hit. It also teaches the baby something about the world. It shows him that when you go, you'll come back. He's reassured.

HE MAY HAVE FEARS

He loves noise, and movement, and the unexpected — in small doses and in familiar surroundings. Loud, unfamiliar noises are apt to frighten him. Occasionally, a baby is quite upset by trains, airplanes, and other rushing sounds such as that of the vacuum cleaner. Try to avoid setting off such fears, and, if unavoidable, anticipate his upset and try to be near him. It's not the time to toughen him up. He's going to surprise you with how fearless and independent he will become when he's older and thinks he can handle the situation. Now he needs to be sure that you're nearby all the time.

Fear of strangers begins around 7 to 8 months, or soon thereafter. It may also start, quite normally, as early as 5 months. Unfortunately, the friendly outgoing baby who at first responded to everybody is apt to become so suspicious later that he won't go to anyone but Mother. His father's feelings are hurt, and his grandmother is sure "you've spoiled that baby" because he whimpers as they come close, or pushes them away. Actually, this new wariness is a good sign. It shows that the baby is getting so he can make distinctions between people. Not very good ones, maybe, but distinctions nevertheless. Don't try to force him to be friendly. He'll resume his outgoing ways later. During this shy stage, assure those who matter most that they need to approach slowly, and let the baby make the first overtures to them. His curiosity is going to overcome his shyness if they sit there wiggling an interesting toy. He finds it easier if strange people do not look at him too closely. He still likes to peer into other people's eyes, but he would rather look at them than have them look at him.

A PLAYPEN IS USEFUL

If you haven't already done so, around 6 months is a good time to get a playpen. You'll probably find it a most useful piece of equipment. Get one which folds so you can move it about easily. A playpen makes a good bed if you take the baby out; it's a playroom which keeps him out of things but near you, in or out of doors. It's a first gym, too. The firm floor helps in learning to sit, the bars are good for pulling up, the top rail gives support for first steps alone.

When you buy a playpen, as with any other equipment, check for safety: slats close enough so the baby's head can't get through, a folding mechanism which can't pinch. If you repaint an old one, use a safe paint.

Start using a playpen before the baby discovers the thrill of moving about on his own, and he may accept it more willingly than if you wait until he's tasted freedom. Babies differ a lot in their feelings about playpens after they learn to creep. Some accept confinement graciously for a good part of the day—playing, napping, and playing again before they howl. This is especially true if you go to them from time to time, or change the location. Others balk. Maybe you can persuade one who doesn't enjoy his playpen to accept it by placing it near you in kitchen or bedroom and seeing that he isn't left in it too long at any one time. Put him where he can see something interesting and give him something to play with. It's all right to let him fuss a little before you take him out. Get the things done which you must do, and don't let his complaints bother you.

But all babies, those who like a pen and those who don't, should have some time out of it. As the baby gets more active, plan to set him free for a part of each day under your watchful eye. He wants to explore on his own, and needs to be right down on the floor at times where he can move when he likes.

FEEDING BECOMES MORE GROWN UP

If you haven't been giving cereal, strained fruits, and vegetables, you can begin to offer them gradually. Once these are well started, meat and egg can be tried. These are good sources of protein and iron.

Some doctors start egg around 3 months; others prefer to wait until the baby is 5 months or more, since some are sensitive to it. If members of your family have allergies, you might want to wait even longer. In any case, begin (as always with a new food) by giving a very small amount. For egg, the amount to start with is about the size of a matchhead.

Begin with yolk only, since it has more food value and seems less apt to cause trouble than the white. Slip the yolk into boiling water and simmer about 10 minutes. Mash or press through a sieve and mix a small amount with milk or add to the cereal. It can be given at any meal. When the baby takes all the yolk, add small amounts of white. Continue to increase amounts if it causes no upset.

The egg can be prepared in any number of ways—soft cooked, poached, scrambled, or steamed in the top of a double boiler. Another way to give egg is to make a custard with 1 egg, 1 cup milk, and 1 teaspoon sugar. Divide the custard into 3 cups, feeding one a day. Over 3 days' time, the baby will get one well-cooked egg, and not too much at any one time.

During the time the baby takes yolk only, you may find it convenient to buy egg yolks canned commercially.

Most mothers today use canned, strained meats for the baby. Beef and liver are good ones to start with. Chicken and others can follow. You can prepare meat at home for the baby by scraping lean beef, but it is a lot of trouble and may be more expensive than buying commercially prepared meat for babies.

After the baby gets used to the strained forms, you may try cooked ground meat—beef, lamb, chicken and their livers. Crisp bacon adds an interesting flavor and texture, but it has little food value.

With meat and eggs added to cereal, fruit, and vegetables, you have many kinds of foods from which to choose the baby's diet. Give one or more of these so-called solid foods several times a day. He needs the nourishment they provide, and it is desirable to get him accustomed to new flavors and textures.

This is a good time also to begin to offer liquids to the baby from a cup. Orange juice, water, or milk in small amounts at first helps him get used to this way of drinking.

THREE MEALS A DAY

Soon you may notice that the baby eats less at one or the other of his four meals. If this is so, and if he is taking fairly substantial amounts of foods other than milk, try shifting him to three meals a day. Some babies are ready by 4 months, but for most the shift is appropriate between 6 and 8 months. Possibly the baby will need some nourishment to tide him over between meals. If so give orange juice midmorning and milk midafternoon. Some babies prefer the extra milk before bed.

Your meal plan may look something like this: *Breakfast*: cereal, egg, milk, orange juice. *Midmorning*: orange juice if not given at breakfast. *Noon meal*: vegetables, meat, milk. *Midafternoon*: milk, crusty bread or crackers. *Evening meal*: cereal, fruit, milk.

As time goes by, you'll be free to experiment with other items. Keep encouraging fruits, vegetables, and meats, however. For variety and interest, add foods cooked for the family, such as spaghetti, rice, noodles, macaroni, or grits. Many babies gag on potatoes as they tend to form a pasty ball in the mouth. Baking the potato may keep it more flaky. Mix with milk, salt, and a bit of butter or margarine. Some babies enjoy cottage cheese, plain or with milk.

Gelatin desserts, custard, and various puddings can be tried. Some mothers buy a lot of puddings because the baby takes these better, but they are not as nutritious. It is usually wise to wait until the child is approaching 2 years of age before using chocolate flavoring. Many children are allergic to chocolate.

After 6 months of age, a baby can be given bread in the form of hard toast or zwieback, crackers, and simple cookies such as arrowroot. Make bread into melba toast by drying it thoroughly in the oven. Butter or margarine can be added to bread and vegetables in the second half of the first year.

As the bottle-fed baby gets more nourishment from other foods, he doesn't need calories from sugar in his formula. Gradually leave out the sugar. Either a breast- or bottle-fed baby can be shifted to fresh whole milk (pasteurized), but there's no reason to stop using evaporated milk.

However, if you are going to stop using evaporated milk for the formula, at first give the baby only one bottle of boiled fresh milk a day. Other bottles should be the same as before. You get him used to the new taste, and you can see if it agrees with him. The same plan can be used if you have been breast-feeding the baby.

WHEN TO STOP BOILING THINGS

If you live in reasonably healthful surroundings, it is safe to stop boiling bottles and milk for most babies when they're getting around a good bit, out on the floor and into places where the surfaces aren't exactly spotless. But you still take precautions with the baby's milk longer than with other foods because germs multiply so rapidly in milk and babies catch intestinal infections so easily.

If things are going well, you can stop boiling bottles when you are no longer mixing a formula to store in them. But scald the bottle with boiling water. If you have heat-resistant bottles, take the milk from the refrigerator and pour it into the bottle just before use. Most people warm the milk a little then, but there is evidence that it might be unnecessary. If your bottles are not heat-resistant, warm the milk before putting it into the bottle.

If your baby is particularly susceptible to diarrhea, if the weather is very hot, or if your refrigerator doesn't keep things very cold, continue to boil everything until the baby is weaned to a cup. Always boil raw milk. Be careful to keep milk and opened jars or cans of milk and other foods for the baby's use under refrigeration.

THE BABY'S CHAIR

It's a great day when the baby sits well by himself and you can pop him into a chair for meals. He loves to join the family for meals even if he has already eaten. Lots of babies have fallen out of high chairs when left unattended, so a low chair is a lot safer. Best of all is a chair which will serve either way—as a high chair on some occasions, as a low chair on others. Some types have a table attached which doubles as a play and feeding surface. If the chair you've got isn't so flexible, make it as safe as possible for the baby. A waist or crotch strap to hold him in is helpful.

You really don't have to have a special chair, but do arrange a way to feed the baby so that when the time comes he can begin to help feed himself. If you sit with baby food jar or dish in one hand, spoon in the other, and tuck bites into the baby's mouth when he opens up, he can't get into the game. And he very much wants to. If you discourage a baby from "helping" to feed himself when he's so eager to try, you may find that later on he'll sit back and expect you to continue doing the work. If you encourage his awkward first attempts, messy though they are, he gets the idea and becomes more skillful. The baby who is allowed to experiment in feeding himself early becomes neater sooner than one denied the chance to practice.

Furthermore, the baby who feeds himself isn't quite so apt to let food enter into the general pattern of resistance which occurs around the first birthday. At this time, they not only are reaching an independent frame of mind where they want to call the tune on everything, but they also have a less ravenous appetite because their growth rate is decreasing. The combination of independence and decreased appetite makes it easy for meals to become a time to battle over food. If you let the baby decide how much he wants to eat, and let him feed himself as much as he will, arguments over food are less apt to occur.

A TOOTH MAY APPEAR

There's an old saying, "One tooth at 6 months, six teeth at a year." This may be true on average, but there are wide variations. Some babies are born with a tooth; just as often, parents have to wait till the first birthday or later for that event. Brothers and sisters are apt to be like each other in the time their teeth appear. Usually, but by no means always, the first to come are two center teeth of the lower jaw, followed by four center upper teeth. They are called incisors because of their sharp cutting edges.

After a pause of several months, six more teeth will erupt: the two remaining lower incisors are followed by four molars with flat grinding surfaces, set back a little. Toward the second birthday, four pointed teeth, called canine or "dog" teeth, come through in the spaces between the incisors and the molars. Later,

Baby's first tooth!

A big day in his life, and yours. One to remember always. Not that it was all smiles and laughter! Poor baby shed many a tear — and you spent many a sleepless night — before you discovered Dr. Hand's Teething Lotion.

Developed by a doctor over 70 years ago, Dr. Hand's is the only leading teething lotion that stops the pain of baby's sore, swollen gums without the use of benzocaine. Besides being safe and effective, Dr. Hand's is pleasant tasting. Stops baby's tears within seconds.

When your baby suffers from teething pains, give him the fine relief he deserves. And make this time a time to remember with joy.
DR. HAND'S Teething Lotion

four more molars appear behind the first ones to complete the first set of 20 teeth. These are the baby or "milk" teeth which will be shed as the permanent teeth come in, starting around age 6. A baby's teeth may appear in a somewhat different order than the one listed. It won't matter.

Sometimes you don't know that your baby has a tooth until you get bitten or hear the click of the spoon against it. You may notice some drooling, but this happens anyhow while he learns to control his saliva better. Frequently, however, a baby is cross and fretful, may lose his appetite for a few days or waken at night crying. He may suck his fingers or fist more than usual. Many households more or less proudly display a ring of tiny toothmarks in the coffee table or the leg of a chair made by a teething baby who is also learning to pull up.

But teething rarely accounts for an illness. If the baby is feverish or coughing, has prolonged loss of appetite or other signs of illness, it is probably not related to teething, and you should check for other causes.

To ease the baby's discomfort while he is teething, probably the best thing is to be patient with him and soothe him every way you know how. Give him zwieback, hard toast, or a teething ring of hard rubber or plastic. Be sure he doesn't chew on things that would break or splinter in his mouth. Watch that he doesn't gnaw wood finished with paint containing lead. If he wakens at night, he may need a warm bottle to help him go back to sleep. When the discomfort of teething is over, he'll be eating better during the day and less fretful at night. When he's again ready, he will give up the night bottle.

The health of the gums and teeth is directly connected to the baby's diet. Even while he's cutting baby teeth, buds of his permanent teeth are being laid down in the jaw. For this reason, a diet which provides plenty of vitamins and minerals is important throughout infancy.

Fluorine is a mineral that is especially important for sound tooth development. Many communities add small amounts of fluorine to their water supply if it does not naturally contain enough. Some doctors prescribe small doses of fluorine for babies who do not get as much as they need from the water they drink. Since too much fluorine can be harmful to tooth development, it is important to follow the doctor's directions carefully if he prescribes it for your baby.

SLEEPING PATTERNS ARE SET

Once they're on three meals a day, most babies settle down to two fairly long naps, one in the morning, one in the afternoon. For many babies, the morning nap, strangely enough, is the longest. After a long sleep at night, it seems hard to believe that the baby is ready to snooze some more.

Two naps continue to be the pattern until a year or more of age. Then for awhile, the baby may take one nap some days, and two others, and neither system works very well. With one nap, he's tired and eventually he gets cross and may fall asleep over his supper. With two, he's on the go too late at night. Eventually he gets it worked out and stays with one nap, usually after lunch, for the next several years.

As the baby reaches a more active stage, he may resist going to sleep at night, even though he's tired. This occurs around the first birthday for some, but others fight saying goodnight by 6 months or so. Resisting bedtime may be caused by the accumulation of several things. For one, he's more sociable, and loves to be with people, so he hates to have you leave.

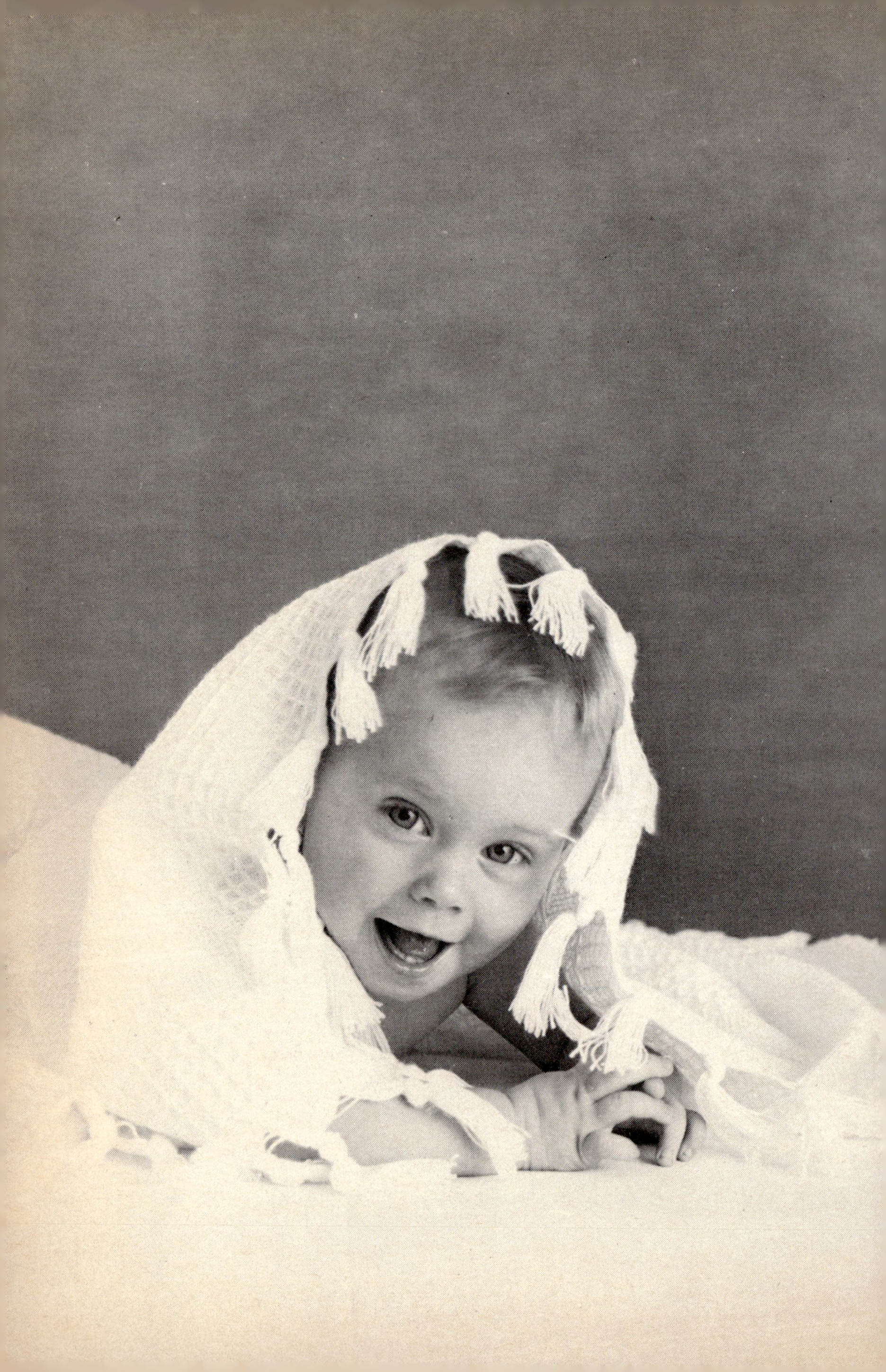

In addition, he's hungry to see more of what's going on in the world, and is eager to keep moving about.

You can do something about this urge to keep moving. If he's at the point where he's learning to sit, he fights against being laid flat, even to change a diaper. He's like a toy that bobs upright when pushed over. Place a baby who is in this frame of mind in bed sitting up. Sooner or later he'll topple over in sleep, and you can cover him then. It's the lying down, not sleep in itself, that bothers him so. As for his reluctance to see you go, just be sure he sees enough of you at other times.

Once you've got him settled for the night, it isn't usually necessary to go back into the room. If he calls to you, call back to assure him you're nearby. But don't go in unless you sense an urgency to his cry that tells you he really needs you. The fretful cry of a sleepy baby may just be his way of unwinding.

It is worth being firm about the importance of going to bed, and staying in bed, from the very beginning. The baby who knows you mean it when you say goodnight is really more comfortable about bed than the one who feels he ought to put up a fuss just to see what you'll do next. At around 2½ years of age, many toddlers are up and out of bed at all hours of the night. This is a trying stage for everybody. But the child who knows your clear expectations about staying in his own room will give up night prowling sooner than one who's been in doubt all along about what you expect of him.

THUMBSUCKING AND OTHER COMFORTS

Babies invent fascinating little tricks to comfort themselves as they fall asleep. One will rub the satin edge of the blanket, another will pull at his ear, suck his thumb, or twirl a lock of hair. No two are exactly alike. These little movements become a kind of language. When the baby begins to pull at his ear, for instance, you know that he's tired and tuck him in bed.

Thumbsucking often worries parents. But babies need to suck, some more and for a longer time than others. Be sure that yours has plenty of opportunity to do so. Some doctors believe that giving a pacifier to a baby in the early months of life will give him enough sucking so that he won't turn to his thumb later.

There are a lot of opinions about thumbsucking, why it starts and what it means. A baby who feels left out, has nothing to do, or who doesn't get enough food to nourish his body or enough love to nourish his spirit is probably going to suck his thumb in an effort to make up for these shortcomings. On the other hand, some babies suck their thumbs in the midst of plenty of everything.

Anyway, don't fuss at the baby about sucking his thumb. And don't resort to mittens or stiff cuffs or any other restrictive devices to try to make him stop. By age 3, he'll probably quit of his own accord.

13. Eight to twelve months

By the last quarter of the first year, a baby has a personality all his own. He's a full-fledged member of the family, and it's hard to do much of anything without him there, insisting that he be in on it, too. He's quite a handful in more ways than just his size.

He trails around after his mother, creeping or beginning to walk. He horns in on every conversation, and laughs gustily, whether he's in on the joke or not. He cries if someone is upset with him, and shows in other ways how sensitive he is to the feelings of those about him. He likes to be the center of attention, but may shyly hang his head if he thinks you find him foolish.

He's into everything—poking, dumping, licking, squeezing, tossing, climbing. He may begin to be choosy about his food, and is very apt to pour his milk or his cereal on the highchair tray, splashing in the mess. He plays with the light cord, or fiddles with the stove. He won't even stay dressed, taking off his shoes the minute you get them on.

Sometimes, in a gay spirit of defiance, he deliberately teases. He heads straight for the trash basket to upset it, making sure you notice what he's doing. He reaches for his father's newspaper, or book, mischief in his eyes, waiting to hear your ready "no, no." At such moments you find yourself joining the age-old dilemma of parenthood, wondering when to stop the child and when to laugh and enjoy his newest success, when to encourage and when to forbid.

Yet discipline cannot be separated from the whole business of just living with a baby or a child. The relationship between the two of you is the outgrowth of everything you do for and with him. And it is from this relationship that good discipline springs. As he grows to love and trust you, he wants to please you and to behave to suit you. Obedience, or discipline, then, is not so much a matter of making the baby mind as it is a process of making it easy for the baby to do the right thing.

DISCIPLINE IN LITTLE WAYS

Everything in this pamphlet contributes to good discipline. When we talk about feeding or sleep or comfortable clothing, we make it possible for the baby to be a good baby because he is full, rested, and at ease. Knowing that you will bring his dinner as fast as you can when he is hungry, he learns to wait patiently while you fix it. When you recognize the baby's need for attention, you make him contented and sure of the world. He learns that you'll come when he calls. But with time, he also learns to control his wishes to have you nearby. He learns that he must not call out in the morning until it is time for the household to get up. So he begins to play cheerfully, if not very quietly, until the household stirs.

We make it easy for the baby to be good when we don't ask too much of him. Keep the household as free as possible of attractive knickknacks and precious objects which will attract him. If he sees something bright and pretty, he must investigate it. His curiosity is boundless, and he can only learn about things by tasting and feeling them. Merely looking at them tells him little.

There's no doubt that the baby has to be kept from doing things which are dangerous to himself or to others. This is a good time to read the chapter on accident prevention, for many of the dangerous situations a baby can get into are avoidable; and the ones which can't be avoided can be handled quickly and firmly. Distract him with another interesting object or activity, or pick him up and take him elsewhere. He doesn't need to be punished for investigating things—he needs information. Give him words to use instead of a flat "no." You say "Hot." "Tastes bad." "Stop." He learns from your voice and the expression on your face, as well as the words.

Some parents reinforce their commands with a sharp tap on the child's hand. Surely nothing more than this is necessary. Even so, they run the risk of teaching the baby to slap them if he doesn't like what they do. You're trying to teach the baby what is dangerous, not to punish him for his natural curiosity or lack of knowledge. Never spank a baby under a year of age. He simply does not understand what you mean, and learns only to fear you. The impulse to strike a baby often comes from anger within the adult over things which have nothing to do with the act of the baby. Although the impulse to strike a baby may be strong, especially when you are tired or worried, you will find that it is deeply upsetting to him and that it does not improve his behavior.

Much of the annoying behavior of a baby is the result of his efforts to control his body, to make it work according to his wishes. Gradually, for instance, he begins to use thumb and finger separately, so he practices diligently at picking things up—a speck of dust, a piece of food, a wooden block. When mastered, he then must learn how to let an object go. He carefully drops his cup off the high-chair tray, the car keys behind the seat or out of the window, his teddy bear into the toilet. You can't help noticing these feats, although you may have failed to notice that he's been dropping other objects all day long, with increasingly accurate aim.

If he's learning how to walk, he works at this task endlessly, right through mealtime, bedtime, and toilet time. For he's a wholehearted creature and what he thinks is good, he finds very, very good. He's an all-or-nothing-at-all-type. Content yourself with the knowledge that once he perfects the skill, he'll move on to something new. You needn't worry about breaking him of the habit of dropping things, or shoving chairs around, or anything else of this nature. He'll be bored with it when he has it mastered. It is foolish to punish a child for actions which are a part of his effort to control his body. He can't help what he does.

In general, then, you are teaching a baby how to behave all through the day. It isn't just when you say "no" or scold him for his mischief. You are teaching him good discipline when you simply accept behavior which you recognize is part of his babyhood. You give him simple, interesting toys and safe places to play. You allow him as much freedom as you safely can. You cheerfully accept his awkward attempts to do things and don't punish him for accidents. Meantime, you stop him promptly from getting into danger, every time, consistently.

And you guide him into behavior which makes him fit into your household ways, knowing that he is happier if you are happy with him. Be patient, gentle, and understanding about the many things he needs to learn, but keep showing him what you expect. As for his mischievous tricks, perhaps you can laugh with him over these, to let him see that you, too, have a sense of humor.

CHANGES IN FEEDING

Whether he has teeth or not, a baby is ready to deal with foods of a coarser consistency anywhere from 7 to 9 months of age. It's no use waiting for teeth. The molars which grind food won't appear until he's 12 to 18 months of age, and it will be some time thereafter before he learns to use them for that purpose. His gums serve to bite things off if he still lacks the front teeth with cutting edges.

For some months, you have probably been giving a full range of strained and soft foods, including cereal, fruits, vegetables, meats, eggs, simple puddings, orange and other fruit juices. Now's the time to nudge him into accepting food in a more adult form. If you wait too long, the baby gets accustomed to his smooth diet and may balk at lumps. Make the change before he gets set in his ways and bossy about things, as he's apt to be for a time after his first birthday.

To start on chopped foods, use either or both of the following plans: Cook vegetables or fruits, mashing them rather finely with a fork, but leave some larger pieces. Let him pick these up himself, if he wishes, or offer him the mixture on a spoon. If you use canned baby foods, buy both chopped (junior) and strained. Mix them, using more of the strained and perhaps reducing the size of the chopped pieces at first. Gradually decrease the strained portion.

Or you can give the baby a piece of food — a bit of ground meat, a cooked vegetable (such as a carrot or stringbean) or slice of raw fruit (banana, peeled apple or pear), or a piece of cheese. Let him gnaw off as much as he wants. Go slowly with uncooked fruits at first, as they may tend to make the baby's bowels loose. Use only those you can wash and peel.

A baby enjoys bits of meat or a chicken leg to work over, sucking and chewing on its goodness. Chopped crisp bacon or dry breakfast cereal will please him also. Gradually, you will be able to feed him what you prepare for the rest of the family. A menu selected from the basic food groups, simply prepared, can be enjoyed by all the family. However, if the family tastes run to highly spiced dishes, rich pastries, many sweets, and fatty foods, you should make special plans for the baby. Babies need plain, nourishing food to help them grow—food to build muscle, bones, blood, and sound teeth. They need food which provides the tremendous amount of energy they use in pushing, shoving, walking, exploring. They need food which helps to keep them well. They have no room in their stomachs for foods which do not serve these purposes. And most of them like the simple foods better.

One caution: Never give a baby nuts, corn or popcorn, raisins, hard candy, or other hard foods which could cause him to choke and possibly inhale bits into his lungs.

Chunks of imperfectly digested foods may appear in the bowel movements as he is learning to manage chopped foods. The color may change, too, with new foods. The movement may become red from gelatin dessert or dark green from spinach. These are normal changes.

WEANING THE BABY

As your baby's menu takes on a more adult texture, you may be thinking about weaning next. Possibly, you've been offering him liquids from a cup for some time. Often babies

Young children rarely do things because of a belief that they are right or wrong but usually to achieve a desired goal. This goal is often to attract attention. Keeping this in mind, be liberal in your praise when the child is good and try to find a substitute for physical punishment when he misbehaves. Quietly withdrawing one of his privileges is more effective discipline than a noisy spanking that simply draws more attention to him.

will accept water or orange juice from a cup—practically anything except milk—from age 6 months on.

But when it comes to milk, babies differ a great deal in the age they are ready to give up the familiar method. A few are bored with nursing by 10 months of age, more by a year. Those who haven't given up breast or bottle by then may cling to sucking for some time thereafter. At a year or so of age, a baby becomes very possessive about his mother and finds it hard to become separated from her, even in the next room. It is easy to see why nursing, whether breast or bottle, has become associated with her. The baby who is not already weaned may be most reluctant to give up sucking his milk until he grows a little and is less panic stricken about losing his mother (often at around 18 months).

There is no fixed age when weaning should be done. Try to follow the baby's lead. If he appears to enjoy the cup, encourage it. He'll chew the lip at first, and spill a lot, but with practice he learns to swallow smoothly. Put in a little milk, only a tablespoon at first, and let him handle the cup himself. Gradually eliminate bottles as he takes more from the cup. If you feel strongly about getting the baby off the bottle, stop giving him a bedtime bottle first. He probably enjoys this one most, and would continue to ask for it long after he's given up daytime bottles. If you aren't concerned about it, he may enjoy falling asleep over a bottle well into his second year.

It is easy to overlook a baby's readiness to give up the bottle if you're worried about getting a lot of milk into him. Some mothers almost force bottles on babies who would otherwise have cheerfully dispensed with them. Most babies take both milk and solid foods equally well. But some prefer solid foods to milk, others favor the opposite, tending to carry a preference for one or the other far into life. Their mothers are often concerned lest the baby not get a sufficient amount of the type not so well liked. Those who prefer solid foods are apt to remain pretty good eaters throughout childhood, but their mothers may keep them on a bottle longer than necessary because they feel that, in addition to all the solid food, they must get in a full quart of milk as well.

Whichever kind of baby you have, do not force him to eat, or drink. Offer him a well-rounded diet, at regular intervals throughout the day. Let his appetite guide you in the amount to give. And don't make too much of an issue over bottles.

WHEN HE STARTS TO WALK

Everybody knows that some babies walk early and some walk late, and it really doesn't matter in the long run whether it's at 8 months, 13 months, or later when the baby starts. Unless yours happens to be one of the late ones. Then you don't like the idea at all. Somehow, the day the baby takes his first step is so important you almost feel like declaring a national holiday. If it's delayed, you're first irritated, then worried.

Many factors enter into the age a baby walks. Among them are his weight and his temperament—whether he is eager and aggressive or passive and timid. Also, his general rate of development or the speed at which his bones, muscles, and ligaments mature. Children tend to keep the same over-all pace in their growth. Some are first in the block to do everything; others take their time.

There's really not much you can do to hurry the day. He's going to walk when he's ready. It does help to encourage the baby to use his muscles freely, to kick and splash in his bath, to wiggle his toes, to stretch and roll over, unhampered by restrictive clothing. It helps to give him a good place to pull up, a

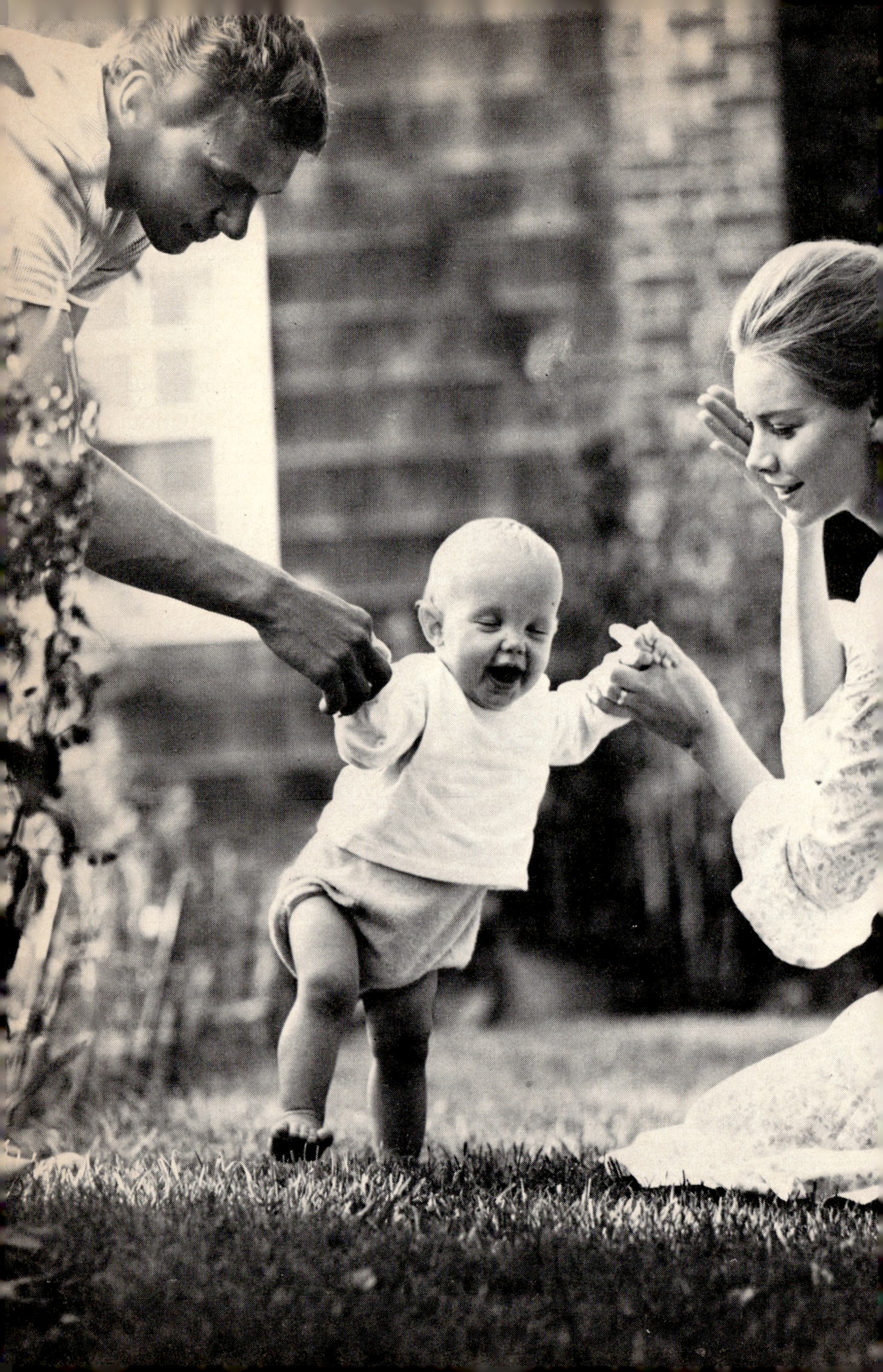

playpen or furniture to grab, and to hold him with your strong hands so he can dance on tiptoe at your feet.

When he begins to stand alone, a child plants his feet wide apart and bends his knees a little. His feet are flat, often with a thick padding of fat in the arch. He puts his weight on the inner part of the foot, and tends to toe out. This gives him a knock-kneed appearance. As his body adjusts to standing, the stomach becomes round and prominent, and a curve appears at the lower part of his back. The hips tip forward. The line of the upper back and head is straight.

The protruding stomach won't flatten out for some years, probably around age 6. By then his feet will point ahead, and the legs will be straight. That is, if you stand and walk straight yourself. Children are such great imitators that their posture and way of walking are apt to be much the same as yours. Inherited body structure contributes; but example is powerful indeed.

When he takes a step, the baby stretches his arms up and out for balance, as if he were a tightrope walker in the circus. The distance to the floor must seem equally great to each performer, the baby and the aerial artist, for the baby needs a lot of courage to sit down. For a time, someone has to rush to his aid when he gets tired of standing. Soon as he's helped down, he bounces right up again and you have to do it over. Eventually, he learns to make it to the floor by himself, and everyone heaves a sigh of relief.

Once he's mastered sitting down, he's up and down all day long. Mostly up, as the drive to walk pushes everything else out of his mind—sleep, food, cuddling—and he struggles to keep on his feet at all costs. He lurches here and staggers there, a determined smile on his face. He frequently loses balance, sitting down hard. When he falls, he bumps his forehead every time. Later, as his center of gravity changes, he hits his nose or cheek. Finally, it's the chin. You can almost guess the age of the child by the location of his battle scars.

His energy and drive seem boundless. He scarcely notices the falls, but occasionally will check your face after a bump to see if he should cry or not. Try to save your sympathy for the really tough falls. He can take the minor ones in stride, and gains so much satisfaction from the sheer joy of walking that he doesn't count the price. It is easy to make him fearful if you rush to comfort him after each tumble.

WHAT KIND OF SHOES?

Until the baby walks, he really needs no covering for his feet. In very cold weather you might use knitted bootees or stockings much as you add a sweater or mittens. Some mothers like to use soft shoes when the baby crawls to protect the tender skin. Unless there is a foot problem, the baby doesn't need a well-built shoe until he begins to walk on hard or rough surfaces. Shoes won't make him walk any sooner than he would otherwise; and a very stiff shoe with a slippery sole can actually make it harder for him to balance.

When he's walking, get a well-built shoe with some support in the arch, a firm sole which is flexible at the widest part, and the upper made of soft, porous leather. For the most part, the shoes on the market for children of this age are made according to recommendations of foot specialists. Good ones aren't necessarily expensive. The important thing is to be sure your baby is properly fitted. Take him along, and be sure to check the length and width of the shoe carefully, on his foot. It should be half an inch longer than his foot and wide enough to allow room on the side for his foot to expand as he stands. It isn't a good idea to buy shoes the next size larger than an outgrown pair without first trying them on the baby. Different companies make shoes slightly different as to size, and the baby may have grown more than one size anyhow.

Unless a doctor prescribes high-top shoes, they aren't necessary. High tops stay on better, but they don't strengthen the ankle. It is natural for a baby to walk on the inner surface of his foot and to toe out at first. Practice and exercise strengthen the muscles to hold his foot and ankle straight.

During the first years, the baby outgrows shoes quickly. If he starts wearing shoes at around 8 months, he may need a new pair almost every month for a while. By 18 months, shoes may last for 2 or 3 months before they are too small. Examine the baby's foot often to see if there is any thickening of the skin or any spot which reveals pressure.

Remember that the baby outgrows socks as fast as shoes. Be sure that his socks are not tight enough to curl or cramp his toes. When put on, they should extend beyond the toe a quarter of an inch.

A LOOK AHEAD

On his first birthday, you can scarcely remember how fragile the baby once seemed. Now it's all you can do to hold him as he gaily bounces, using your lap as a springboard. He reaches for the candle on his cake, determined to make it his own.

Proud as you are, you may have some twinges of sadness that he is growing up. You already see some hints that his helpless sweetness will be replaced by a husky independence. It is hard to be wholehearted in welcoming the changes to come. At the same time, your mind rushes ahead to tricycles and roller skates, to storybooks and first days at school.

While the first birthday appears to be a dividing line between baby and childhood, it does not mark any great change in the baby's day-to-day behavior. The tasks which absorb him at a year will continue to challenge him for some time to come. He has made a grand beginning, but has a good way to go.

As the baby becomes more proficient in walking, he increases his range of activity. The sights and sounds of the world flood upon him, and he must develop words to express the ideas which they produce. He must have names for everything he sees, for he's a social fellow and wants to tell you all about it.

He has little sense of right and wrong, but depends on you to keep him out of trouble. He's not a bit cautious, either, and needs your careful supervision every minute he's loose. His circle of friends grows wider and he reaches out to others, as long as he knows you're nearby. He enjoys the company of grandparents, soberly watches other children at play, and waves to the milkman. Somehow your circle of friends grows, too, as the baby brings you closer to others who have babies.

PLAN YOUR NEXT BABY

A new baby can be a happy event in a family, especially if he is wanted and planned. When you plan your family, both you and your husband can be happier because you won't be worrying about having another baby until you are ready. There are many ways to be sure you will have your babies only when you want them. Your doctor will help you find a way that best suits both you and your husband.

14. Ages one and two

Your baby has now lived a whole year. You may think that you've done all the work in the first year, but your baby has been working too. He's made a start on the learning that will absorb him for the rest of his preschool years. He has felt to some degree all the emotions he will feel during the rest of his life.

He has learned a great deal about people from you, his parents. But he's also been teaching you. His arrival has pushed you into a new understanding of yourself. You have gained in confidence, and your baby has added to your confidence, by becoming more predictable as well as by thriving on your care.

TAKE STOCK AT FIRST BIRTHDAY

From fitting comfortably in the crook of your arm, your baby has grown about half as much again as his birth length, and he's probably tripled his birth weight. From being altogether helpless, he learned to control his head and trunk, and later his arms and legs. He can hold a rattle with his toes and use his fingers and thumb to pick up a speck of dust.

He may drink from a cup and perform juggler tricks with

his bottle. He reflectively tastes everything and decides what he considers edible, whether it's good for him or not. He gets about rapidly, creeping and crawling, perhaps even walking. He crawls up stairs and possibly worms down a few; he gets in and out of furniture. He contributes a few words to the conversation—hi, bye-bye, mama, dada. He has sounds which stand for many other words, and he understands even more.

By his first birthday he wakes, sleeps, and eats in a definite pattern. Usually he enjoys a long sleep and one or two naps. He's reduced his meals from six or more a day to three. He has learned to chew vigorously, although he may still have need to suck. He may exhibit from four to six teeth, which make his biting businesslike.

He knows his mother and father and other members of his family. Just as clearly, he distinguishes strangers, and somehow makes a quick decision on whether he can trust them. He's more interested in people than in toys, and loves to play little games such as pattycake and peek-a-boo. Nevertheless, he can spend half an hour alone with his playthings.

At this age physical play, even roughhousing, is endlessly satisfying to him, especially if the game has an element of surprise or if you noisily follow him as he creeps away, then delightedly catch or find him. When his father gets down on the floor to play with him, the baby shouts with delight and nearly bursts in his enthusiasm for the game and for life. He also knows when you're not pleased with him. He can tell how the people around him feel—if they are afraid, angry, anxious, affectionate, or upset. He catches his mood from them.

Through the first year he has begun to decide whether or not the world is a safe and dependable place. For most babies, the answer is loud and clear—the world is wonderful. They have developed a deep attachment for the people who take care of them. Through this attachment they become human beings who can, in turn, care for others.

All in all, the first birthday finds most babies at a serene stage, responsive and absorbed in every detail of the world. Sociable and fun to be with, they anticipate with delight each step of the daily routine.

HE BECOMES A TODDLER

About this time, the baby begins to slide into a much more independently active and vigorous stage. He matches his new physical abilities with ideas and energy that seem boundless. The docile, manageable baby disappears and parents are dismayed at what a suspicious, bossy fellow they have on their hands.

Strange as it seems, the older the baby, the more he wants his mother. He doesn't want anybody else either, and may fuss if a familiar grandmother comes to fondle him, or Daddy wants to pick him up. Even though he rejects them, at times he behaves better with them than he does with his mother. His father, for instance, may get him to eat better; Grandma or a sitter may get him to sleep more quickly than either parent.

To explain these contradictions, it helps to know that a child's dependence on his mother, or the one who has taken the most care of him, is really a sign that the job has been well done. He now begins to understand that he is a separate person. At first, he probably felt he was a part of his mother. It might be better to say he felt his mother was a part of him—the part that gets things done. She brought what he wanted, sometimes even before he was sure what it was.

As he grew, he became able to move away from his mother, by crawling or creeping. He could control his world to a much larger extent by fetching his own toys himself. Now he is on his own! This is a thrilling—and fearful—discovery, for he has learned to love his mother and responds to her intimately, finding assurance from her nearness that he is safe and all is well.

So, as he pulls away from her, he runs back even faster. This is shown clearly when a child crawls away from his mother to a different room. Suddenly he realizes that he is alone and howls, frantically eager to be "found" and reassured.

The toddler or creeper fares better when we don't add to his fears about losing his mother, so be cautious about planning any separation. This is not a good time for you to return to work. It's too soon to plan a vacation away from him. If the doctor feels that an operation for your child can be postponed, it is far better to wait. If a separation must occur, you will need to understand how deeply upsetting it is to the child, and be prepared for extra clinging and fearfulness afterwards.

At the same time the toddler is developing an increased awareness of how much he needs his mother, he is complicating life by wanting to run everything himself—without her. He wants to open doors even though he can't reach the knob. He sees steps and must march up them. He grabs the steering wheel. Parents are now faced with the problem of how much to restrict and how much to give in. If they overrestrict him, he may feel he must battle every step of the way and become rebellious. Or he may lose faith in himself and become too docile, always seeking approval before he tries anything new.

EARLY EXPERIENCES COUNT HEAVILY

This baby, entering childhood, is really at a crossroads. If he continues to receive the warm assurance he has had, he will

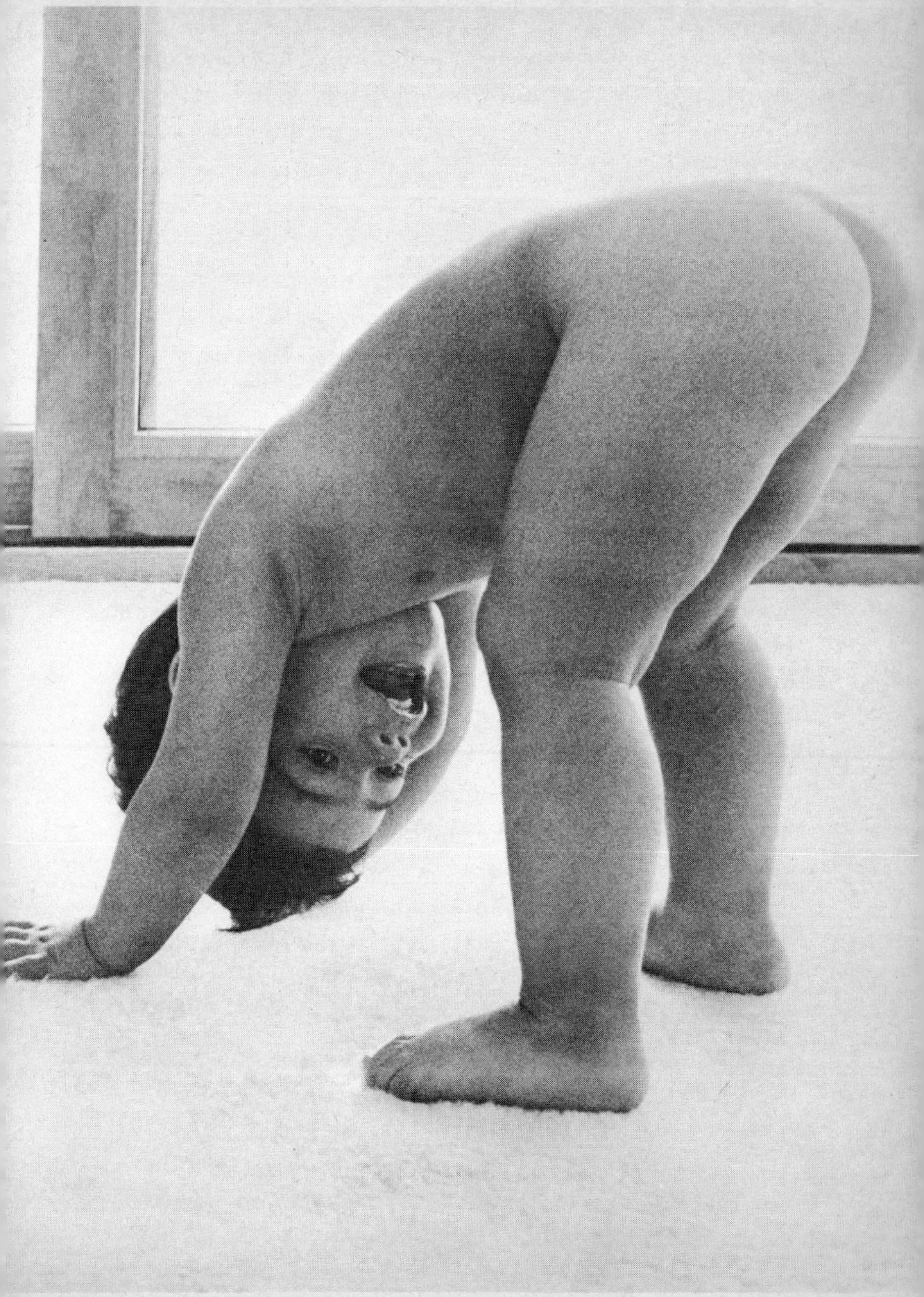

grow more sure of himself. If he is pushed out faster than he is ready to go, he will always be a little less confident and a little more dependent on others than he might otherwise have been.

These early experiences have a lifelong effect. Even though the child doesn't remember what actually happened, and lacks words to give it shape in his mind, the feelings remain. He learns that he can count on people—or that he cannot; that he will be allowed to try things out—or that he'll be constantly thwarted. These characteristic ways of looking at things tend to persist and become a fixed part of personality.

Many problems of the preschool years result from normal growth, which pushes the child into contradictions within himself. A serene, cooperative stage will be replaced by one in which nothing seems to go smoothly. Parents may find it hard to accept the changes in the child, and their mixed feelings may contribute to the child's lack of balance. If they do not understand the change as a result of growth, they are apt to struggle unsuccessfully to keep the child as he was. Even though they are proud their child can do more things, they naturally mourn the lost babyhood.

The contradiction within the toddler of the urge to be on his own and his increased awareness of his need for his parents obviously produces problems for him, too. He can't have both at once. Gradually, he gives in a little at each end of his desire to be independent and dependent at the same time. Most of the rough spots in a day with a toddler occur over routines —meals, dressing, naps, going to bed.

WALKING ENLARGES HIS WORLD

The age at which children walk alone varies widely. First they learn to move arms and legs together with swimming motions to propel themselves forward or backward—creeping, scooting, or crawling. Later they begin to pull up, stand with support, and then move about, still holding on. Children tend to keep the same over-all pace in their development. Some are quick, some slow at everything.

While some babies walk at 9 to 10 months of age, it is more common at 13 to 15 months. The actual age depends on many things: the heaviness of the child, how cautious or courageous he is, and his general body build. These might be expressed as what he inherits.

His daily life influences the age of walking as well. Good nourishing food helps. So does an opportunity to kick and wiggle toes, to stretch and roll over, unhampered by restrictive clothing. As you encourage him and provide a safe place for his natural urge to use his muscles, you contribute to later walking skill.

A child can't be taught to walk until he is ready. And when he gets ready, it is almost impossible to stop him. He will spend most of his energy and time practicing. Once up, he hates to get down or be put down at all. He springs to his feet in the morning and walks all day long, frequently fussing about being stopped—even to eat. After he is put to bed, he may struggle to his feet again and again, practically walking in his sleep.

Keeping up with a child at this stage can be strenuous. If you interfere with his upright posture or with his movements, he gives battle. He hates to be stopped or laid down to be dressed. It requires strength and determination just to get a diaper changed.

To balance when he begins to stand and walk, a child plants his feet wide apart and bends his knees a little. This tends to make him more steady. His feet are flat pads with no noticeable arch at all. His weight tends to fall on the inner part of the foot, so he may toe out.

His body makes other adjustments as well. The stomach becomes prominent and a curve develops at the lower part of the back. The pelvis will be tipped forward. The line of the upper back and head, however, is straight. He may be knock-kneed or bowlegged. He'll hold his hands up and out, and keep his elbows in to increase balance. Diapers give him a bunchy look. Precariously poised, he can be knocked over with a feather.

Balance and coordination will increase as he grows and uses his muscles. By 6 years of age, the feet should point straight ahead, knock-knees will have straightened out, and the foot no longer tilts. His posture is greatly changed.

Nowadays we place more value on natural development of good posture than on teaching exercises or reminding the child to stand properly. The way you yourself stand and move will influence your child's posture, too.

Good posture is the result of good nutrition, plenty of fresh air and exercise, sleeping on a firm flat bed, special attention to rest after an illness, properly fitted clothes, and a happy home atmosphere in which the child feels confident and loved.

THE AGE OF ACCIDENTS

The ability to move around by himself makes it possible for a toddler to get everywhere. This, however, isn't the only reason toddlers need so much supervision. As a part of becoming more independent, they wish to investigate everything.

During the first year, a baby is kept in a crib, a playpen, a high chair, a stroller or carriage, or held on a lap most of the time. It is not right to keep him so confined now. He must explore the world for himself. No one can do it for him. It is next to impossible to confine him, anyhow. So make the household and yard as safe for this venturesome little person as possible. And be sure he gets constant supervision.

Before a child takes his first step, check your home for safety. Remember he doesn't use his eyes alone in learning about the world; he will lick, taste, punch, squeeze, listen, and toss. He has keen interest and no sense about danger. Just how little we can rely on him is proved by the number of accidents which occur to adventurous and curious toddlers.

Accidents are the leading cause of death in children, and a fifth of all poisonings happen at just this age. Poisons kill more children than polio, diphtheria, scarlet fever, whooping cough, and streptococcal infections combined. Other leading causes of deaths in young children are cars, falls, fire, and drowning.

Bathrooms, kitchens, and basements are apt to contain the worst traps. And they are most hazardous to children as they begin to walk. Among the common dangers then are lamp cords, electric sockets, ashtrays, fireplaces, bottled beverages, irons left with cords dangling down, dressing table items such as pins and scissors, and pans with handles which protrude over the edge of the stove. Remove what you can. It is your job to protect a child from those items which can't be spared.

Telling him isn't enough. Firmly and consistently, remove him from danger. His ability to get around is considerably ahead of his ability to stop himself. A child may tamper with forbidden items to get attention. When he seems unreasonably stubborn about returning to dangerous objects, be sure he is not being ignored or overrestricted in other ways.

Safety is the most important consideration in buying equipment for a child. Buy a playpen that will not pinch him if he works the mechanism himself. He should not be able to get his head through the bars. Strollers, high chairs, and bouncing chairs should be well balanced.

Select a high chair that won't tip over. As a child grows older, he's going to insist on getting in and out by himself. For many children a high chair becomes his first jungle gym. For this reason, a low feeding table may be the better choice.

"GROWING PAINS"

In spite of all care, children do get hurt. They fall off beds, tumble down stairs, find broken glass and "help" by picking it up. Parents—and children, too—have to learn to accept some accidents as a part of growing up. It is possible to make a child fearful instead of confident if you are overzealous or constantly remind him to be careful. Through a reasonable amount of experience with heat, sharpness, and pain, a child learns to temper his zest for exploration with caution.

SLEEPING HABITS CHANGE

The infant who snuggled willingly into bed may become a toddler who puts up a fuss. Going to bed interrupts everything he values—play and the nearness of people. He lives in the present moment and feels that he is being deprived forever. Tomorrow seems not to exist. Tired after a busy day, even groggy with fatigue, he battles to stay awake to keep his parents near and "the show on the road."

Some toddlers fight against bed because they aren't sleepy. A toddler may have somewhat lower sleep requirements than a baby and is ready to omit one of his daytime naps. Just which one will vary from child to child and may be unsettled from day to day. For a few weeks, the household may face almost daily readjustment. The toddler who didn't sleep in the morning sleeps long and late in the afternoon, and is ready to go until midnight. In this transition period, try moving the noon meal to 11:30 or so, and arrange for a nap in the early afternoon.

All of us vary in the amount of sleep we need and no one can tell you exactly how much sleep your child will require. As long as he seems contented and satisfied with life, be relaxed about the exact amount. Around 12 hours at night, plus a daytime nap, seems to be the average until 6 or so. Small bodies need a balance of rest and activity. So rest or sleep during the day is better for most children than one long sleep at night.

From early infancy, a child should sleep in a room away from his parents. Everybody gets a better rest. Your activities can be very disturbing to the child. Your relationship with each other can be interfered with by the presence of even a very small outsider, as well as possibly being upsetting to him. Since children are apt to be restless sleepers, they are apt, in turn, to disturb the adults.

Whether the child is to sleep in a room with other children depends upon many things. The most important, of course, is how many rooms you have. Try various combinations of children for the one which works best. It may change from time to time. Partnerships may be made on the basis of temperament, feelings of importance, soundness of sleep, as well as those of age and sex. It sometimes works better to put the oldest and youngest together as their bedtimes may come at quite different hours.

Many sleeping difficulties can be avoided if you think of

bedtime as a matter of course, as something not open to question. Make a plan for the day which allows for plenty of interesting activity, as much as possible out of doors. Then it is easier to be firm and clear about the bedtime hour. You're not so apt to feel you're depriving the child; in fact, you'll know you are offering him what he needs.

Allow plenty of time to get your child to bed. If he senses your haste, he'll find ways to prolong the performance just to keep you around. Do something with him for a few moments before bedtime, such as reading a story or listening to a record. He may have been kept more or less at a distance from you by household and work demands all day. He will find it easier to say goodnight after you've shared some time together.

Reserve going to bed for times to rest and sleep. If you put him there as a punishment, he may resist bed for sleep.

Most children take a long time to settle down. They practice new sounds, and sing, and call out — just to be sure you're there. You rarely need to look in after a child is comfortably settled unless there is an imperative note to his call. Fretful, whining crying is usually to attract attention, which might better have been given at another time.

When the child first gets out of bed by himself and arrives in the living room, sweet from his before-bed bath and flushed with the success of "jail breaking," the achievement may both dismay and secretly delight you. Many toddlers go through a period of bouncing up and out of bed at all hours of the night for a while. Like the 2 a.m. feeding for the infant, this intrusion into the family's night rest will end, but it is a trying time.

The crib rocker and head banger. Some children get up on their hands and knees to rock in bed, roll their heads from side to side, or bang their heads against the crib. Some children do this only at bedtime. Others do it during the day or when they wake up from their naps. Some children may do it only now and then, while others keep at it every day or night for months or even years. Usually a child begins in the second half of the first year if he is going to do it at all; most children stop by 2½ or 3 years.

No one is quite sure why some children do this. Rocking and head banging may first occur when a child is passing from one stage of development to another, such as going from sitting to standing or from standing to walking. High-strung, sensitive children are more prone to become rockers than those who are more placid and easygoing. Many more boys than girls rock. Children who have suffered earaches may do so.

The sleep of the household may be disturbed, but you're more concerned lest the child hurt himself. While he probably won't, it may help to pad the sides of the crib with thick cotton quilting, or to remove the wooden headboard and replace it with canvas or sail cloth. To cut down on the noise, try shoving the crib against the wall, and tie it in position, placing padding between it and the wall. The crib itself may be placed on a thick carpet. It may help him to stop rocking if another rhythm is introduced, such as a metronome or a loud alarm-clock tick.

You might encourage the child to use his body in rhythm at other times with a rocking chair, a hobby horse or rocking boat, a swing, seesaw, or dancing to music. Be sure he has plenty of freedom to run about. Don't keep him in a playpen a great deal of the time, especially if he objects. Also look for sources of tension such as differences in parents' handling of him, or an oversevere relative in the home. Spanking or other punishment does not discourage this activity but rather seems to increase it.

Someone should always be around when the infant is first attempting to chew such foods as hard toast. Then, if he has a choking spell, he can be helped promptly.

FEEDING THE TODDLER

Since how and what toddlers eat is tied in closely with their independent, crotchety stage, a few suggestions about this age follow.

By the end of the first year, a child usually has been having semisolid food for several months and has learned to chew. He has three meals a day, perhaps with planned snacks to supplement them. He's probably taking milk from a cup, even though he may still want to nurse from breast or bottle. You plan to increase the amount of solid food you give him as you cut down on nursing. But this isn't what he has in mind at all.

It is a surprise to find that he loses interest in his food and may actually eat less. What he does eat, he wants on his own terms, with his own method of getting it from dish to mouth. He may take a sudden dislike to foods which he has liked before, perhaps his cereal or vegetables. His behavior fluctuates from meal to meal. You had enjoyed feeding the baby, but now this satisfying time of the day for both you and the child has vanished.

It helps to know that these ups and downs are normal. The baby's rapid growth is slowing down, and he actually needs less food in proportion to his body size than he did a few months before.

You can't depend on the old system of feeding your baby with a spoonful of cereal first, a bite of fruit, and tucking in the less-cherished vegetable. He may snatch the spoon, as if simply possessing it is all there is to eating. When he finds this isn't the case, he may throw the spoon away and begin to eat with his fingers. As soon as you get another spoon, he may grab it and the struggle begins all over again.

Your child's desire to feed himself is, in the long run, exactly what you want. Therefore, let him do as much as he can, even if he is awkward. By 2 years of age, many children can do a pretty complete feeding job, if not a neat one. If you place a toy in his hands to keep them out of his food, you miss a good chance to let him begin. It also confuses him by making it a playtime. He's willing enough to play with his food already.

What seems like deliberate messiness may have a purpose all its own. A child feels his food and pours his milk on the tray and onto the floor because he is so interested in how things behave. What will pour? Is this cold or hot? What will happen if I bite the cup? A child does not see the difference between pouring his milk and pouring water in his bath. He does not yet know about the proper place for his experiments.

There is a big difference between the awkwardness of a child who is trying hard to manage food and one who plays with his food because he is being forced to eat more than he wants, is getting tired, or has found this gets his mother upset.

You will want to help a child who has stopped eating because he is tired of feeding himself, although he is still hungry. And you'll try to give him food which is easy to handle, spacing his meals and time of rest so that he is not overtired before he starts. Cut down on distractions which pull him away from his food before he has had enough to eat. Such wise planning helps to make mealtimes smoother for the toddler.

When a child has had all he wants to eat, he knows it. You may deftly squeeze in another bite or two, but you run the risk of losing his natural appetite as the best incentive to enjoyment of meals. Remove the food when he refuses the next bite or begins to play. If he is too hungry before the next meal, give him a nourishing snack.

If he won't chew. A few children have trouble chewing

solid foods. The longer you let them stay on strained or mashed food, the harder it is to get them to accept lumps. Frequently, these children will accept cookies or toast, but they refuse chewy or chopped items such as meats and vegetables.

Such a child may chew if you give him larger pieces of food and let him bite off what he wants. A leaf of lettuce, crisp bacon, a wedge of apple, or a whole cooked green bean may get him started. Permitting him to finger-feed himself seems to work better than shoving food into his mouth on a spoon. Start the meal with something he must chew. A lazy chewer needs a lot of encouragement. It rarely works to wait for him to change by himself. Peas, beans, and other foods with tough skins are frequently not popular with children and are especially unpleasant to a child who still prefers to have his food mashed.

The time for weaning. Children vary a great deal in the time they are ready to give up breast or bottle, and there is no reason to be in a hurry about it. Some are weaned by the time they are a year old. Many continue to get much of their milk by sucking until well into the second year. Some wean themselves overnight; usually it is done gradually. Around a year of age, children are very sensitive to being separated from their mothers and it is easy to see why nursing is associated with mother. The child of 12 to 18 months who still wants to suck, especially at bedtime, may need extra reassurance and would be especially upset if deprived of it. Later, he'll probably give it up more gracefully.

Help your child in this gradual process by offering him liquids in a cup for some months before you expect him to give up bottle or breast. Don't worry if he doesn't drink all the milk you offer him. If you're inclined to worry, you may worry about whether weaning will mean that the child gets less milk. Be assured that many children at this age drink less than a quart of milk a day, yet are well nourished because their diet as a whole is adequate.

Worrying mothers often defeat their purpose, anyhow. They go along with nursing for months and months. Suddenly one day they decide that the child is too old for this sort of thing and they throw all the bottles away or abruptly withdraw the breast. In this way, despite their initial indulgence, they end by forceful and sudden weaning. An earlier start and more gradual reduction would have been less upsetting.

SUCKING MAY CONTINUE

Nursing from breast or bottle satisfies a deep need. A child who has not had a chance to suck sufficiently as he drinks milk may begin to suck his fingers, his thumb, or a blanket. Some children suck such objects practically from birth. Nursing is more than just getting milk, however. The feel of warm milk flowing into an empty stomach and the comfort of being cozily held bring emotional satisfactions as well. So what started out to be a physical response soon carries deeper meanings. Sucking re-creates the contentment of being held and fed.

In most cases, the child who is going to suck his thumb begins before he has been completely weaned. If he hasn't started by then, he probably won't except for brief trials during a time of particular stress, such as during the discomfort of teething.

Many children give up thumbsucking of their own accord by the age of 3 or $3\frac{1}{2}$. They outgrow the need for this type of comfort. Occasionally a child will suck his thumb when he is tired, or finds himself at loose ends, or feels temporarily unsure. At other times, he is his busy, sunny self.

A few children persist in sucking their thumbs long past the age of 4. They may suck so vigorously and for such a long period that they push the roof of the mouth up and may change the position of the upper teeth. Such children usually show in other ways that they are unhappy or feel discouraged.

It works better to try to find out what the matter is than to interfere directly with the thumbsucking. Splints, bad tasting medicine, and mittens do not work because they intensify the child's feelings of being unloved.

Parents who object to thumbsucking may say that they are worried about germs or that it looks babyish. They may feel uneasy about the pleasure the child gets from his body. Yet the germs a child will get from his thumb are no more numerous than those he gets in the natural course of his day. Remember, he's at the stage where he puts everything he can into his mouth. It's a way of learning. If you object to the appearance, remind yourself that the child is, after all, quite a young thing and has years ahead of himself to look grownup.

Some parents prefer to give the young baby a pacifier to give him all the sucking he needs. While it seems like the same thing, pacifiers and thumbs are different. Unlike a thumb, a pacifier can get lost, or become weakened by use and can cause choking if bits are swallowed the wrong way. If you decide to use a pacifier, keep two or three spares on hand in case one becomes mislaid or worn out.

One problem with a pacifier is that parents may reach for it automatically at the first whimper. They thus encourage the child to suck long past the time he might have stopped naturally. They need to be alert to little signs that the child is ready to give it up.

WHEN TO START TOILET TRAINING

The time to begin to toilet train depends on the child. How can you tell if a child is ready? Physically he needs enough muscle control to stop a natural release. He has formerly let go whenever he felt pressure of urine or bowel material. Training involves teaching him to hold back. Just holding back isn't all, however. He needs to be able to tell you with a word or a sound, or a look on his face—or be able to get to the bathroom by himself. Even so, he'll probably need help with his clothing. Good toilet habits are a complicated business and require timing. To stop a natural release, to hold, and then to let go at the right time and place is what we are asking the child to do. You help, but it is up to him to manage it somehow.

Here is another clue to success in toilet training. Take advantage of his eagerness to be on his own and independent of you. This is quite different from punishing him for his "misdeeds" by confining him to the toilet or by using other harsh methods.

When the baby is 8 or 9 months old, some mothers begin to place him on a potty or toilet at a time when he usually has a bowel movement. If he is regular about his movements, they will be successful at catching him.

Success depends upon intimate knowledge of the child's pattern and the fact that they began to place him on the toilet before he reached the stage where he wanted to be on the go every minute. They may proudly announce that they haven't had a messy diaper in weeks. As soon as their star pupil learns to crawl or walk, however, or if the rhythm changes, many find they are back where they started. The toddler acts as if he never heard of toilet training.

Real bowel control can be taught to most children only after they learn to walk. If you're eager to get started, try it out to see if the child catches on. Supply a word he can use to announce his wish to go to the toilet, or use his own sound. Place him for brief intervals on the toilet with the diaper on or off—so he learns how it feels.

Comfort and stability on the toilet are important. A child should have good support for his back and feet. He may find a low seat less frightening than an adult fixture, with a child's toilet seat added. Bring him when you expect a bowel movement. Stay and talk with him. Take him off the toilet, success or no, after a while—seldom longer than 5 minutes.

If he struggles to be free, you gain nothing by forcing him to stay longer. He may be content to stand beside the toilet without removing his diaper. While this doesn't save a diaper, that isn't the goal here anyhow. The goal is gradually to get him to accept the idea of the right place, at the right time.

Little children feel quite possessive about the products of their bodies, and don't view bowel movements with disgust. They are sure, at some point, to dabble in the toilet bowl or smear a bowel movement on the crib or walls. Try to temper your dismay as you clean up with an understanding of the child's experimental frame of mind. Some authorities observe that it must seem quite callous to a child when his mother noisily flushes his bowel movements away. For this reason, or because the child may fear being flushed down himself, some mothers tactfully wait until the child has left the bathroom. Later on, of course, children enjoy working the handle themselves.

Fear of being flushed down the toilet occurs at a time when a child may also fear that he will slip down the drain in his bath. Such fears seem ridiculous to adults, but the child has a very poor notion of relative size. He experiments with the bulk of things in his play, fitting little things into big ones, and tries to shove big things into small spaces. It takes months of practice to get it all figured out. He hasn't much of an idea of his own size, either, in relation to doors, drains, chairs, or doll carriages.

Regular daily bowel movements have become a symbol of good health in the minds of many people, but such a pattern is not necessary at all. Many children have movements every other day or so. Unless the doctor prescribes it during an illness, the use of suppositories or enemas is unwise. A diet which helps to keep the mass soft, plenty of exercise, and fluids are better than medicines which lead to overconcern about a natural process.

Training the bladder. Training a child to stay dry is the next step. Without pressure, the child will gradually shift from wetness to dryness. This is better than an all-out push. "I'm training Bobby this week" implies that everything else is forgotten except concentrating on trips to the bathroom. There may be tension about the state of the diaper at any time of day. Wet? A defeat. Dry? Run up the flag!

Around $1\frac{1}{2}$ or 2, a child will tend to increase the time between voidings, as the bladder will fill up instead of emptying automatically. He understands more and has a few words he can use. He may be in a more cooperative frame of mind than he was at 1 year. He will be wanting to imitate others. He isn't so completely wrapped up in learning to walk and has a little extra time on his hands. Training will probably go faster if you wait until 18 months or so to start. Girls may be ready somewhat sooner than boys, as they are with other activities which require control and maturity.

Start by taking the child to the toilet when you find him dry. Very often this will be after a nap if you've gone to the child promptly when he wakens. Put a child in training pants.

They are easier for him to manage and may give an incentive to stay dry. If you've been premature about making the change, though, don't threaten him about returning to "baby" diapers.

Some parents set up a regular schedule, such as before and midway between meals. The child's own rhythm is the best schedule to follow at the beginning, however.

Frequently, a child who has been doing well will have relapses. His learning is not fixed and for months will be easily unsettled by such things as cooler weather, a cold, a visitor in the house, or excitement about a trip. Try to take these relapses without fuss or comment.

Sometimes even more serious troubles show up. A child may refuse to go to the bathroom at all, or will plainly show that he is so worried about having an accident he can scarcely do anything else. When this happens, relax your training, or give it up for a while. Disturbances may show up that seem not connected to training at all. He may be quite upset about getting his clothes dirty, for instance, or avoid touching soft or gooey things, or refuse to cooperate at mealtimes.

A child who has shown for a time that he understands what the toilet is for does not forget it easily. He probably catches on to things very quickly, much quicker than you want him to—such as where you keep the lemon drops. Therefore it is not necessary to scold or punish to fix the idea of toilet training in his head.

You may have started too soon. Or, he may feel he needs to boss this himself. A look at his life may give an answer. Does he have a chance to make decisions about how and what things are done to him? Is he getting any satisfactions from growing up, or has he decided that it is better to be a baby? Is he so afraid he'll have an accident that he can't help having one?

Whatever the cause, you help him most by encouragement, not by punishment. Most children are 3 years old before they stay clean and dry in the daytime.

A child working on his toilet habits may be unable to perform in a strange bathroom or out of doors. The 2-year-old easily gets into a rut and depends on familiar surroundings to respond. So it is a good idea to vary the place and get him used to changes. On a trip, take along his toilet seat. You might tell him in advance that he will be using a new bathroom or will have to urinate in the woods. Since his toilet seat may be a sign for release, parents may be able to hold the seat for him, over the grass or any suitable spot.

Little boys first urinate sitting down. The age when a boy learns to stand probably varies with the amount of male company he keeps (including father, of course) more than anything else. Male example will give the little girl ideas about a new way to urinate as well. While the results are discouraging to her, she will doubtless keep trying, on and off, until she accepts herself as she is.

Night dryness. Staying dry at night comes later and hardly belongs in a chapter on toddlers. However, since parents want to be consistent, night dryness can be placed here. Before 4 years of age, occasional night wetting is to be expected, although some children are dry at nights even though wetting in the daytime. If you haven't struggled over daytime training, you'll usually find that night dryness comes just as easily with your encouragement.

Some parents take their child to the toilet about the time they themselves are going to bed or very early in the morning. Some children are able to perform quickly, still almost asleep. If the child doesn't succeed so easily, is annoyed or upset, give it up. Some people feel that taking a sleeping child to the toilet

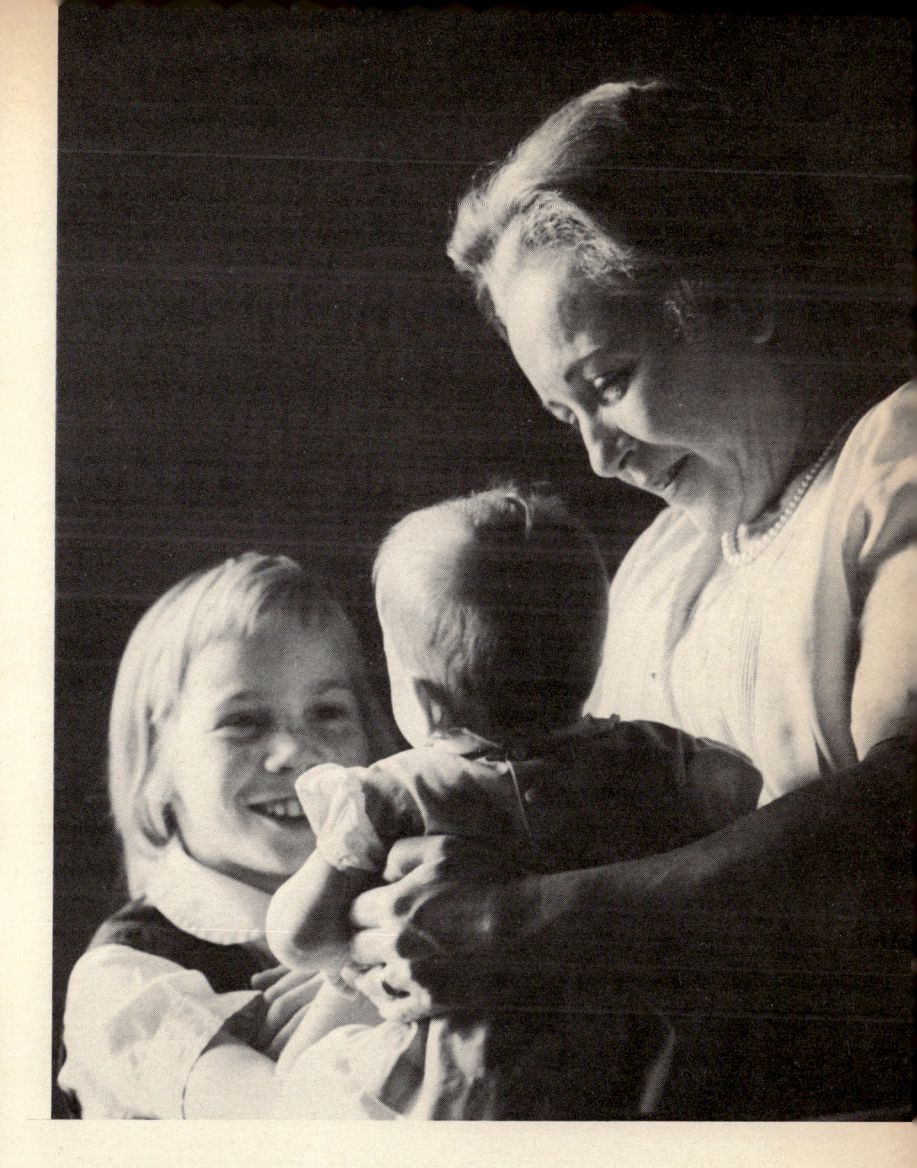

Grandparents who come to visit the new baby should be reminded to pay equal attention to any older child. It's all too easy for an older child who used to be first in their affection to feel slighted by effusive displays over the new child.

may make him urinate in his sleep longer than if he were let alone.

Cutting down on liquids after 5 p.m. may help a child who understands the connection between drinks and an overfull bladder. However, if he regards this as a deprivation or a punishment, he may become rebellious or fearful of an accident. When a child who has been dry at night feels unsure about the way things are going (when a new baby comes, for instance), wetting the bed may be a symptom of his doubts.

Attitudes toward the body. Long before training starts, a child senses how his parents feel about changing diapers. It is fortunate if you've been able to handle this chore matter of factly. While training, parents may become so absorbed in their teaching they scold the child for mishaps. He may get the notion that this part of him is disgusting. It is easy for him to confuse his waste processes with the genital organs themselves, and a shamed attitude toward his body may result.

Children learn very readily that society demands a certain amount of reserve about elimination. They can acquire this reserve, however, without shame.

Some children discover one way or another that they can produce pleasant and soothing sensations by stroking or touching their genitals. They explore sensitive parts of their bodies as they do other interesting things. Their attention quickly wanders. Therefore, you don't need to do anything about it. If you're really upset, casually place a toy in his hands. Quietly pick him up and talk or play with him, offer him a drink of water, or occupy him in some other way. If you interfere every time you see him reach for himself, you may give him the idea his body is bad or dangerous.

HE LEARNS TO TALK

When a baby first utters a sound which seems to have meaning, parents spring into action and think about the child differently than before. They welcome him into the human race. Everyone was delighted with the first tooth, or the first steps. But these purely physical accomplishments do not carry the exciting promise of the first word, the delight of experiences shared through speech, the comfort of talking together.

The infant amuses himself with throaty noises and bubbles, coos and chuckles; authorities assure us he's learning how to talk. Before long, he'll have hit upon a great many sounds, some of which he'll discard because he won't need them.

From the very beginning he uses his voice by pitch and intensity changes, by crying, chuckling, or fearfully shrieking to tell you how he feels. Very quickly he selects your voice out of the other sounds around him and recognizes its friendly or unfriendly tones.

As time goes by, he hears a lot of talking around him—and to him—as you chat to him while bathing or feeding him. In his play with sounds, he begins to imitate the rhythm of the language he hears. He seems to converse with characteristic pauses and inflections, although the individual sounds are meaningless.

Around 6 months of age, he can reproduce some of these random sounds at will. By the time he's a year old, through the encouragement and attention he got when he just happened to make a sound, and through having it repeated back to him, he begins to associate sounds with objects and persons. In this way, speech comes into being. It is the result of the maturing of the tongue and throat muscles (which have been strengthened by sucking), learning to hear what he's done, a desire to communicate, and sufficient intelligence so that he can associate a sound with the meaning it has to others.

Learning to speak is the chief way a child becomes clear about what he knows. Of course, he thinks and feels before he can talk, but what he thinks and feels becomes clear to him as he learns to say it. He can use words to remember past events and to anticipate future ones.

He finds that words are very powerful, too. When a child can begin to command some language, he can begin to control his world. Parents are relieved to find that it is much easier to manage a child who can talk.

The child is apt to overdo the power of words for a time, particularly when he discovers the strength of "No." Slowly he gains the ability to express his desires in more detail. He can say "In a minute," rather than "No." And he can be helped to use words to defend himself, rather than to rely on biting or hitting, crying or running away. Through language, then, he gradually becomes able to manage his affairs in a way to bring himself satisfaction in a manner acceptable to society.

The chatterbox stage. Some bright children begin to use half a dozen words before they walk. The exact age will vary. For most children, addition of words may be delayed as they concentrate on learning to walk, but by the second birthday usually they hit a tremendous spurt and may add 300 or 400 new words in the next year. They add new words by asking constantly "What's that?" A 3-year-old uses the words he knows over and over again. "Talks all the time," says his father. And it's true. He may be saying 11,000 or 12,000 words a day. He'll keep adding new words to his vocabulary all through the preschool years and to some extent all through life, but the rate is never so great again.

At first he uses single words to express whole thoughts—"light," "car," "hat," "dinner." You know by his gestures and tone of voice what he means.

Soon the child, who is so active himself, wants to express action, so he begins to use verbs too: "Daddy go," "dog bark."

Learning to use pronouns correctly comes somewhat later because they change constantly as they identify self and others, and he has a self-centered view of the world. He still feels that he is the only "me" that counts. He is frequently addressed as "Baby" or "Tom." So he will tend to say, "Tom get up." Don't make an issue of it, but sometimes you can phrase an idea correctly and have him imitate you.

Baby talk. Children make up wonderfully expressive words, which become a part of the family vocabulary. An excited 3-year-old, hearing a siren, shouts: "A sirengine." A breakfast cereal is christened "scrippies." As others in the family delightedly pick up these inventions, they help the child to fix meanings to words. They serve as a bridge between the child's words and adult language. Talking this kind of baby talk, in which the child's own words and simple sentence structures are copied by the adults, helps him to catch on to spoken language. He is baffled by long, elaborate sentences.

Children love to play with sounds long after they learn to speak, and 3- and 4-year-olds giggle over nonsense such as "gaggle, goggle, zoom, zoom, zoom." A good beat to a string of nonsense is all that is required to keep a group of preschoolers amused. Along with their pleasure, they are perfecting difficult consonants and emphasizing the last or middle syllables of words, which improves their articulation, too. These word games are good practice.

Preschoolers like to play with words of doubtful social

use—"pee pee" and "wee wee," as well as any other they happen to hear. They enjoy getting a shocked reaction; but if you ignore this kind of talk or substitute your own nonsense, you usually keep word play from becoming a problem. "You're an old mashed potato yourself" delights him just as much as his naughty word.

Neither of the above examples is to be confused with baby talk of the kind that keeps a child using immature sounds he long ago would have dropped had he not discovered that baby talk gets results from parents who think it is cute. Children who hear good speech tend to copy it. Usually a child will outgrow baby talk when his parents do.

Late talkers. The age at which a child will talk and the amount of talking he does are highly individual matters. Girls tend to start talking sooner than boys, and may talk more clearly. Older brothers and sisters may interpret for the younger child so skillfully he does not need to talk. Twins and triplets are apt to be late in talking and may continue to be hard to understand because they spend so much time with a partner who speaks no better than they do. The amount of talking a child hears influences the amount he will produce, too.

Children who live in institutions talk later than those under their mother's care. Temperament is also a factor. Some children are full of chatter from dawn until dark; others watch and observe silently. Some children begin to play with words early; others wait until 2 or 3 years of age to begin. Children talk more when they have something to talk about. A vacation trip to the beach, for instance, gives a great boost to the new words a child will learn as well as the amount he wants to say.

Circumstances sometimes require the child to learn two languages at once. They astonish us by knowing when they should use one language and when the other. Often the child's skill in both languages will be slowed down by the double task, but he'll catch up.

If you're worried because a child is slow in talking or because no one can understand him, recognize that there are many reasons for poor or delayed speech and each of them requires a different approach.

If a child does not talk by the age of 3 years, your doctor may refer you to a speech or guidance clinic. Or the Children's Bureau, U.S. Department of Health, Education, and Welfare, Washington 25, D.C., can tell you where clinics are located. Since the public schools are very much interested in providing speech correction for children who need it, you may also be able to get diagnosis and help through your local school district.

Stuttering is common. To think of the right word and get it said is a hard job for a child. It becomes even harder around 2½ or 3 years of age when his ideas get bigger than his vocabulary. All through the preschool years children find it difficult to express their ideas smoothly, particularly if they are excited or upset. They may get in the habit of repeating everything to be sure that they'll be heard by an absentminded parent who is tired of hearing them chatter. Or they may hesitate and fumble over words if they fear that another child will beat them to the punchline.

Parents who have had problems in speaking themselves, or have had someone in their own family with speech difficulties, will be apt to worry about the jerky uneven speech of the child. They are sure he's beginning to stutter or stammer.

In worrying about it, parents are sure to show their concern. Then the child becomes worried about it, too. Parents are tempted to help by saying "Take your time," "Start over, now," "Say it slowly, Jimmy." The child realizes that he does not please his listeners and becomes more hesitant. Next time he wants to tell them something, he can scarcely get the first word out. Then his speech does, in fact, become disturbed.

This is one way stuttering may begin. There are probably other causes as well.

All this can usually be prevented. Here are some simple suggestions for helping your child to develop good speech. They are the same as helping to prevent stuttering:

Allow your child to speak like a child. Children are still learning to manage words and ideas. They should never be teased about faulty pronunciation.

Allow your child to behave like a child as well. Children who are expected to be perfect and to excel in neatness, staying clean and dry, manners, quietness, and obedience are sure to show the strain in some way. It often shows up in speech problems, or even refusal to talk, since talking is so closely tied up with what a person thinks about himself.

Listen to him. Talking takes two: one to speak and one to listen. Your child will be vastly encouraged if you listen attentively to what he has to say. Much of the time a little child is shut out of adult conversations—at meals, when guests drop in, when mothers talk on the telephone. It may take special effort to include the child.

Most children become self-conscious about speaking before strangers if forced to say nursery rhymes or to show off. They may wish to share their own ideas, however, if given a chance with a friendly audience of one or two guests or a familiar neighbor.

Read to your child, sing with him, talk with him. Jokes, word games, and nonsense are good fun and valuable, too. Little children gain much from sharing words with others.

TODDLERS PLAY WITH EVERYTHING

A little child makes no distinction between work and play. Adults envy the way a child can lose himself in what he's doing—in a story, a toy, the running of the bathwater, the dance of a butterfly. At the same time they become impatient that the child shows no sense of time ("Don't you know it's lunchtime?") or annoyed when he finds it hard to tear himself away from whatever is so compelling.

The toddler squats on the kitchen floor amusing himself with a big spoon and a pan. He licks the metal, listens to the bang, polishes the rivets, puts the spoon in, tries to put the pan in the spoon, shoves it across the floor, turns it upside down to hide the spoon, finds the spoon again. When he can find no fresh discovery, we say he is bored with them. He'll start all over again if other items are added—sand, water, pebbles, smaller toys, clothespins, a lid, more spoons, other pans. He hits on new possibilities, he masters the old tricks. Then he trots off, finished.

He's not aimless; his play has a purpose, even though it may not be clear what he has in mind or just what he is accomplishing. What does he learn as he plays?

He first learns how to manage his body—to shove and push, lift and throw, climb and jump, pinch and squeeze, poke and break off. Awkward and clumsy at the beginning, he learns to guide his arms and legs and trunk, then his fingers and hands, into smooth performance by the time he is 4 or 5.

Then he must find out how things work, where they go, what fits into what. He must try out everything he sees others doing, be it sweeping or cooking or cutting the grass.

Gradually a new element appears. A block of wood be-

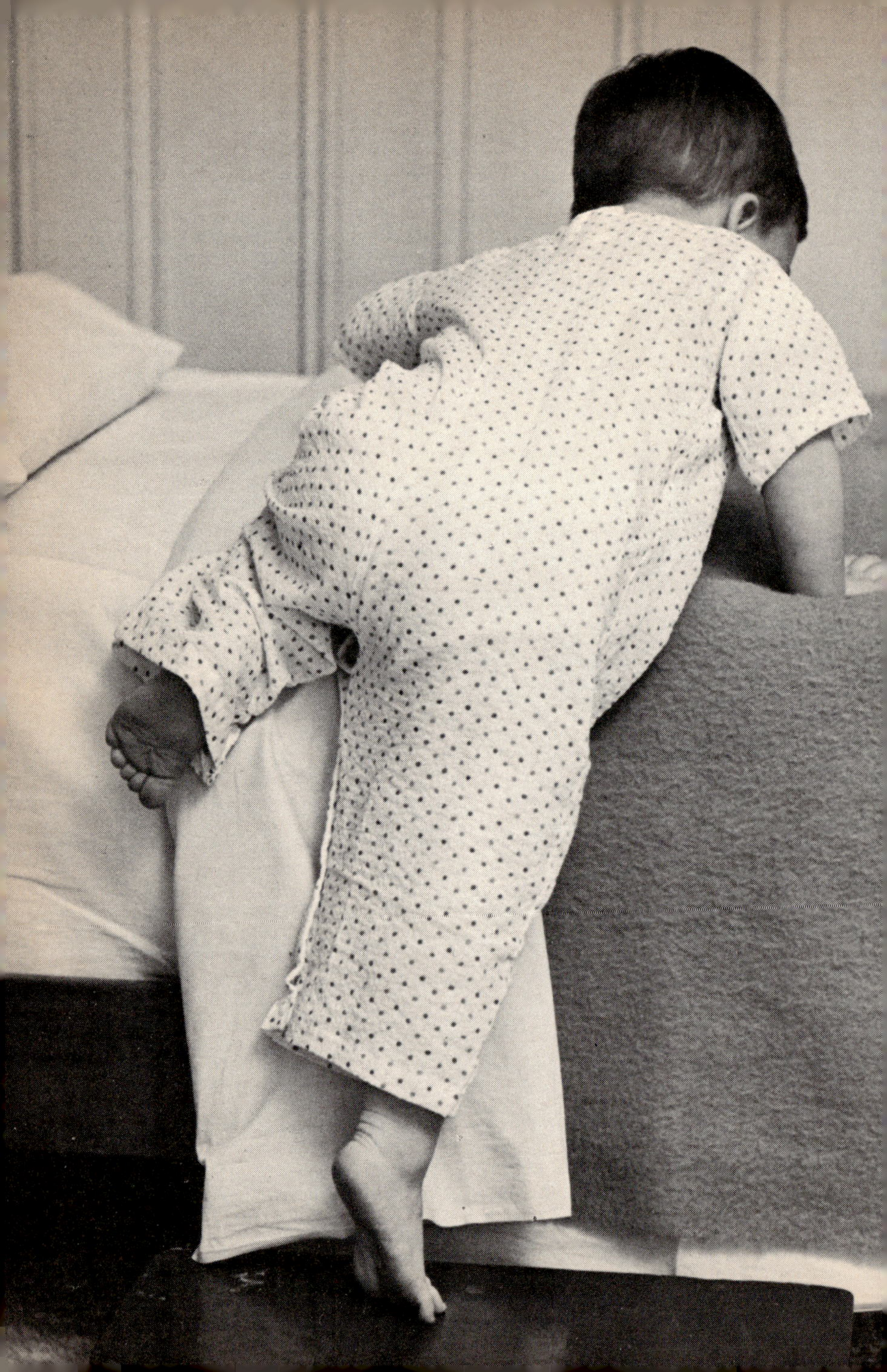

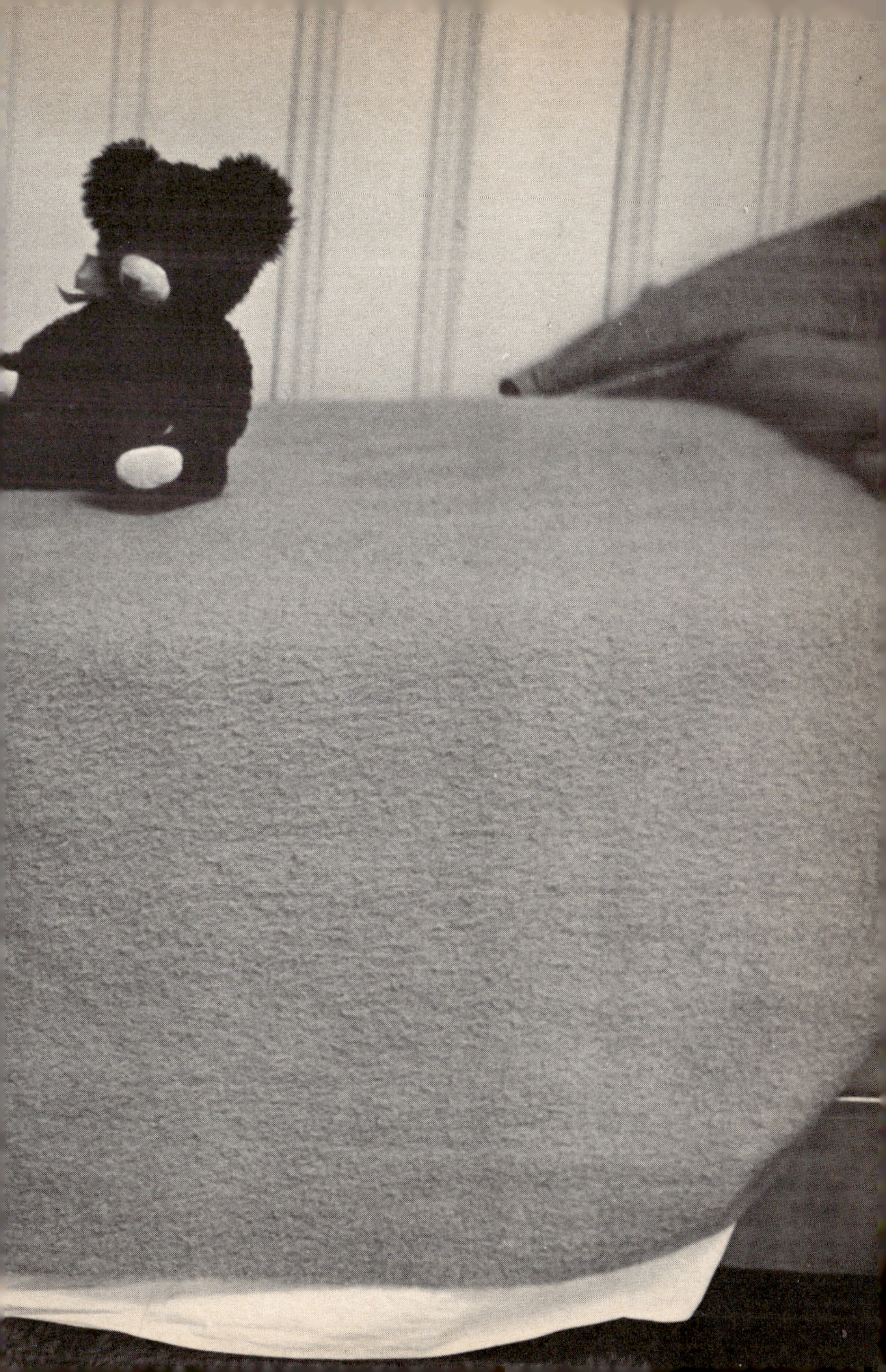

comes a car, and the toddler makes convincing motor sounds. He drives in and out of traffic. He lines bits of cereal up to become marching men. He himself becomes a dog, or an airplane. In most children's lives, such imaginative behavior begins around 18 months. The brighter the child, the more imagination and the earlier it begins. Imaginative play increases rapidly to the age of 4 or 5, when it crowds out the world of reality.

Through imaginative play, he learns how it feels to be something—or somebody—else. He expresses how he feels as a little person in a world of big people and strong forces. He plays out real life roles, faithfully copying gestures and voice inflections; he releases angry or frustrated feelings; he relives experiences which have been upsetting, mysterious, or enjoyable.

Where will he play? As soon as the child begins to get about, he'll want to be wherever his mother is—in the kitchen, laundry, or bathtub. Parents who dream "the child's in his playroom and all's right with the world" are doomed to disappointment. A recreation room, removed from the hub of activity, is seldom used willingly by little children unless others are there, too. Since the child wants nearness to you so strongly, try to let him play nearby while you work. Your companionship is dearly important to him; your supervision is vital to his safety.

Even though you can have him near you much of the time, you'll want him to have a place of his own to play. It may be his own room or an area elsewhere which he knows as his own and where his main possessions are kept. Hopefully, there he can be free of many restrictions required in other parts of the house. If he has his own place, you have a right to expect him to begin to respect the difference between his and your phonograph records, his dishes and your best china, a place he can climb and your upholstered furniture.

If he has his own place, don't lock him in or send him there as punishment. He can't enjoy a spot which is used as a jail. It seems to work well if a child has regular playtimes in his room each day, as well as regularly recurring times to be out of the place. You may find you need an hour in the morning to get a good start on household chores. Again, in the afternoon, expect him to play there quietly alone as you prepare dinner.

At times a child who usually is contented in his room alone becomes restless and bored. He needs some deft "first aid." If you can take a few minutes to join the fretful child and "play" with him (by which he means having you accompany him in his activities), he may be contented again for a while alone. He may be showing that he needs greater variety in his experiences, more interesting things to do, or some friends to play with.

To be orderly, a child needs to have a place to store his things. It can be simple—an orange crate, a cardboard carton, or low open shelves which are deep enough to keep things from tumbling off. Very early, a child can begin to help put his toys away at the end of play. This is a good moment for friendly talk as you share the task. It will be many years before he can do it all alone.

Encourage him to put away as he goes along, too, but at best this takes a lot of adult supervision. Little children do not play with one thing at a time, returning it to the shelf before selecting another; and it is not reasonable to expect it.

One way to cut down on confusion and clutter is to keep only a few toys available at any one time. If a child has many playthings, put some away to be rotated or brought out on special occasions. Too many toys distract him and keep him flitting from one to another.

Even though he has his own place, reserve a certain area

for him in other rooms, too—a shelf in the living room for old magazines and his books, a low drawer in the kitchen for safe kitchen playthings.

A child will play on the floor a great deal of the time. Minimize drafts by using weather stripping, heavy drapes, or a screen made stable by hooking it to the wall. Select a floor covering which can take frequent washings. Wax linoleum or wooden floors only enough to make them dirt resistant, not slippery. Small scatter rugs cause falls.

Wall surfaces also require frequent washing. You might attach hard-surfaced masonite or a protective fabric to the lower third of the wall. Use only washable paints. Check the label on all paint used in the child's room, to be sure it is safe to use on surfaces which might be chewed by children. Wall plaster contains lead, and if eaten by a child can cause poisoning.

Fun out of doors. Out of doors, a child needs a safe place where he can run about freely and climb. Ideally, he should have ground to play on. He likes to sit in the grass, to watch ants running in and out of their hills, to pick up pebbles, and to pull his wagon over bumps. He likes to have a place to dig. If there is no yard space, a portion of a porch away from the steps can be fenced off. Be sure the railing is secure. Or check your neighborhood to see if a public park is within walking distance for periods of outdoor play.

Hours and hours of happy play, alone or with companions, are afforded by a sandbox. At first the child fills cups and digs with a spoon. Later he builds roads, tunnels, and forts. Sandbox play remains a favorite sociable activity well into the elementary school years, so it will pay the family to build a large, sturdy enclosure for sand.

Sun and air can aid in keeping the sand clean, but it is well to provide shade for part of the day. If there are no trees, use a beach umbrella, sail cloth, or canvas stretched on a frame. It is helpful to locate the box where it can readily be filled by a dump truck or wheelbarrow.

Fencing a portion of the yard gives both you and your child peace of mind. Within it, he doesn't get into trouble, making you angry because he destroys flowers or precious shrubbery. He's safe from a spanking he might otherwise get if he ran into the street after his ball.

If you have a choice, locate the enclosed area where you can see it from within the house. If you rent, you can use inexpensive wire mesh or snow fencing stretched between posts embedded in the ground. One wall of the house may serve for a side of the play yard. A folding gate can often be adapted to close the entry. To keep a child happy, provide boards and boxes, an automobile tire swing, sandbox, assortment of sandbox toys, wheeled toys, and a place to climb.

An agile child can get out of almost any enclosure if he really wants to, so the fence is more a reminder of safe boundaries than a corral. Cheerfully assume that the child will play in the fenced area because he belongs there. Visit with him often, or provide a playmate if you can. Even a pet can give a child a sense of companionship.

What will he play with? A few simple toys, carefully selected for the child's interests and abilities, are all that is needed. Remember, he wants to play with everything that he is allowed to. Many of his play materials he finds around the house: pots and pans, clothespins, rolling pin, potato masher, plastic containers with lids, spoons, pie tins, empty boxes, spools, and so on.

Check all items for safety. Are edges sharp? Are they safe

to lick? When broken, would they puncture or cut? Could parts be swallowed or inhaled, as with pieces of a rubber balloon, buttons, or marbles?

Many "educational" toys can be made at home. With few tools, a handy mother or father can saw out a puzzle, or make a pyramid of gaily painted wooden disks to slip over a dowel, or a floor train of boxes hooked together with screen door hooks and eyes.

Other suggested toys for the toddler, somewhat in order of advancing age are:

Sturdy rattles, telephones, a large ball, noisy squeak toys;
Floating toys for the bath;
Push-and-pull toys such as a bell mounted on wheels;
Low rocking horse or seat on rockers;
Stuffed animals or dolls;
Sandbox toys that don't rust, including a plastic pail;
A nest of blocks and a pounding set;
Small sturdy wagon or wheelbarrow, kiddy car or tricycle;
Small chair (which he'll carry around) and table;
Simple take-apart-and-put-together toys;
Simple musical toys (triangle, bells, tambourine);
Bright picture books with large pictures;
Cars, boats, trains that interlock;
Rubber dolls and animals;
A suitcase or large pocketbook;
Big wooden beads (1 inch) to string on thick string;
Puzzles with 3 to 8 pieces;
Wooden planks, hollow blocks, sawhorses (low).

Avoid toys which (1) have small or easily removable parts such as eyes on a teddy bear; (2) are fragile and easily broken; (3) are electrical or need winding up.

First friends. The toddler enjoys friends. He gets along

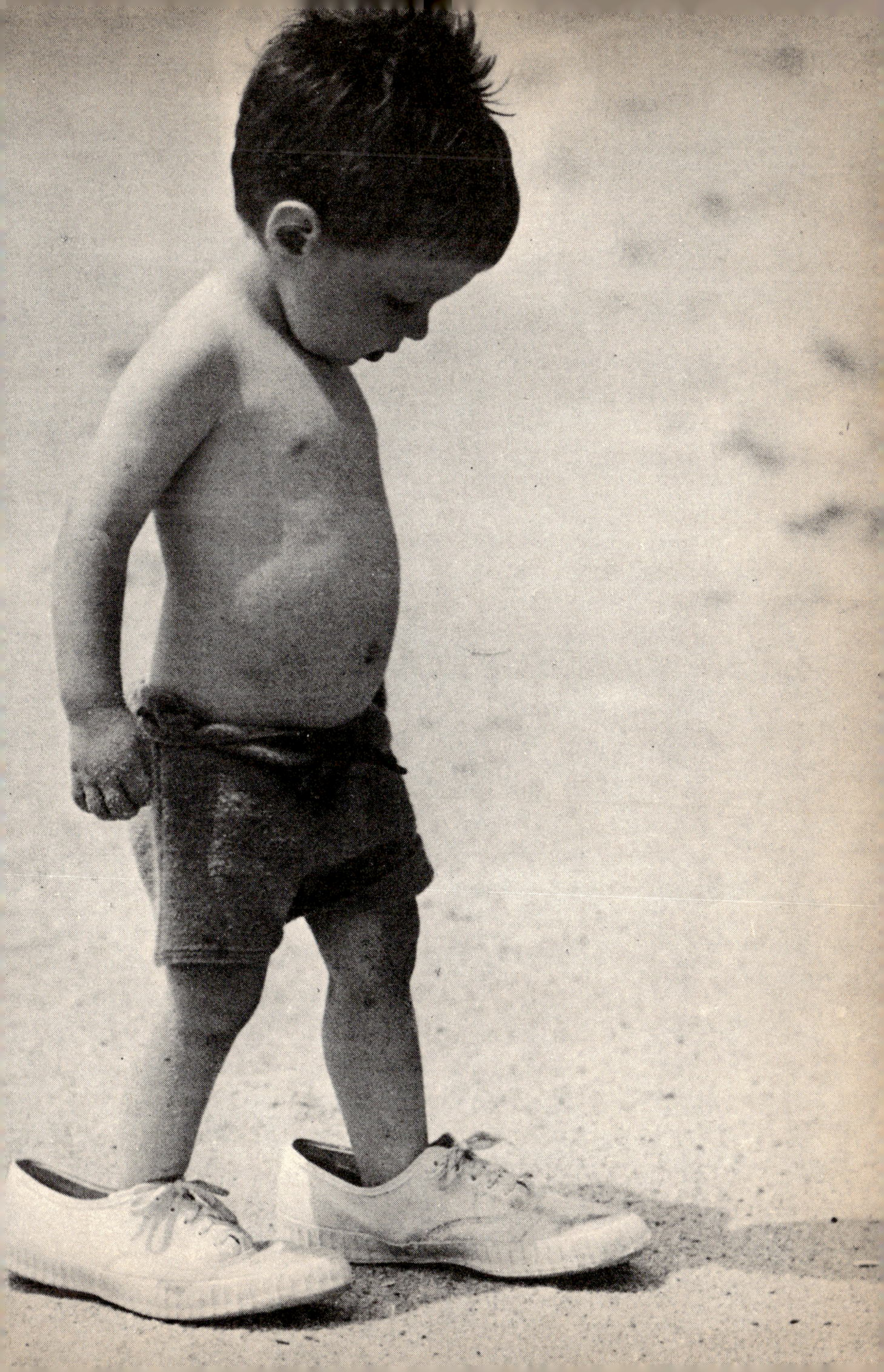

best with one or two. His first meetings will be most pleasant if short, simple, and supervised. An occasional half-hour with another child is much better than the free-for-all of a large birthday party. As a matter of fact, birthday parties are most pleasant for host and guests if kept small. One guest for each year of the child's age is a good formula to use.

Even with friends, he is apt to play by himself, stop to watch occasionally, argue over possession of a truck, or briefly get sociable with a ball. Toddlers seem to understand each other without words, and just like the idea of having someone their own size around.

They aren't born with a spirit of generosity and are apt to be fiercely possessive about their toys. "Mine" is one of the first words children use. They're willing to let others use their things only if they don't happen to want them at the moment. To take turns and to share require years to learn—in fact, some adults are more lacking in such graces than their own toddlers.

Adults can't force a spirit of generosity, but they can help. Be sure your child doesn't have to share too much, too often. If you suggest that a child share a toy, see that he gets it back in a reasonable time. If he's not forced to give up his possessions, he'll discover that it is fun to share—that two people can put blocks into a wagon together, with one to push and one to pull the load. Such brief encounters will tend to increase as children learn to trust each other and become better at talking about their ideas.

To make playtime with others satisfying, an adult needs to be nearby. But don't be so quick to interfere that the children have no chance to settle anything themselves or get to know each other in the process.

You're sure to be distressed when your toddler bites or hits another child. You're apt to be amazed at the interested, detached look on his face as he studies the tears of the injured party, apparently unaware that he caused them. As a matter of fact, he probably didn't plan it this way. He may have punched or squeezed his friends much as he does his beloved teddy bear. He is apt to regard them as similar. He needs information, then, not punishment: "Your teeth hurt Sally. See—she's crying." If he has bitten because he is angry, tell him he can't do it. Don't make him feel that he's "bad," though, because he was angry.

Occasionally, toddlers who resort to biting are provoked beyond their endurance, and may need closer supervision to protect them from equally immature or unfair playmates. At any rate, biting a child back to teach him *not* to bite seems useless. "I'll show him that it hurts" usually fails. You've shown him instead that you hurt, too, and have taken advantage of his small size.

The child nearing 3 years of age who repeatedly bites or hits other children probably has some reason other than simply not knowing any better. Try to find out *why* he wants to hurt others. Usually his victim is a substitute. He may feel that he is hemmed in by his parents' demands or gets so little support from them he's unsure of their love. Or he may constantly be faced with competition against which he can never win—the competition of a baby or an older child. He's ready to charge at the slightest opposition.

It's bad enough when your child bites another, but it's even harder for most parents when their own child is hurt by another. Before you rush to send the visitor home ("the little savage!"), be sure that your interference doesn't keep your own child from learning a valuable lesson—that of defending himself. Little children are assured when their parents treat their friends with as much understanding as they themselves receive.

Going visiting. Short daytime visits to the homes of your friends can be pleasant and beneficial to a child. He's especially lucky if he has grandparents close enough for frequent, casual calls. From such contacts he can learn to know people of several generations and the rules of different households. He can begin to form a picture of what old people are like and may profit from a little wholesome indulgence.

When he's out to visit, or friends come to your home, you're apt to be conscious suddenly of his manners. Preaching a company set of manners is probably useless for preschool children. It seems to work better to encourage a child to express his friendly feelings naturally. Ignore adults who demand formal manners in these early years. It does help a child to be given simple tasks he can perform to add to the comfort and welcome you give your guests.

Long visits away from home without you don't always work well for little children. Frequently grandparents who live far away desire a long visit, especially if they seldom have the pleasure of "spoiling" their little ones, putting them to bed, fussing over a hairdo, and telling stories about the days when Mommy or Daddy were little. Despite their wishes, shorter visits usually work better for all three generations. Little children become homesick, even though they're with loving grandparents. Parents may resent the difference in methods *their* parents use. And the grandparents, in spite of themselves, are apt to find the care of active little ones more than they bargained for.

MANAGING A TODDLER

Life with a toddler is a compromise between his fierce desire to manage everything and your good sense about what is harmful to him or to others. Through the routines of the day —

such as feeding, toilet training, and play—you give the child his first lessons in how to behave. Thus begins discipline; yet it has less to do with obedience or disobedience than with patient teaching.

When a child adjusts to your wishes, he exchanges some of his strong ideas for your loving approval. It is one of life's first business deals. He behaves to suit you because he values you and depends upon you. Later, his behavior will be geared to enlist the approval of friends, teachers, and others; but right now his parents are all.

It is easy to expect too much of a toddler. As soon as the child begins to walk and talk, people tend to forget how immature he is, and they expect too much. Especially unfortunate in this regard are children who happen to be big for their age.

Those responsible for a toddler's well-being have to see that he gets sufficient rest so he doesn't add fatigue to his immaturity. Most difficult of all, they have to give him enough freedom that he doesn't become entirely dependent on them or rebellious about restrictions.

Some suggestions for handling a toddler follow:

Keep life simple. From the repeated routines of the day a little child learns to trust in the world and do what is expected of him. Remove knickknacks and breakables you cherish. They can be brought out again when the child has more control.

Crowds and noise and confusion should be the exception, not the rule. The modern supermarket, with its crowded aisles, flags that wave, and piles of cookies attractively stacked in arm's reach, is an everyday example of a situation which is almost more than a child can bear. It is no wonder he is frequently in tears at the checkout counter and his mother worn out with "You can't have that," "Don't eat the ice," and "Come here."

Mothers who can accept the child's plodding help in taking items in and out of the basket seem to fare better on marketing trips than those who try to keep their helper from touching anything. A lightweight stroller will keep the toddler confined. Some mothers like a harness as a way to give a child some freedom within a safe radius.

Try to avoid head-on clashes. Channel the child's actions by suggesting something more—or equally—interesting. Avoid a battle of wills. "Here is a ball" is enough to make him absentmindedly hand over the cigar butt he has discovered. "I'll put your cup here" helps direct the child's interest away from your hot coffee.

Actions speak louder than words to him. If you begin to do the things you want done, he'll often go along while muttering "No." Walk toward the house when it is time to go in, start the bath water running when it is near bedtime, and he tends to trundle along. Doing something is what he likes best. Not doing is hard for him.

The words you do use should be simple and clear. Long speeches confuse him. "Now, your boots" is a short way to phrase "You have to wear your galoshes because it's raining." Stand beside the child, or kneel to be at eye level. This puts you on a more equal basis, and you're not so apt to shout when confronted with the solemn, steady gaze of a toddler.

Teach him the meaning of "hot," "hurt," "tastes bad" rather than just saying "don't" or "no." Try whispering your suggestions from time to time. He'll whisper back, enchanted with the air of mystery and often astonishingly cooperative.

Follow through on your decisions. A child depends on you to help control impulses, whether they be physically dangerous or simply sufficiently annoying to cause him trouble. It

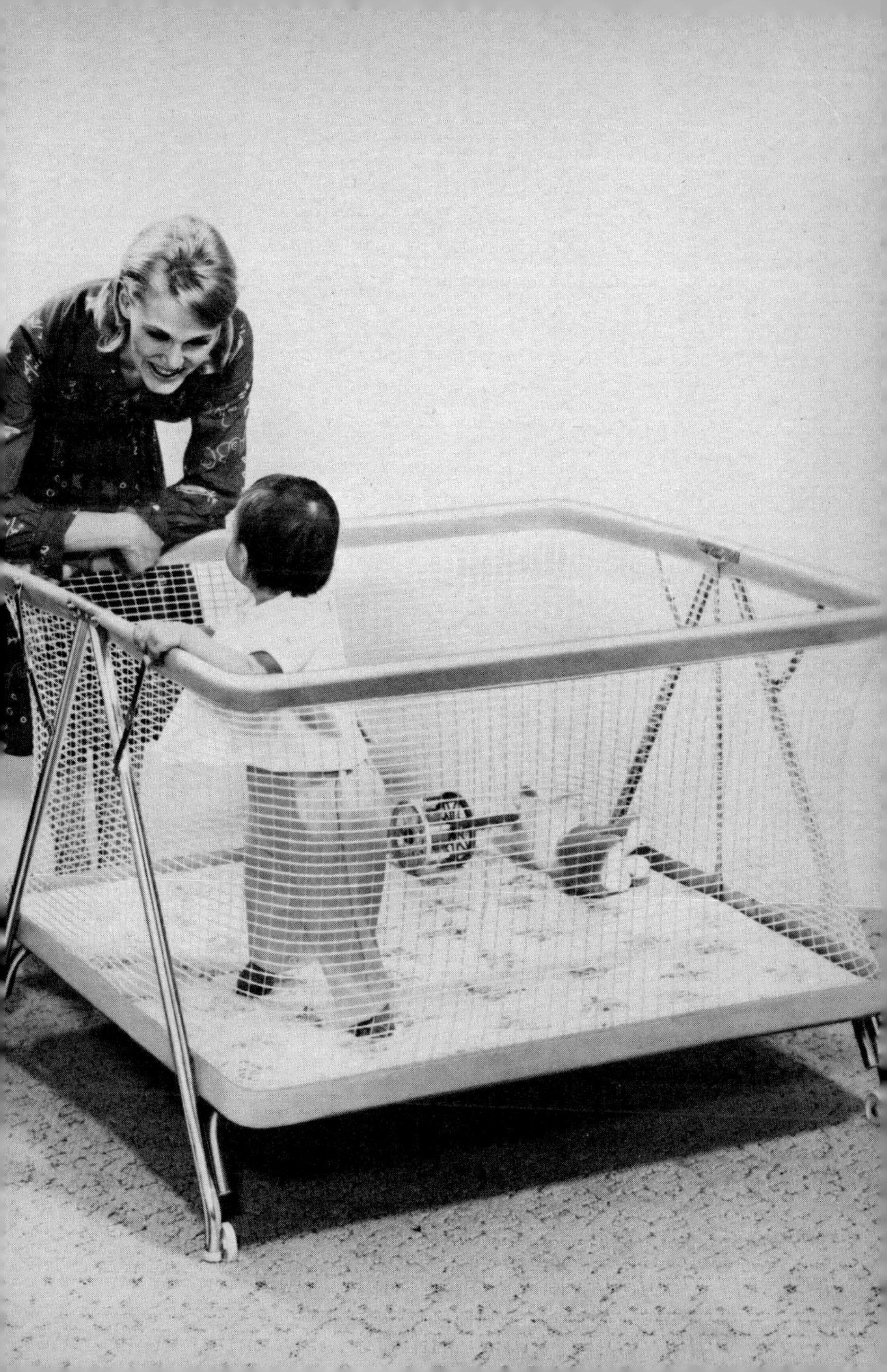

is better for little Alice when her parents stop her, and are strong enough to weather the temper she displays, than when they let things go on too long and wind up furious at her stubbornness. When Alice needs to be stopped, her mother will substitute another activity or give simple directions. If these fail, her mother quietly picks her up and takes her where she wants her to be.

Sometimes Alice's mother will decide, on second thought, that she can accept her refusal gracefully because it really doesn't matter so much. Alice cheerfully patters off about her business when her mother says "Time to come in." Her mother may decide that a minute out of doors would be fun for them both, so she lets the nap wait awhile.

If a change in activity does matter, though, both will feel better if her mother sees it through promptly and without spite. If her mother strikes Alice in anger, it may give Alice the idea that temper tantrums and hitting are acceptable, and she'll use them, too. She may anyhow at this age; but the example of the adult convinces her the method is good. Alice's mother, being sure of herself, can take the time to make her point tactfully. The time saved by abruptly stopping a child usually gets used up in drying angry tears which follow hasty or harsh commands.

When a child continues to disobey, it may express an inner drive over which he has little control. For example, around a year of age he may throw toys constantly. At this time, he is learning to let go of things, as well as testing weight and whether it will bounce or break.

It's best not to start picking things up for him. If you do, he'll think you've made it a twosome and go at it even harder. Put him on the floor so he can fetch his toys himself. Save your breath. This is temporary.

YOUR BABYSITTER

The babysitter is an important member of most households. We know that everybody is happier if parents can get out with each other now and then. Couples need to continue to enjoy community affairs and personal interests after the baby is born. We know, too, that sometimes children are better off at home than being dragged around from store to store.

Regardless of how long or how often you use a sitter, she must be someone who can be trusted. It is best if you use the same or few persons. Both sitter and children are more at ease when they know each other. When you hire anyone who will have more or less regular contact with your children, ask for references and a current physical examination, including a test for tuberculosis. Teenagers often have these tests at school.

The first time ask the sitter to arrive well before you expect to leave so that all can become acquainted. Even if you expect the child to be asleep while you are away, be sure he knows the sitter. The soundest sleeper has a way of awakening on such occasions. Then both the child and the sitter have a harder time because the child is frightened by the stranger and your unexpected absence.

Such an episode can start persistent sleeping difficulties. Once frightened, the child may wake up crying night after night, or refuse to go to bed, until reassured that he can trust you again.

By the time a child is 2 or 3, after he and the sitter have become old friends, he can be told ahead of time that you are going out. Put him to bed and he'll be able to remember that you'll be gone.

Many young couples band together as a club to exchange

sitting for each other. A volunteer secretary keeps track of the hours. By this plan many different mothers and fathers may be used, but the problem presented by the changing faces will be offset, somewhat, because they usually have other contacts with the child and are also likely to be familiar with the routines at his home.

Teenagers do a lot of babysitting. They may or may not be experienced with the ways of young children and feel more confident if you take the time to show them how you feed, diaper, and care for your child. For that matter, any sitter, old or young, appreciates full information about your ways of doing things. As the child grows older, he's sure to announce "Mother always does it this way," or "Mother lets me have that." If you've talked your ways over with her, the sitter will be able to distinguish fact from the child's understandable wish to try her out.

Among the items a sitter likes to know are: Does the child expect food or drink before bed? What time does he go to bed? Is he supposed to have any medicine? Should he have any medicine if he asks for it? What is his favorite toy? How do you arrange the covers? Does he go to the bathroom during the evenings? Where may he play—indoors and out?

In addition, the sitter should have other information: the telephone number where you will be or where some responsible person can be reached; the telephone number of your doctor and the fire department. How do you regulate the heat? Are there any extra jobs you have in mind? How about snacks, use of radio or TV? Do or don't you permit the sitter to have companions? What time will you return? If you are to be delayed more than 15 minutes, phone. People who are otherwise conscientious about promptness are frequently careless in their commitments to sitters.

15. Ages three and four

As the third birthday nears, a youngster gradually ceases to be a baby and enters early childhood. Often this is called the preschool age; but since thousands of children ages 3 and 4 go to some school for part of each weekday, their parents will tell you they are not "pre" anything.

In the next 2 or 3 years, a child becomes much more skillful in managing his body. He learns to run easily and freely, climb surefootedly, jump, hop, and handle a tricycle well.

If his growing interest in taking off and putting on clothing has been encouraged all along, he will be able to do a complete dressing job, except for tying shoestrings or bows, by the time he is 4. He'll need help still with a snowsuit, tight rubbers, or buttons in the back.

He is efficient with glass, spoon and fork, and he eats more neatly. Managing his utensils is not so all-absorbing and he is able to talk and eat at the same time. He gets carried away with his story, or with watching and enjoying other people, and a good many glasses of milk are spilled as his attention is directed elsewhere.

He no longer needs to concentrate to get up steps, one foot at a time. Now he runs up the stairs, one foot after another,

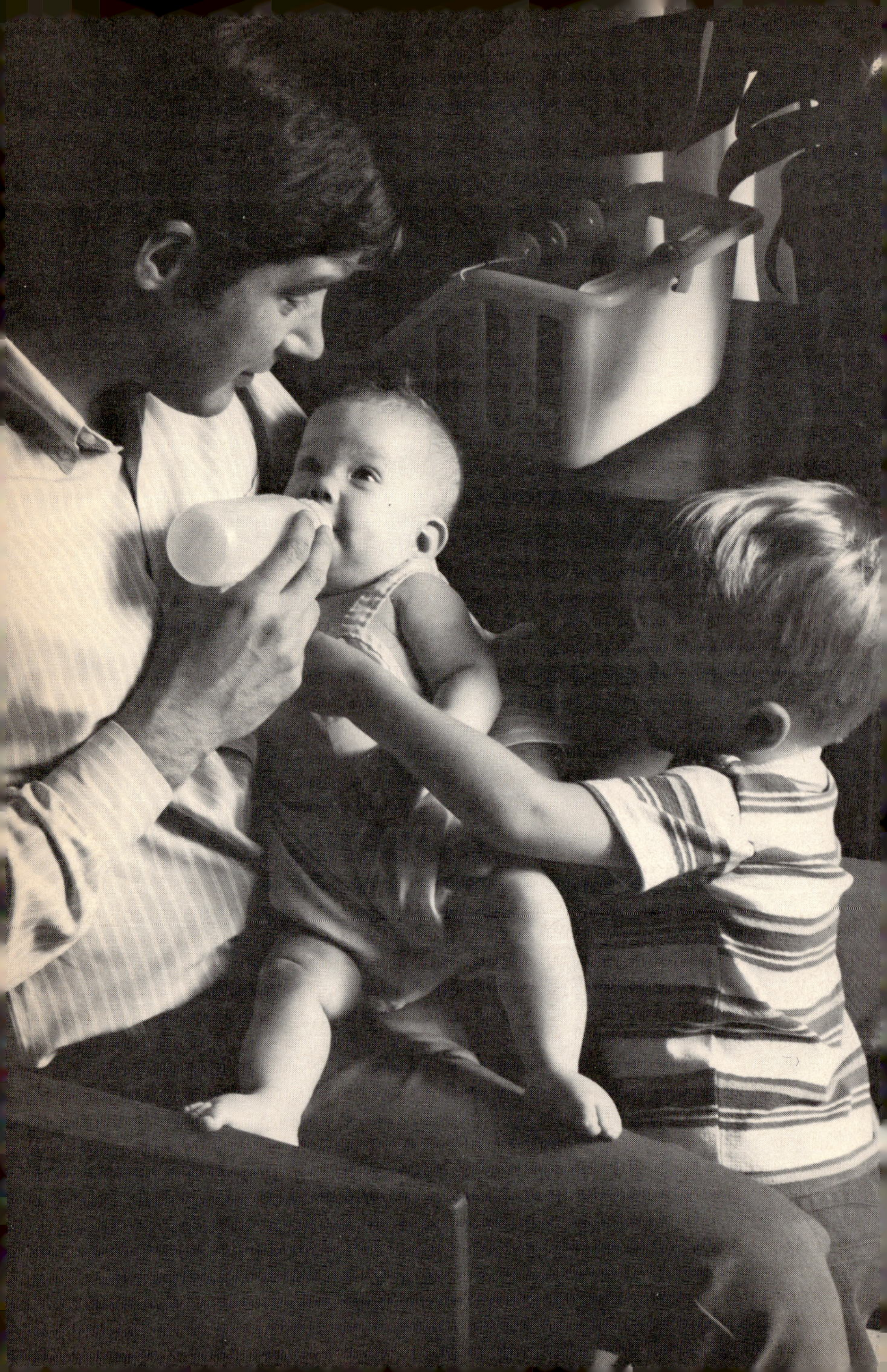

in order to find his mother to tell her the ice cream man is outside ringing his bell.

Going to the toilet no longer requires much thought, either. He makes a hurried stop as he rushes to his play. Even the hurried stop may be postponed until too late because of the press of other interests.

Once a child can do a thing easily, it gets shoved to the background in his thinking. As his horizons widen and he is absorbed in new skills, he may relapse noticeably in his eating, toileting, and dressing habits. Later on, when he reaches school age, routines will seem important to him again.

Your job as a parent changes, too. You had to do literally everything for the infant. You taught the toddler how to do things for himself. By the third birthday he has learned, so you mostly guide. This means you have to be willing to "let go" a little. While many parents welcome this relief, others may find it hard to let the child learn by making mistakes. Yet if he does, he actually becomes more trustworthy. He finds that people listen to him and let him make some decisions. He may then even ask for help. He tries to understand. He takes refusals more easily. He can wait a little. What a child learns now depends less upon what his body can do and more upon outside factors. Those around him determine to a large extent how much stimulation and challenge he gets, communicating to him their sense of values and their ways of life. Opportunities for him to learn come from a wide variety of materials, ideas, and experiences; his life is enriched by a wider circle of people important to him.

FATHERS BECOME IMPORTANT

The child naturally turns to the one who has had the closest physical contact with him. Usually this is the mother. Yet many fathers slip comfortably into supervising supper, bathtime fun, or the business of getting ready for bed.

Actually taking care of a child does much to foster understanding. Some fathers who appreciate that fact make a point of giving some physical attention to their babies right from the start. Others come into fuller appreciation of their children when they learn to talk; still others, not until the child can share more adult activities. Fathers don't have to be like mothers. Their own way of doing things is equally valuable.

Children turn to their father more and more; and, as they do, he is apt to feel more fatherly. Daddy's arrival home from work is greeted with glee. While he may have hoped to slump into a chair, he now finds it better to give 15 or 20 minutes of undivided attention to his clamoring youngster in, say, a rousing game of ball. Then he can tell the child, "Go along now, Daddy wants to read." This may satisfy him somewhat and keep him from pestering and begging for attention all evening.

By the time a child is 3, he studies others and begins to see the differences in the way men and women act. Fathers, as men, become patterns for male behavior. Mothers show both their boys and their girls what women are like. The child carries this even further, and for a while wishes to become the husband or wife of his respective parent when he grows up. Little girls practice on their fathers how to win a man's heart; little boys fall in love with their mothers, see how a man earns a living, treats women, and—in short—behaves like a man.

WHEN PARENTS DISAGREE

If Mother and Father don't always see eye to eye on the way to handle the child, it's hard—but not necessarily a catastrophe. Children can become accustomed to different ways of doing things. By the time they are 3 or 4 they have adjusted to quite different sets of expectations. There's one set among the neighborhood children, another in the house with the family. Grandparents do things differently than parents. Dinner, when the father is home, may be unlike lunch when only the mother is present.

As long as the behavior patterns of people are relatively uniform in various situations, children seem able to adapt to suit the occasion. They become confused only when things are forever changing in the same situation.

If the mother says one thing and the father another, the child becomes uneasy because he needs approval from both. He'll continue to try to get his way, from one or the other, but he feels lost when his two protectors so betray him.

Of course, differences, even occasional quarrels, are to be expected. Friction is bound to occur between parents and between child and parents. People who love and trust each other may honestly disagree now and then, but can resolve their differences through discussion, even heated debates, or sharp conflict. A good row may clear the air.

There is evidence, however, that when the mother and the father disagree about almost everything involved in raising their child, the child suffers. He is apt to become aggressive and quarrelsome himself. This feeds the tension between the parents, and the home becomes heavy with outbursts and resentments.

It helps immensely if parents can frankly discuss their feelings about raising children. Only when they recognize differences can they work out a solution or, failing that, agree on a truce. Sometimes one parent lacks information known to the other. Talking it over helps them see things more the same way.

Parents may find it a good rule to back each other up, even if the solution proposed is not one that either would have selected. The child suffers less from what might seem to one parent to be too easy or too strict, than he does from fear of losing the love of the other parent.

BROTHER-AND-SISTER QUARRELS

Some days children in a family don't get along at all. Neighborhood play doesn't always go well either, and loud shouts and cries pierce the air.

When quarreling and fighting break out, you may feel that you've spotted the troublemaker right off, and know just what to do—send him home, or off to his room if he's yours. But this isn't necessarily the best way to handle it. Instead of fixing blame on somebody, try to get the children to work out a solution. Frequently, their ideas are more fair, and their understanding of each other's motives more correct, than yours.

Quietly join the group. Your presence alone may help. You may suggest a new game or see further possibilities in the old one. "How about that train over there—doesn't it need a station?"

If you fall into the habit of playing referee, quarreling may increase as children try to use you in order to get even with each other. When a child whines "What can I do now, Mommy?" it rarely means he doesn't have toys aplenty. Also if you do think up something for him to do, he is apt to turn it down. Behind his plea he may really be saying "What will you let me do now?" He may be implying that you'll stop him from any-

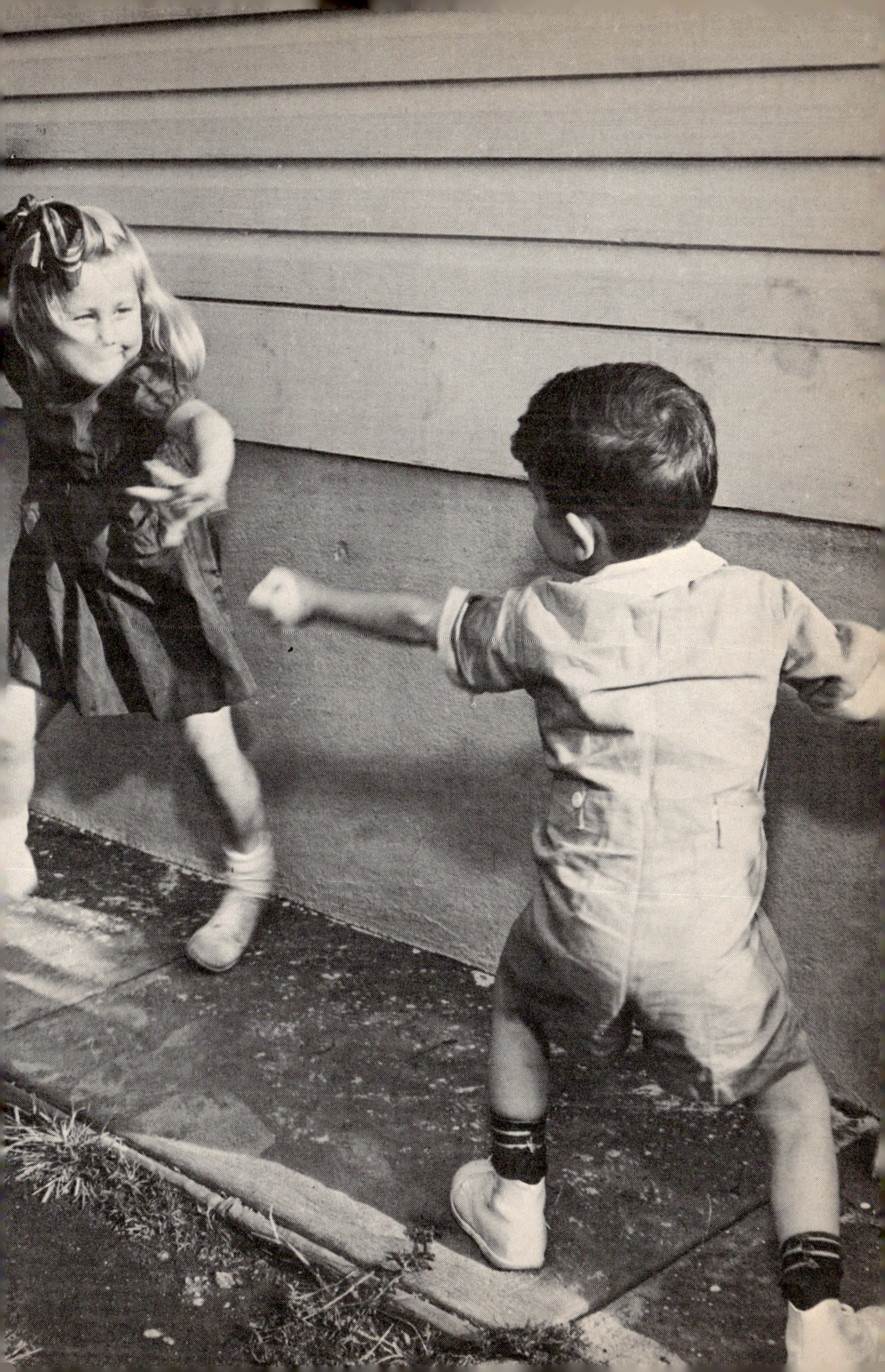

thing he thinks up. Or he may be saying, "Please pay some attention to me for a change." The suggestion that you need his help to select buttons for his winter coat, or that you'll read him a story, often works like magic. "Let's do . . ." usually works better than "Why don't you . . . ?"

JEALOUSY OCCURS IN FAMILIES, TOO

A child may feel jealous when another gets what he considers to be his. One of the commonest times is when a new baby arrives. The child feels anger toward his parents for having let someone else take his place. Fearing further loss, he dares not express his anger directly toward the parent. Therefore, he's apt to display his feelings to the baby, who stands between. He may try to remove the baby himself, or suggest that his parents return the baby to the hospital. He may decide that if they're so eager to have a baby around, *he'll* be one. So he goes back to his baby ways, crawling, asking for a bottle, wetting his pants.

He may disguise his feelings completely in a show of love for the newcomer, hoping to win back the affection of the parent who has betrayed him. But such strong feelings usually find another way to come out. He may begin to have nightmares, dawdle over his food, whine or cling, or give in to sudden temper outbursts. He may mistreat younger companions or animals, taking out on them what he'd like to do to his mother or the baby.

Yet his anger cannot be expressed directly toward the baby either. Real harm might come to the baby, or the child might feel too guilty about what he has done. He needs to be protected from these results of his actions. He should never be teased about "having his nose out of joint."

Preventing jealousy is the best method. This cannot be

done in bits and pieces, simply telling the child ahead of time, for instance, or verbally assuring him that he is still loved. Months and years of steady loving care must have given him reason to feel valued for himself alone. If he does feel so, his hurt or jealousy will not last too long or be too overwhelming.

Whatever parents can do to prepare the older child is good. As they talk and plan with him about the baby to come, they themselves understand more fully what the older child is going to feel, whether he be the first born or one of several children.

Such preparations should not be started until the child asks about changes in his mother or, if he fails to ask, a few weeks before the expected delivery. Any shifts which will be necessary—a change in sleeping arrangements, handing down equipment, or starting to nursery school—should be done well ahead of the event, not at the time. The older children can wash the small new garments, help arrange the nursery corner, or go to buy talcum powder. Talk about the baby as he really will be, instead of promising a future playmate. Babies really aren't good playmates, and the child who expects an instant companion is sure to be disappointed.

How to help. The older child cannot really be prepared for the intensity of his feelings when his mother leaves him to "get" the new baby. Nor can he be expected to like it when she later gives the new baby a great deal of attention or is short-tempered because she has lost her usual night's sleep.

Mothers aren't adequately prepared, either, for their own feelings of outrage as they see their older child start to squeeze or pinch the little one. Without thinking, they are tempted to punish the child and thereby make him feel even less loved.

Everybody in the household, and those who come to visit, should be careful not to overlook the older child or children.

When visitors come to admire and bring presents to the baby, the older child should be given a share of attention. You may have to discreetly coach Aunt Sally to remember to include older Tommy in her conversation. Tell about the new tricks Tommy has learned with his tricycle, or how tall he can build with blocks. Possibly the older child can be permitted to open gift boxes, take the rattle to the baby, or place a new garment where it belongs. Thoughtful visitors sometimes bring a gift to the older child as well.

A jealous youngster under 3 gets the most relief from being babied himself again. A somewhat older child has friends and interests outside the home, and may be less keenly upset by a new arrival. You help him most by encouraging these interests and seeing to it that he gets special treats from which the baby is left out. Sometimes mothers can give a half hour of attention to an older child when the baby is asleep. They join the child outdoors in the sun, read to him, make cupcakes together, or whatever seems fun for them both.

Jealousy is not always felt at the time the new baby comes. Rivalry may appear only when the new baby begins to intrude by learning how to creep and get into things. Jealousy may also flare up when one of the children achieves a new skill. When the baby walks, for instance, the old balance between the children is upset. Mothers notice increased quarreling until the children establish new ways of living together. Circumstances must permit the one left out or left behind to feel important again in ways peculiarly his own.

LEARNING RIGHT FROM WRONG

By the age of 3, a child begins to know pretty well what you approve of and what you don't. From you—your example, your teaching, your facial expressions—he gets his sense of right and wrong. He's not born with it. Unless you know what you think yourself and stay reasonably consistent from day to day, the child is unable to know either.

At first you have to be there to tell him—or stop him. Later, your presence nearby is enough. As time goes on, he can apply brakes to forbidden actions by himself. He knows what you want him to do and tries to do it, even when you are not there. After a while, he is thinking for himself. This is the beginning of what is called a conscience. A little boy refrains from raiding the cooky jar when his mother is at a neighbor's house. Jenny shouts "It's mine!" instead of pinching or kicking her playmate. Such restraint on behavior shows real growth.

Over the years, a conscience becomes more reliable as a stop to misbehavior and as a guide to good. A useful, working conscience develops most readily in an atmosphere of kindly patience which makes the child want to be like his parents. It's not much of a conscience at all when it operates only because of fear—of you or your punishment, of being found out, or of encountering a bigger opponent.

Fear of the consequences seldom stops a child anyway. He may well decide he'll trade a punishment in the future for the immediate pleasure—or take a chance on no reckoning at all. This is scarcely a way to develop a conscience which, in the long run, will mean the child can be trusted without supervision. You really are seeking to support him as he develops an inner control over his behavior.

The child learns what is right by being told, even more by observation, and to some extent by praise or punishment. Unfortunately, some parents spend a great deal more time scolding their children for errors than praising them for their goodness.

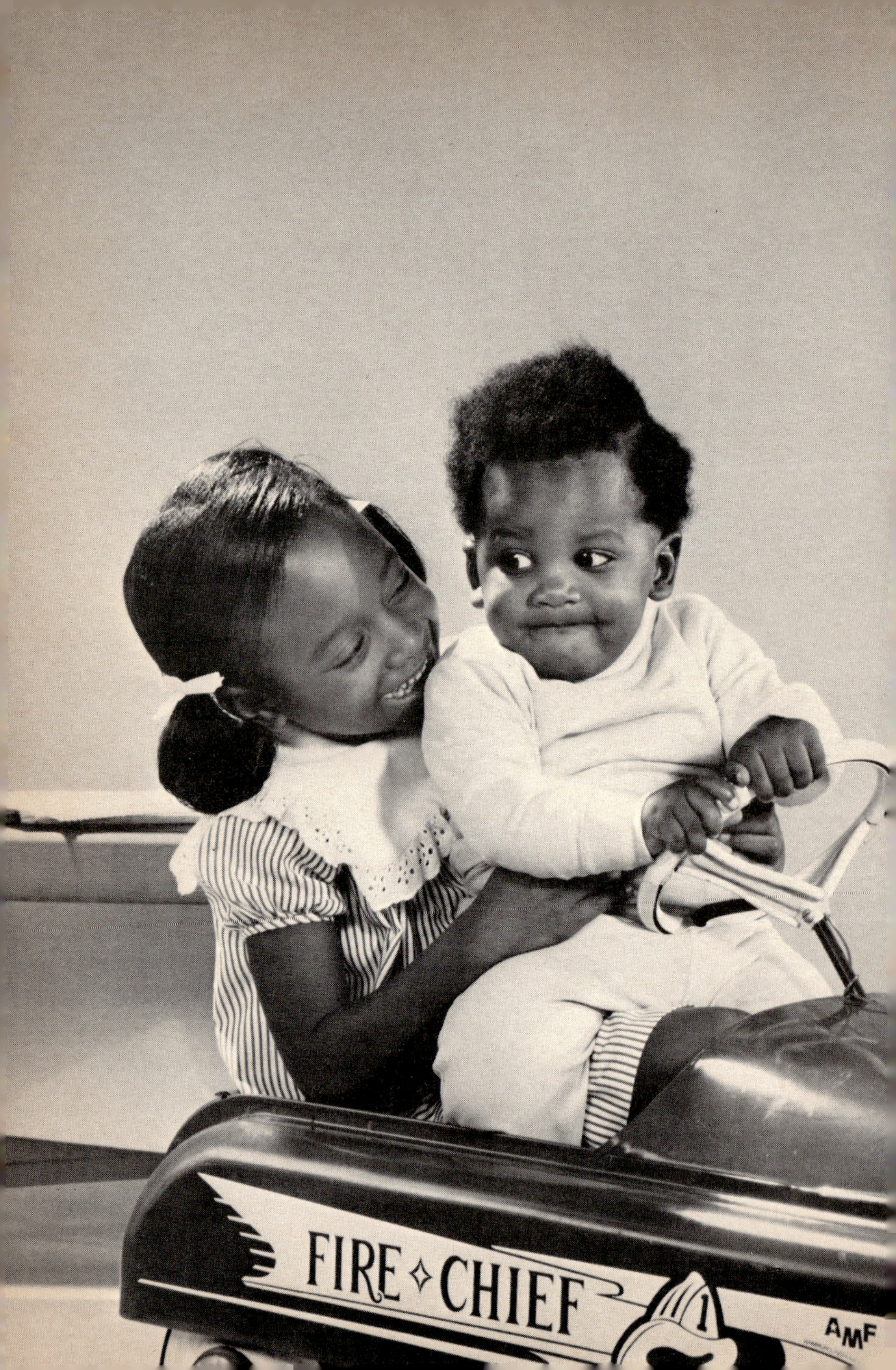
FIRE CHIEF
1
AMF

Hard as it is for anyone to learn to control impulses, it becomes even harder for the preschooler, because he scarcely can distinguish between what he has done and what he has imagined or wished he could do. Wishing he's a cowboy makes him one. But if he wishes that his baby sister would go away—a wish common to most children at some time—and the infant gets sick, he's bound to worry. Did his wish do that?

He hates his mother when she makes him come indoors from play. Did that hate-wish send her away—to work, on a trip, or out for the evening? He may feel he's responsible for all that goes wrong. He may try very hard to keep things in order, or do them in the same way every day. He works out rituals for going to bed, or for saying goodby. In his way he thinks he can control the world.

We certainly don't want a child's conscience to be so overstrict that he loses joy in simply being alive. Probably you can help most by showing your youngster that you accept his conflicting emotions—his loves and hates, his bigness and littleness, his tenderness and destructiveness—and that you have confidence in him.

Parents also help a great deal when they assist a child to sort out fantasy from reality. "That's just pretend, you know" or "You're mad at Tom, but you can't kick him" are examples of the way you can assure the child that his feelings and wishes are natural and that they harm no one.

LEARNING TO TELL THE TRUTH

What a child wants to be he is. With his space helmet on, he's an astronaut. His piled-up boxes are an apartment. The sandbox furrow is a road.

Parents find it easy to go along with the "pretend" game. They may even extend the pretend to their suggestions for behavior. For example: "Drive your truck over here to the diner." The driver will then have to eat his dinner.

Little boys who can spot minute differences in aircraft as skillfully as a trained sky observer, can readily accept the story of the jolly fat man and his bundle of toys, drawn through the sky by flying reindeer. Children who know all about chickens and eggs — and rabbits and their babies — find the Easter bunny just as plausible. The whole world is full of wonders, and magic is expected.

Parents get upset, though, when a child says, "I didn't break that dish" — wishing it hadn't happened. Or "Sister ate the cookies" — when he knows perfectly well that *he* ate them. Such untruths show that a child is getting a conscience and knows when he's done wrong. They reveal how poorly he distinguishes wish from truth, or what he'd like to have done from what his awkward and heedless body did do.

Parents help children to tell the truth when they make it not too painful to do so. Getting a confession isn't nearly as important as helping the child acknowledge his mistakes. Perhaps you could say "What's happened?" Don't say, "Did you break the dish?" for that puts him on the spot.

We must remember that our standards for telling the truth are apt to be pretty one-sided. We expect children to tell the unvarnished, incriminating truth, yet charitably call our own untruths "white lies," tact, or kindness. As you mumble some excuse for not coming to dinner to a neighbor you dislike, strict honesty gets blurred a bit. Yet to many people it is a sign of social maturity to refrain from telling the whole truth under such circumstances. Such subtle shades of truth and half-truth are difficult to explain to children.

IMAGINARY COMPANIONS

Every now and then a child will invent an imaginary playmate who becomes as real as life. The family can't sit on a chair or shut the door, lest they squash this friend. Sometimes the friend is horrible, and gets into all kinds of mischief, is responsible for all that goes wrong, doesn't like spinach, hates to pick up his pajamas, and hits his mama.

The friend may be around for only a few days, but some imaginary companions have moved into homes and lived there, getting in everybody's way, for months and years.

Instead of inventing a friend, a child might "become" somebody else. "I'm not Ann, I'm Elsie," announces little Ann. She must be called Elsie and treated as Elsie would be treated, which may mean she doesn't take naps as Ann does or wear rubbers.

Sometimes a child needs an imaginary friend because he has no real friends or can't get along successfully with real children. He may be compensating for being excluded by others who are older and are apt to leave him out. Whatever the situation, his parents should ask themselves if they are being too harsh with the child and need to change their tactics, more in line with what it is reasonable to ask.

If they have any reason to believe the imaginary friend is an expression of a problem too deep for them to fathom, they may wish to seek counsel from a child guidance clinic. Meanwhile, the best thing is to try not to sit on the friend, slam the car door on his toes, or do him any other damage.

HE HAS NEW FEARS

The infant and toddler are afraid of real things, but many of the preschooler's fears are imagined. They seem real to him, nevertheless, and cannot be dismissed.

He may become afraid of dogs, even though he has happily scuffled with his own and, as far as you know, has never been frightened by another dog. He, the most faithful fan of the lion, wolf, and bear at the zoo, dreams of terrible animals. He, who begged to work the vacuum cleaner as a toddler, screams with terror as it is turned on.

The brave 2-year-old is gone; at 4 he puts up such a fuss about shots at the doctor's office that his howls drown out the soothing comments of the nurse. Adhesive patches sell by the thousands, mostly applied to youngsters of this age who are comforted only when the broken skin is held together or hidden by the tape.

Preschoolers are upset by broken toys, because they are no longer whole, not because they do not work. They dislike having only a part of a picture in a book or magazine or a table with only three legs, or only half a toy dog.

To the extent that such fears are common at this age, we can say they are normal. They spring from the child's growing concern about keeping his body intact and from his new awareness of his sex. They are also related to his imperfect sense of what, and who, causes what. He still feels to a large extent that he is the center of the universe and that he controls a lot more things than he really does. With all the power he imagines he has, he is frightened by his own impulses and wishes.

His fears are often the result of understanding hazards better; at the same time, his active body and mind push him into hazardous situations. The toddler's fear of losing his mother was greatest when he himself moved away from her by crawling or walking. The 4-year-old dares to pull away in many fashions. He extends his life out into the neighborhood. His ideas carry him even farther, into the world of space and the

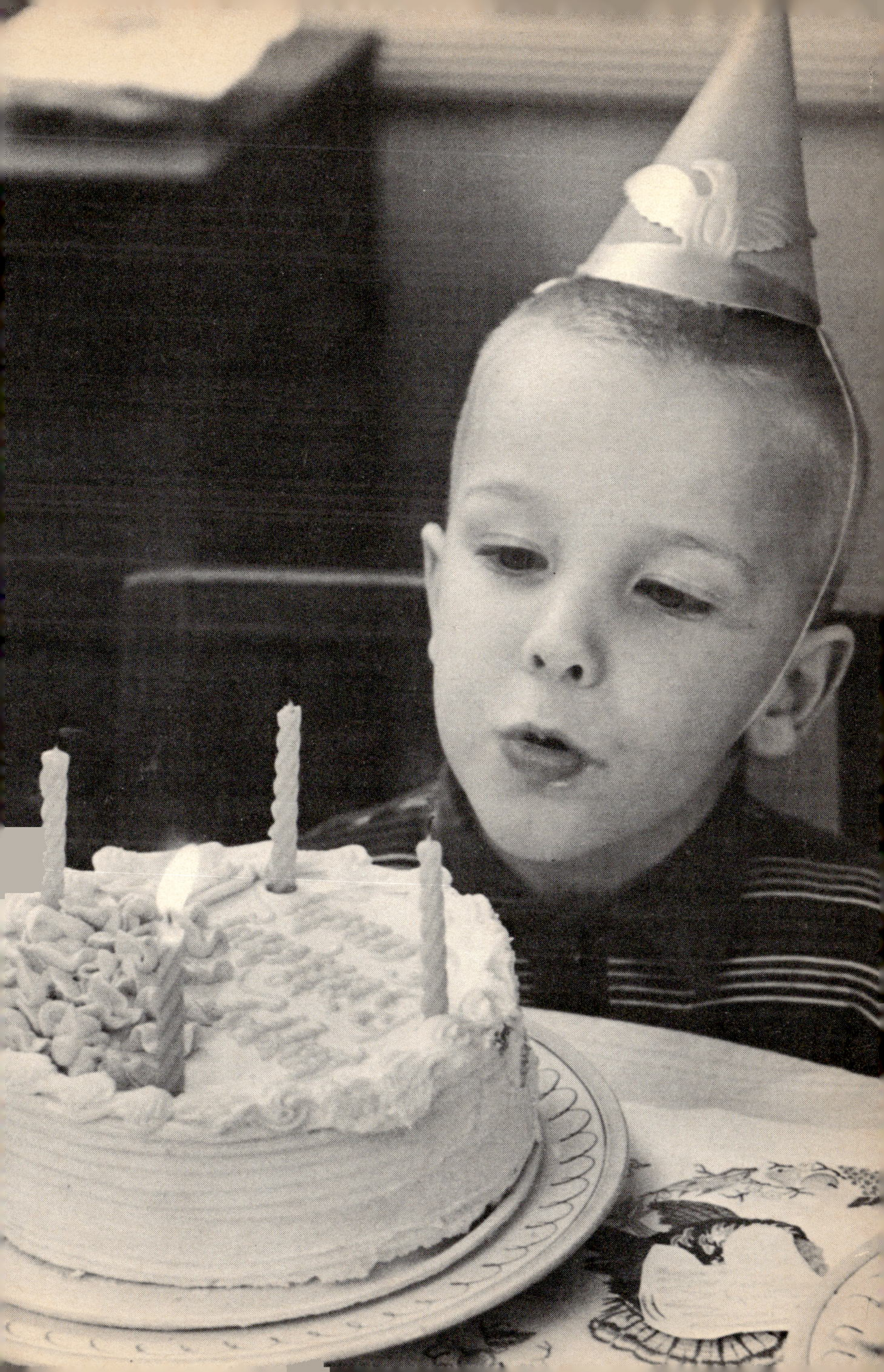

unknown and the depths of the ocean. His mind may be peopled with imaginary animals which scare him.

He overhears fragments of adult conversations about frightening and horrible events which he may or may not understand completely. Violence and injury are made all too real for him as his imagination is reinforced by unsuitable programs on television.

Since most of his fears are the result of a grain of truth embellished with a great deal of imagination, it is difficult to treat them directly. But avoid frightening situations. Never shut him in a dark closet or threaten him with awful people. It may be well to postpone an operation which can safely wait until he is a little older, so that fears of being cut are not verified.

When you show him that you are in control of the situation, you help him shed many of his fears. You carry for him the burden of responsibility that is more than he can handle. You show him daily, in dozens of ways, that you won't let him go too far. When he is frightened, you treat him kindly and gently, giving him the assurance he shows he needs.

All fears cannot be prevented, however, since that grain of truth in them actually does exist. From that grain of truth comes the caution which is necessary for a human being to survive. Parents who strive to protect their children from the knowledge that life is dangerous somehow communicate that life is more dangerous than it really is, and their children are apt to be the most fearful of all. They do not learn prudence and caution, and have not tasted the precious feeling of being able to cope with whatever comes along, be it a close call on a tricycle or the beginnings of courage and bravery in the face of pain.

Many fears of preschoolers have to be dealt with indirectly. It may help to re-educate the child to the vacuum cleaner, patiently having him turn it on and off, experimenting with the power.

You may have to look at the child's whole life. Perhaps you'll find that too much is expected of him in goodness and control and the many virtues which come slowly at best. Your child may live with a growing fear that he can't do anything right.

Sometimes children cover their fears by overreacting and becoming belligerent. Such bluster will melt quickly if the child senses that you'll accept his fears and give him your steady, loving support.

Most fears for which you can find no apparent cause will disappear as the child gains experience and sureness. If teased or shamed, he may learn to hide his fear, but will continue to be upset inside. Nightmares may result. Or misplaced caution and general timidness may dampen the child's soaring spirit.

Frequently, adults continue to fight childish fears because they were never helped to deal with them openly.

IN SEARCH OF ANSWERS: SEX

"What's that?" the child asked when he first began to talk, and you endlessly gave the names of things while he increased his vocabulary. Now he asks, "Why?" Thus:

Some questions show how imperfectly the child's sense of cause and effect is developed: "My baby brother is a month old. You know why? 'Cause he's so little."

A boy might ask: "Why are there mommies and daddies?" "Why don't we have a baby?" "Why doesn't Susie have a thing like mine?"

Though it may not be easy for you to reply, the child

shouldn't feel he's done something wrong when he asks. To the best of your ability, give as much information about the world and its ways as you think he can understand.

"Where do babies come from?" They come from the mother. They grow in her. They grow in a special place. (That's better than in her stomach, and more accurate, besides.)

"How do they get out?" By themselves, when they're ready to be born. They come out of a special place between the mother's legs. The doctor helps.

Of course you'll have your own way of saying these things, and there is no one correct way. Every child will ask the questions differently. Usually they'll pop out when you least expect it, or when it seems least convenient. Postponing the answer until a later time is rarely necessary, since the information asked for is so simple.

The part that father plays in creating a child is the toughest of all for most of us. Usually children don't ask about this until they are 6 or 8 years old. Even then, they may be seeking less information than you think.

It often pays to ask "What do you mean?" and get a better understanding of what the child wants to know before starting a lecture. There is the old story of the child who asked where he came from and was told the whole process of human reproduction. He impatiently replied, "I mean, do we come from New York? Mary does."

Most children are content to be told that the father must start the baby growing. Be sure he knows that both a mother and father are needed to make a baby, just as both are needed to help take care of him. You may wish to use such words as "sperm" without much explanation. Like "radio," the word cannot be simplified much without making it meaningless, so let it go at that. Later on, he can understand more. All along, it is helpful to children if they are given the correct names of parts of their bodies and their products: vagina, penis, bowel movement, urine, and so on.

Telling may not be enough. Simply telling a child the facts of reproduction usually doesn't end the matter. Children rarely take anybody's word for anything. They have to see for themselves. They check and try it out. How many times have you said "I told you so!" after the child has deliberately gone ahead to see if a knife was sharp, or if a balloon would break.

They usually don't take Mother's word for how babies are born, either. It is pretty unbelievable after all. Except for farm children who possibly see animals deliver their young, today's children are accustomed to a world where new things are bought. So they check on this "special place" you've talked about in a young female playmate if they get a chance and they talk it over among their friends. Little girls practically turn themselves inside out to see where "it" is.

This curiosity is perfectly natural. Boys want to see if other boys are like them and if girls are like their sisters. The practice of letting boys and girls use the same bathroom in nursery school provides an easy and natural way for them to satisfy their questions about sex differences. They are as absorbed and scientific as in watching how a turtle eats and as readily distracted by the next thing that comes along.

It may help a child who has no other opportunities to observe human anatomy to take him to see a baby bathed or changed. Plan your visit with the baby's mother so she can tactfully provide an opportunity for such observation.

Only when a child continues to display the need to peek or is morbidly fascinated by such subjects in later years do we worry about it. A child who handles his sexual organs a great deal shows some fear or worry about which you'll need expert

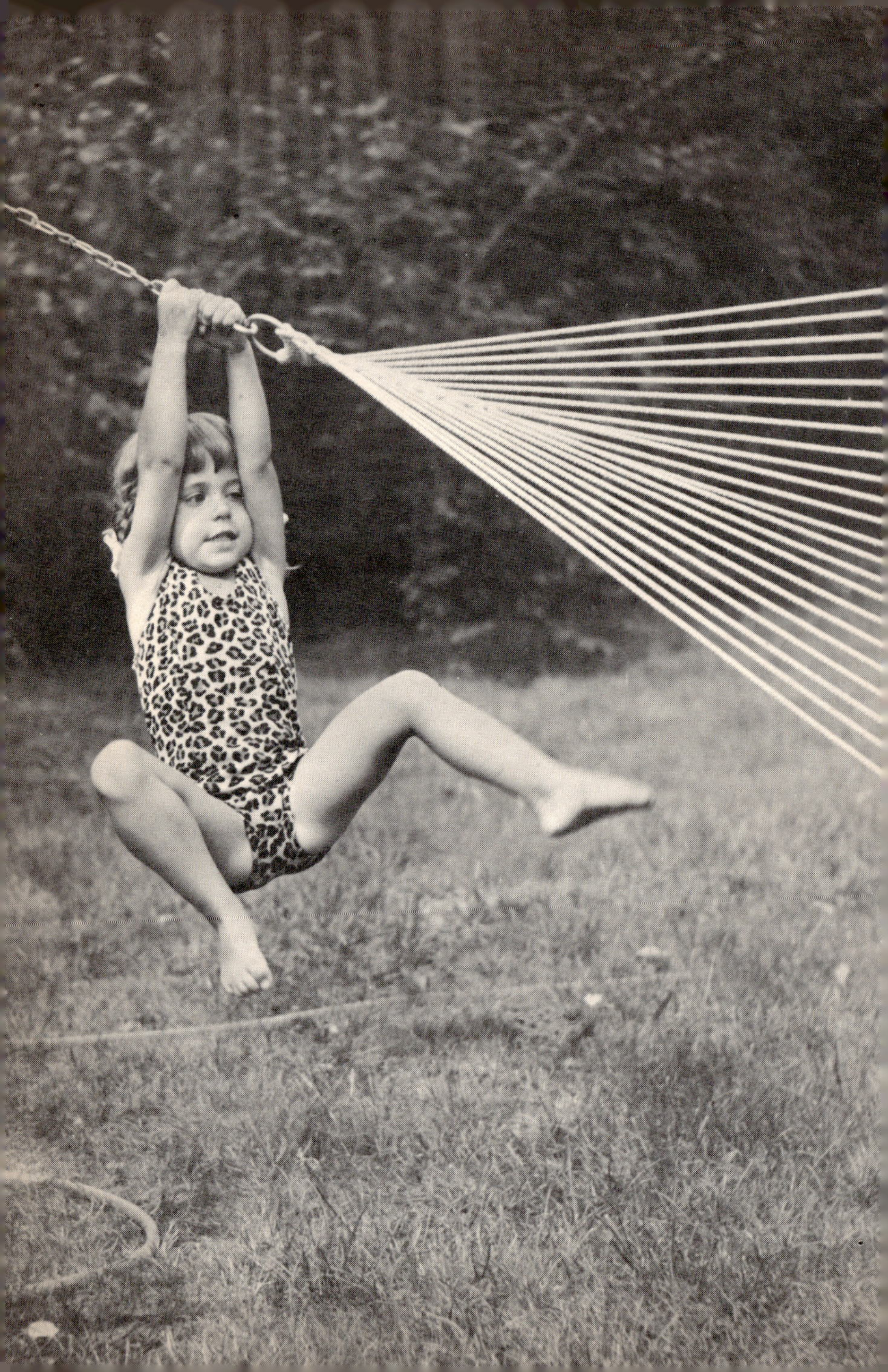

help. By school age, most children have their curiosity satisfied, sense that these are private matters, and have their interest directed to other things.

Remember, when children ask questions about sex or show interest in their own or others' bodies, they deserve to be given correct information—preferably by you and not as twisted or garbled by another. If the child never asks, it may be that he has had his curiosity satisfied in the normal course of events in family living. It is very possible that his friends have communicated to him a secret or frightened notion about anything having to do with sex.

If you feel that for some reason he is ashamed or afraid to ask, you can help him by introducing the topic. "Did you know? Aunt Jane and Uncle Bob are going to have a baby. It is growing right now in a special place." By sharing this fascinating knowledge, you may give your child the reassurance he needs to ask more.

MORE QUESTIONS: DEATH

Sooner or later, your child will learn of death. His grandmother or a playmate may die, his dog gets run over, he discovers a dead bird. Adults feel a sense of loss and grief, and sometimes are revolted by an animal's dead body. Often the child sees the event in a very matter-of-fact way—what once moved is still and he loses interest after a poke or two.

Don't be too surprised if he seems very calm or unfeeling. There are lots of reasons for this. People come and go all the time, as far as he's concerned; and in his play, the "dead" cowboy rises to fight again. He is just beginning to develop a sense of time and to realize that birthdays are repeated at seemingly endless intervals; so "forever" isn't an idea he can grasp, either. He's more apt to feel that you are upset, and much of his response will be determined by your own.

This reassures parents who might otherwise try to protect a child from the knowledge of death by replacing a pet so promptly the child scarcely realizes any sense of loss. Some attempt to soften death by suggesting that Grandma has gone to sleep or gone away.

Actually such evasions may create trouble, for the child may be afraid to go to sleep at night, be upset as you mention "a special sleep" in connection with an operation; or worry as you plan to go "away" on a trip.

Use plain simple words to tell what has happened. If you use flowery or vague words, he may think he somehow caused the death, especially if he has mistreated his pet or been rude to his grandmother or just thinks of himself as a "bad" boy. Sending a child away to relatives, as a way of protecting him or yourself at a time of grief, is usually not wise. Whatever the trouble, he is better able to deal with it in your presence.

Later on, he may reveal that he's been thinking more about the real meaning of death. He may ask if he will die, how it feels to die, and if and when you will die. Associated with these questions concerning death are his fears about losing you, about bodily hurt, and the unknown dark.

Perhaps he will be more satisfied if you attempt to reassure him about these related fears, building up his confidence and trying to clear up any misunderstandings he may have. A philosophy about death itself can only be achieved as the child lives, gains experience, and can begin to understand your own faith in the design of the universe.

TEACHING GOOD BEHAVIOR

When the subject of discipline came up, people used to think of a set of rules they could apply as needed—rules for "What should I do when my child disobeys?" "When should I spank him?"

Nowadays we don't think so much about rules for such occasions. We know—as sensitive parents and teachers have always known—that discipline is the result of everything that goes on between parent and child. It isn't something to be applied only to children, either. Good discipline is essential for grownups as well. It helps us all to be happy and comfortable. It enables us to enjoy others and to be enjoyed by them. It is a day in, day out background for productive living.

In broad terms, discipline is a matter of learning how to behave. We want the lessons to stick, long after children are grown and parents, teachers, or other authorities have bowed out of the picture. Teaching children how to behave is not a simple task. We don't want to merely stop them. Applying brakes does not show them what to do. As children they are active, creative, and positive. They get things done, and we want them to continue to do so. Yet, and here's where discipline comes in, we want them to consider others as well as themselves. We want them to be fair, not cheaters. We want them to be gentle yet strong, cooperative yet able to stand for what they think is right.

Such big goals seem far removed from the playpen and tricycle years. But you begin when you teach the child to hold your hand when you cross a street and to park his tricycle out of the driveway. These learnings add up, and the sum total of your teaching over the weeks and months and years will surely determine how the child behaves.

A good teacher of anything—discipline or arithmetic—is most effective when he keeps the learner in mind. So how and what you teach depends on the child. His age partly determines what is appropriate. As the child grows, you let him take on more responsibility and make more decisions. You often give him reasons for your rules. You are less apt to need physical interference and are more apt to control him with words.

How you discipline also depends on the child's temperament, whether he be sensitive or stubborn, exuberant or quiet, docile or dashing. While such qualities are influenced by the child's experiences, to a large extent they are inborn and persist throughout life. Unless you can adjust your tempo and method to the child, the two of you just won't mesh. You'll be imposing your will on him, and he's sure to become balky. A mother who does everything quickly and efficiently has a hard time slowing down for a plodding, dreamy child. The reverse is just as taxing.

Parents are sometimes surprised to find that the child who is just "like" them is the one hardest to be patient with. Recognizing a trait in the child which they've always disliked in themselves triggers old, unsolved struggles. They may be overstrict with their "chip off the old block."

What is feasible for an only child may not be practical for a house full. Some activities are all right sometimes, but not at others. Most children can go along with very subtle distinctions by the time they are 3. They're bright enough to resent fixed rules that don't make sense. They can accept broken promises or unexpected changes if you are sure and clear about the necessity.

It is good if you can be consistent in dealing with children, or anybody. But in a busy household it is not always possible.

Anyway, no one day settles discipline. You can take your time, knowing that your example and your steady efforts will count.

How you teach discipline. By now we know a good deal about the ways children learn. We know that they learn by experience. So we let them try things out as far as possible. This is as true of the lessons of arithmetic (2 plus 2 makes 4 only after you try it out dozens of times with pebbles and lollipop sticks and marbles) as it is of behavior (if you hit your friends, they will go home).

Of course, you can't let a child try out things that would hurt him. But before you stop him, be sure it really matters. Lots of parents absent-mindedly say "Don't run, you might fall" when a tumble on the grass wouldn't hurt at all.

When you *must* be authoritarian, tell the child firmly and clearly, ahead of time if possible, what he can or can't do. And follow up on it. Fit your directions to the child, and phrase them in a positive way. "You can't do that" is a challenge to a bright, energetic youngster. He says, inwardly or by his actions, "I can, too. Just watch me." On the other hand, if you say, "Keep your tricycle on this side of the street. You can ride from this corner to that one," you've told the child exactly what he can do.

We know that children learn readily when they think they can succeed. But it's up to their parents to create an atmosphere of success. A heady, intoxicating feeling of "I'm all right" or "I'm good" bubbles inside a child whose parents have made him feel that he does things well.

Of course he is childish, immature, has little judgment, gets carried away by the moment, forgets, and loses control of himself. But that's childhood. Let his parents delight in his growing control, his knowledge, his eager attack on life.

We know that children are apt to behave well when they have plenty to do and are challenged. A lot of discipline problems occur when they are bored or overrestricted. They then become busy at producing mischief. Much has been written about the adolescent who rebels against supervision which is too close. The same process occurs at around 5 years of age, but is less obvious because the child is smaller and his range is more limited. The 4- and 5-year-old feels able to lasso a bear, figuratively speaking. Let him try.

Be smart about the kinds of responsibilities you give him. Tailor these to his age and individual interests. He needs materials to work with. You can widen his world by taking him on trips to the zoo, factory, daddy's office, the farm, library, museum, airport, firehouse, and railroad station. He needs friends to play with, space to move about in, places to run and climb. He welcomes fresh ideas from books and conversations with you.

It isn't necessary—or even desirable—to reach into school-type tasks, pressing a child to learn letters and numbers, or anticipating his pleasure in lessons of various sorts, such as piano, dancing, painting, and so on. At 3, 4, and 5, he still needs to experiment freely with a wide variety of materials. He cannot control his body well enough to accomplish delicate or rapid movements. Pressure to do so simply causes frustration.

With friendly reminding, he can be expected to pick up his clothing, help with simple kitchen chores, be responsible for his tricycle and wagon, help care for a pet. He respects the reasons for things and will cooperate more readily if he knows "why" and "how."

Does punishment help? When we look at discipline as a process of *teaching* a child how to behave, the thorny question of punishment becomes less complicated. We can view punish-

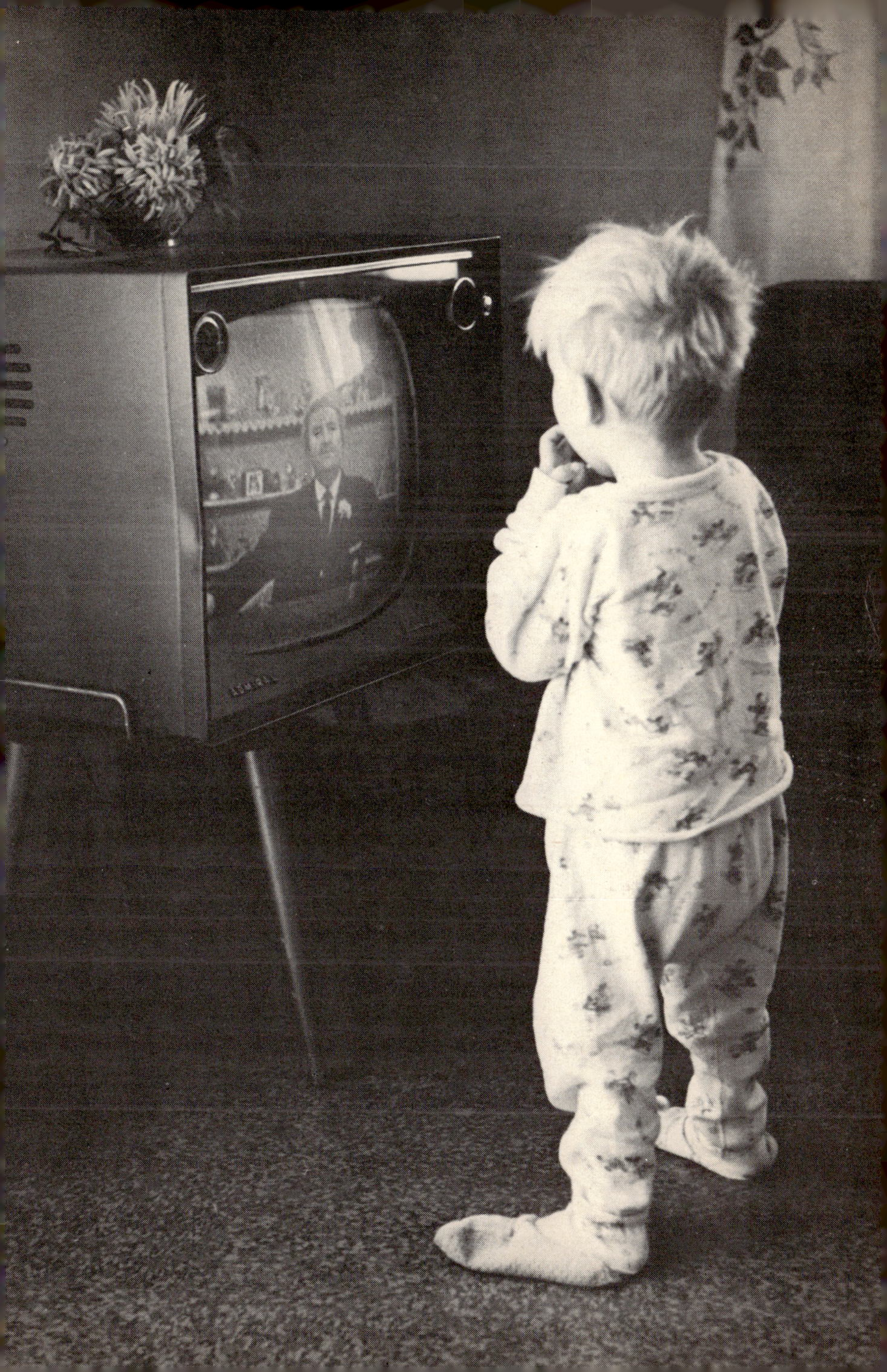

ment as one of the methods you might use to make teaching effective.

Experts who have studied the subject agree that punishment may be useful to teach a specific prohibition: don't walk on the flowers, stay out of that tree. Sometimes you need to teach such lessons, quickly. The rule won't change; you want no exceptions. Punishment may fix the idea and keep a child from repeating that one act.

But most of what you are teaching is more complicated than this. You can't punish to make a child kind, or smart, or fair.

Experts also agree that when punishment is harsh and painful, the child forgets what he's being punished for and remembers only that he wants to get even. That's a healthy reaction. If he doesn't dare to hit back directly, he may inwardly rebel. He may pass on his hurt to the next smallest child, or dawdle and slow everything down. It's a less healthy reaction if he is so overwhelmed that he loses his spirit, and is broken by the attack.

Parents who punish frequently and severely almost always admit frustration. They find that they have to increase the frequency and severity and it does no good. They despair because the child who is spanked for wetting his pants wets again the next day, or that night. The child who is slapped for grabbing, grabs again or slaps to get what he wants. The child who is put to bed for disobeying disobeys again, often when it is most inconvenient to put him to bed.

Most parents feel they need to punish a child sometimes. Mild punishments make them feel they are doing something. Such punishments are much easier for children to take than endless scoldings, strained silence, or the hurt air of being abused that an occasional parent adopts to make a child feel remorseful. Shame or ridicule is the hardest to bear. A mild physical punishment can actually relieve the child who wants to shed his guilty feelings. When mother spanks him, the score is even. He's paid for his misdeed and is free.

Even mild punishments are seldom really necessary, though. And it's so very hard to punish a child without it seeming like revenge. Most times, the child has already learned what he should have done before the blow falls or the toll is extracted. He accepts the punishment as a reflection of the difference in size between himself and his parent; he accepts it as inevitable, but he's already learned what he can from his mistake. Rewards and punishments only work when the feeling between the child and parents is one of mutual respect, of pulling together. A general underlying attitude of "we're together on this" is the best known tool for discipline.

PLAY AT 3 AND 4

Busy from dawn to dark, with enforced stops for eating and napping, the child from 3 to 5 stays on the go. At the end of a breathless day, his mother may wonder what he's been up to.

He has a lot to learn and he doesn't wait to begin until he starts school. Through play, he works on lessons appropriate for his age. He takes on more daring and complex physical feats— running, jumping, and climbing, turning pages, handling a pencil, lacing a shoe, buttoning a doll dress. All the while, he practices talking. Some social skills don't depend solely on language—how to wait for a turn, how to defend oneself. Don't get the idea that these learnings are consciously practiced though. They are the result of his activities, not the cause.

He seldom runs just for the sake of running, or laces and unlaces his shoes for the joy of handling the string and hitting the hole. He does these things as part of getting somewhere or of being somebody. He tries out how it feels to be a mother, a father, a fireman, or a nurse. He imitates the grocery clerk, the trash collector, and any work he observes. When men arrive to build a house next door, there's a rash of carpentry among the neighborhood boys. They beg for odds and ends of lumber and nails for their play.

The 3- to 6-year-old is happiest when other children can join in, and he's fortunate if others are close by. Boys and girls play together enjoying much the same activities until around age 4. Then they like to have pals of the same sex. From casual, almost wordless play near another child, children become able to manage real cooperative efforts, where three or more children shift in and out of a game of playing house, putting out fires, or piloting an airplane.

AIDS TO HAVING FUN

Children of this age use everything in their play. Acorn cups and cookies of leaves make a tea party; a yard of cotton material is a tablecloth, queen's robe, or a baby blanket; a mailing tube is a telescope. A perfect cowboy outfit, complete from hat to spurs, may not be half as grand as what a child could imagine from a coil of rope and wooden gun. The rope may next become a deep sea diver's tube or one connected to a guided missile. Parents who scurry around for a detailed costume rob the child of a chance to imagine things much grander than in real life.

A miniature dollhouse with tiny rooms and furniture doesn't interest children as much as large cartons which they can move about freely and climb in and out of. Girls of school age and grownups are the ones who really like to assemble showplace dollhouses. Boys like trains they can shove about to suit themselves. Later on they respect the fixed track of electric trains.

Today it sometimes seems as if play and toys have become reversed in people's minds and we have permitted toys to come first, as if play depended upon them.

Long ago, mothers lovingly dressed corncob dolls in corn husks, children collected hollyhock blossoms to serve as varicolored ballet dancers, balls were made of fabric or leather stitched and stuffed, and many games were devised using colored pebbles and sticks. Piles of leaves in autumn were the setting for hilarious fun.

Possibly these simple objects and activities were more treasured in the past than are the toys and possessions of today's children, who have far more than they know what to do with.

This does not mean that children should have no toys. It means that toys and play are not identical, not totally dependent upon each other.

Toys can be a means of pushing the child away. A parent may give his child an assortment of toys, hoping he'll take himself off somewhere to play. Or a parent may buy toys in an effort to make up for things he feels he hasn't done well. A mother who works, for instance, may shower things on the child with whom she can spend little time, although she may have made the best possible plan she can.

Nevertheless, wisely selected toys and equipment can enrich play, provide enjoyment, teach and bring beauty or pleasure as well. The best ones appeal for more than one of these values. In planning for happy play hours for your child, you may wish to select some things from each group below. You'll readily see, however, that an item listed under one heading may have value for others as well.

Toys for play that are imitative of adult life

Dolls and housekeeping toys such as dishes, furniture, telephones, broom. For the most part, children get more use out of these if they are somewhat near life size and are sturdy enough to be actually used. The child is going to be the baby himself, and will climb in the doll bed; the ironing board should be steady and strong enough to take pressure when the busy homemaker irons. Tiny, plastic miniatures have a place, but they demand more dexterity than most children this age have achieved.

Dress-up clothes: shoes, hats, pocketbooks, vests, neckties, lengths of fabric, a briefcase.

Hand puppets (animals and people). Wait until the child is older to introduce marionettes operated by strings.

Storekeeping toys: cash register, empty grocery boxes and food containers (except glass).

Farm animals, barn, fences, tractor, trucks.

Trains, trucks, boats, and airplanes, large and small.

Toys for construction and for special skills

Wooden building sets and interlocking blocks.

Puzzles of treated cardboard or wood, with from 4 to 30 pieces, depending on child's ability.

Hammer and peg set, counting frame, magnet.

Live animals such as dog, cat, frog, turtle, salamander, fish, guinea pig, rabbit, hamster, parakeet, canary.

Hammer, nails, saw, pliers, plane, and other sturdy tools which really work. Child-size miniatures which have dull edges and are lightweight frustrate the child. Provide a strong table or workbench with vise to hold wood.

Simple games, such as cards to match, large dominoes.

Musical instruments: bells, xylophone, harmonica, music box, record player and records.

Toys for large-muscle development

Large hollow blocks (painted for outdoor use) and boxes.

Smaller blocks. A handy father can make these of hardwood, cut into lengths based on one unit (that is, 4, 8, 12 inches, etc.) and carefully sanded.

Swing, climbing bars, rope ladder, gym sets. Set the frame into concrete, if possible.

Ladders, barrel, sawhorses, smooth wide boards.

Wagon, sled, scooter, tricycle, doll carriage, wheelbarrow.

Hoop, roller skates, an automobile tire to roll.

Rubber horseshoes, beanbags, small sports equipment.

Inflated balls, bag, or doll to punch.

Sturdy gardening tools — foxhole shovel, spade, rake, trowel.

Toys for sensory and creative experience

Some of the most satisfying materials children can use are artist's supplies: crayon, chalks, paint, paper, clay. Blocks, sand, and water rightfully belong in this list also, for they too have endless possibilities for expression of ideas and feeling and serve as springboards to imagination. You could just as well add mud — for squishing, molding, and making pies. It's really no harder to clean up than finger paint.

With clay and other molding substances, a child creates shapes and forms. He can make and remake, watching changes emerge under his fingers. He enjoys the feel. He can pound, dig, and pinch without harm.

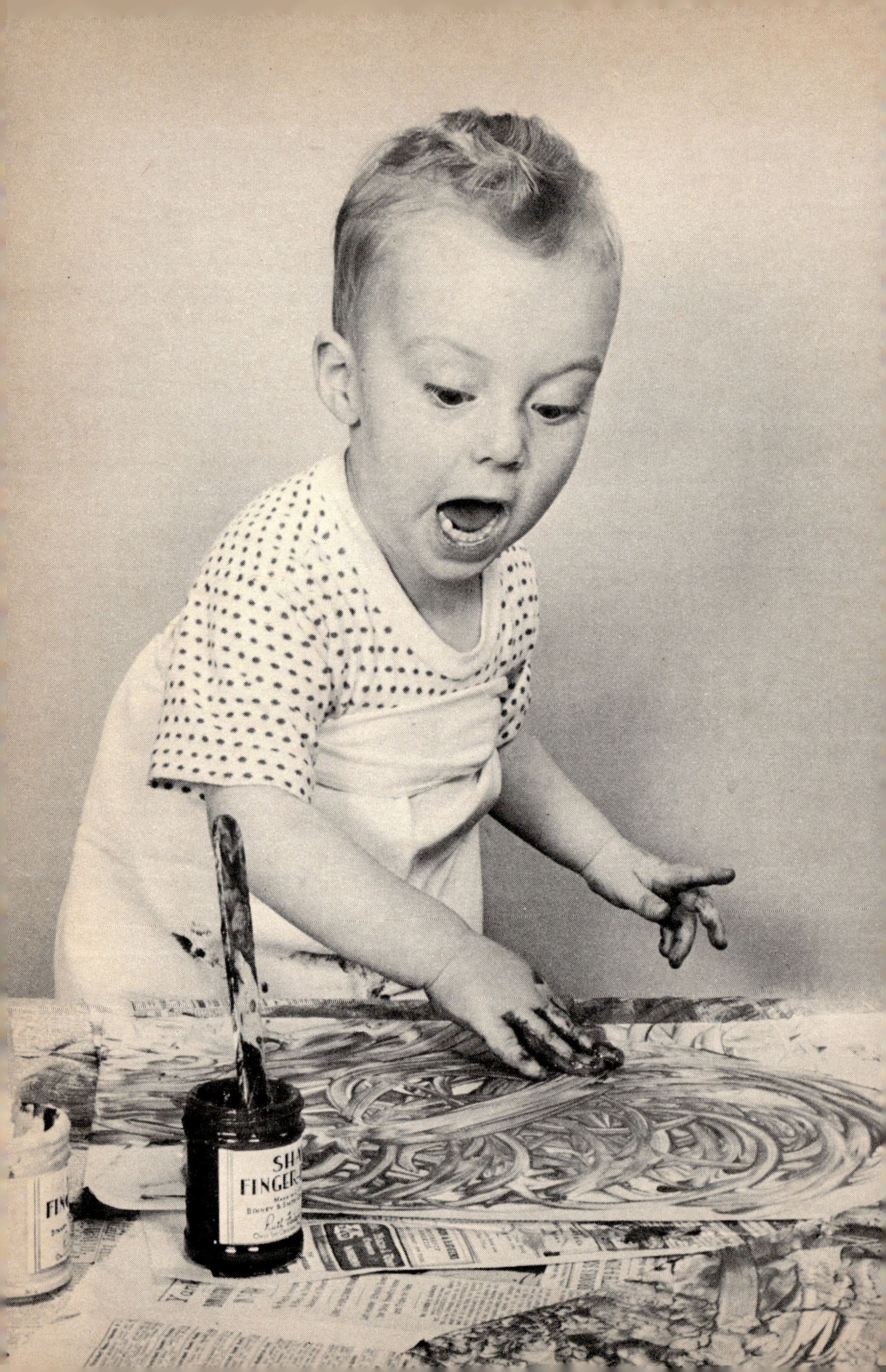

Color alone is sufficient for the beginning painter. Later he'll paint designs and pictures. Through these, he can express beauty, sadness, anger, and other feelings much too hard to say in words. If the child is not expected to paint or mold to suit somebody else, these materials are truly a means of enlarging his life.

They are absorbing, too, and most children will spend more time with "raw" materials than with almost anything else if they can do as they like. This doesn't mean a child should be allowed to mishandle them, of course—to throw clay or paint on the wall—but it does mean that you should confine your comments to appropriate use, not results.

Coloring books don't provide quite the same opportunity. In them the ideas have already been given shape. Lots of parents don't approve when a child becomes creative with a coloring book—giving a lady a green face, or scribbling over the page. Yet most children cannot stay within the lines as they color until age 5 or 6, and often the pictures mean little or nothing to them. A pad of plain paper would do as well.

Paint. Small cups of paint in boxes and tiny brushes are hard for a young child to manage. He wants to make a broad sweep of color in a hurry. Give him a half- or 1-inch brush and a small jar—or several jars—containing tempera or showcard colors. They readily wash out of clothing or off hands (as well as floors or walls). An easel, or other device to hold the paper at a good height for work standing up, makes a wonderful gift. The young painter may be just as happy with his paper on the floor, though. Put the paint in a muffin tin to help minimize spills.

You may feel at first that you just can't put up with paint or give the time to supervising and keeping the paints in working condition. You may feel better if you save paint for special occasions or rainy days, or decide that the easel should only be used outdoors, perhaps in the garage.

If you just can't see a way to have paint in your home, it won't change the child's whole future, of course; but be sure you don't tend to keep him from all other outlets for his feelings. Permit him to enjoy textures, colors, and the feel of things in other ways. Let him stir and "mess about." Painting with water, out of doors, satisfies children, too, while it pleases their mothers because it is clean.

Finger painting presents similar advantages and problems. When a child paints with his fingers—or elbows, fists, or arms—he gets tremendous pleasure from direct contact with the paint, blending and erasing color and pattern. He doesn't have to worry about a brush or crayon. Finger painting is deeply enjoyed by children of all ages, except by some who have become afraid to get messy as they are being taught to keep clean.

You can buy finger paint or make it by adding color (watercolor, tempera, powdered paint, or food coloring) to cooked or readymade starch or wallpaper paste. If you make a quantity at a time, store it in a covered container in the refrigerator. You can combine a dab of color and a dab of starch directly on the surface where the child is working.

You'll need paper with a high gloss so it won't scuff off as the child whirls and circles. Shelf paper, freezer wrap, or butcher paper work fine. You may have a formica tabletop or a piece of linoleum on which the child can work directly without paper. The paint has to be washed away when the child is finished, but as with most of the work children do, the doing is more meaningful than the result anyhow.

Finger painting with nice thick soapsuds sometimes follows a soap-bubbling session. While the child may start out with soap and water (detergents sting a child's throat if he accidentally inhales) and paper straws, empty thread spools, or a bubble pipe, he may wind up dabbling directly.

Clay and dough. You may be lucky enough to have a riverbank nearby which has a deposit of clay. Or you can buy modeling clay economically. Add water from time to time to keep it in working condition. Keep it in a covered rustproof container or tight plastic bag. Modeling clay hardens when exposed to air.

Plasticene is clay treated to keep permanent softness. It stays pliable. Plasticene has an oily base and will stain furniture or floors.

Dough for play can be made of flour and salt, half as much salt as flour. Add enough water to make a workable mass. A small amount of salad oil produces a smooth texture. The salt acts as a preservative, so the mix will keep for a long time, especially if covered and refrigerated. Sometimes add food coloring to the water for a change. Play dough is a cheap, clean modeling substance, and stimulates domestic play with cooky cutters and rolling pins.

Paper. All kinds of paper have possibilities. Unprinted newspaper by the ream is the cheapest. Cut it in half or quarters as needed. A sheet 18 by 24 inches seems right for painting. A smaller size will do for crayons.

Printed newspapers can be used for painting, too. Smoothed paperbags make a good surface for crayon, chalk, or paint. Save colored papers from gift wrappings and attractive packages for use with paste and blunt-pointed scissors. An assortment of colored manila paper has special charm, too.

Books. While books can scarcely be called playthings, they do become treasured possessions, hauled around and taken to bed. A good story can bind all the family—even a nation—together. Children who are read to frequently are fortunate.

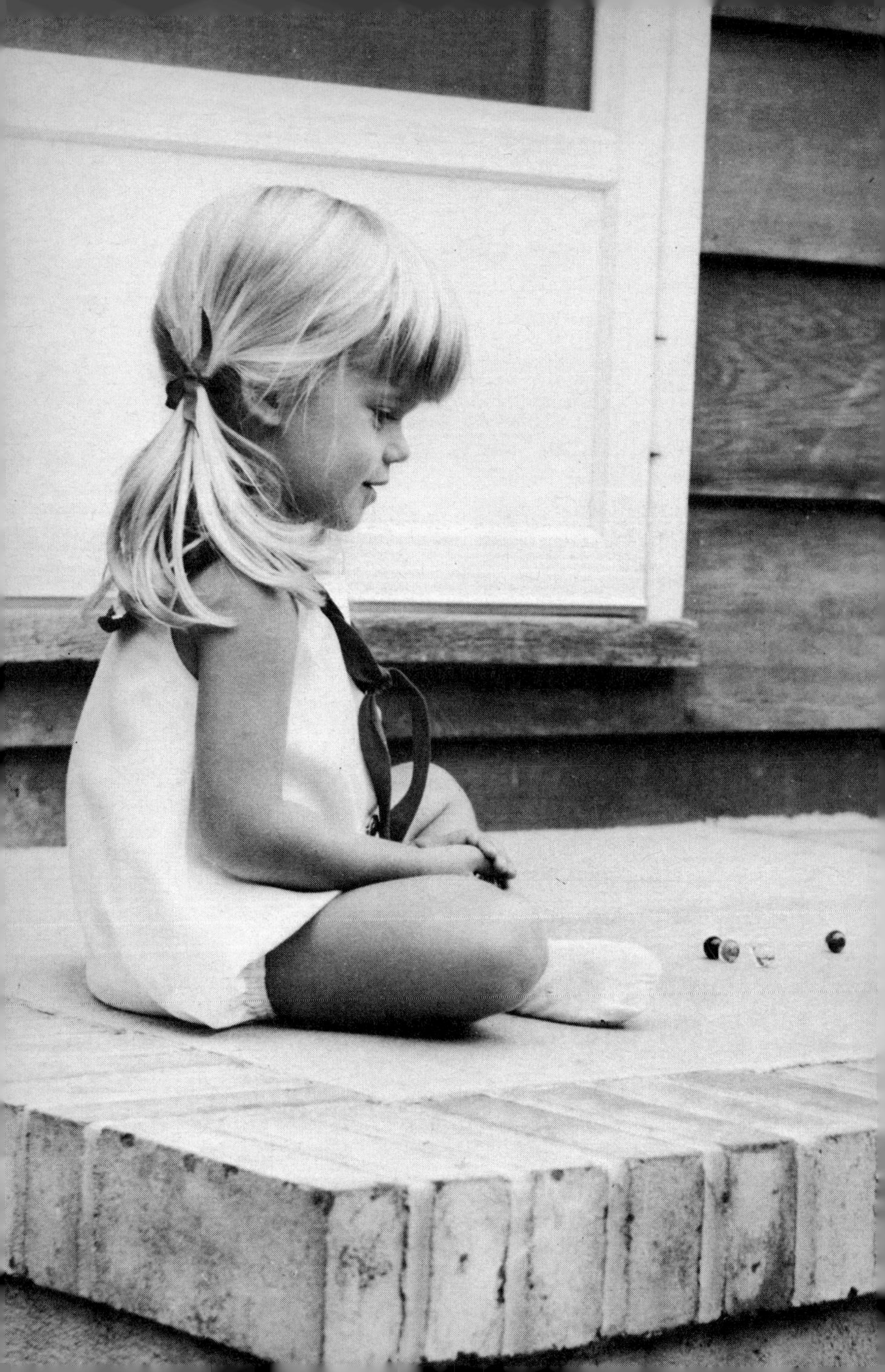

Select short, simple stories for the youngest children. Expect to read them again and again. The 2- and 3-year-olds like to hear about everyday events and people. You'll get rapt attention if you make up a story about the child's own daily experiences, but beware of changing even a sentence as you repeat it!

As children grow older, they like books about insects and shells, fire engines and dinosaurs, stories of faraway lands, and olden times. They can understand a more involved plot. Still, the characters should be doing things they know about; they should be able to understand the thinking and motives.

For this reason, many people feel that preschool children are not ready for fairytales yet. As they learn to tell fact from fancy they are better able to deal with dragons, fairy princesses, wicked witches, and animals that change into people.

You may wish to spend several dollars for a good book which will be enjoyed for its pictures first, loved when heard aloud, and rediscovered at age 8 or 9 as the child reads by himself. But most books need not be expensive. Well-written books, skillfully illustrated, abound. You will want to select carefully, however, for not all books published for children are worth their time or your money.

A good children's book will have a timeless quality, and appeal to adults as much as to children. It need not be dull or pointless, inaccurate or shabbily written.

Regular use of the library increases the variety of books available as well as introducing the child early to the delights of his public library.

16. The mother's personal well-being

Motherhood needs to be approached in a positive and happy frame of mind. This is important, for if things are right on the inside you'll reflect it on the outside; and your baby and those around you will respond accordingly.

Maintaining your good appearance during and after pregnancy calls for somewhat more vigilance than at other times in your life because of the many hormonal, metabolic, and other changes that occur in your system then. This chapter explains how those changes affect your hair, skin, nails, and body in general, and what you can do about their care and about diet, weight, bathing, exercise, clothing, and personal grooming.

HAIR

When you're pregnant, your hair may take on new characteristics. Some women find their hair becoming dull and dry; others find theirs becoming excessively oily. Most women need to shampoo their hair more often during pregnancy because sweat glands work overtime then.

Some loss of hair may occur during pregnancy; but it is commoner in the post-natal period. If you find yourself losing

Let *condition** baby your hair back to beautiful.

Now that you've got a beautiful baby, it's time to baby your hair back to beautiful again. If you can check any one of these trouble symptoms, your hair needs *condition**: The Beauty Prescription For Troubled Hair®

☐ Dry, brittle hair? ☐ No bounce, no body?
☐ Split, wispy ends? ☐ Hair won't hold set?
☐ Dull, unhealthy look? ☐ Weak, spongy texture?

condition* by Clairol is the unique corrective that's enriched with protein to make your hair feel stronger right away. The lively body comes back. A healthy glow returns. Suddenly your hair is beautiful again. And it stays beautiful through shampoo after shampoo. Recondition your hair with Instant *condition** Lotion Treatment or *condition** Beauty Pack by Clairol.

© Clairol Inc. 1970 *TM

much hair, you probably should not tint it or have a permanent wave until the condition corrects itself. Like other bodily changes, hair loss is only temporary. After your baby is born, your hair will return to normal.

If you find your hair becoming oily, wash it thoroughly and often. Oily hair cannot be harmed if it is washed even daily. It should be washed at least twice a week. Buy a shampoo especially for oily hair. Use hot or very warm water. Massage the shampoo into your hair and scalp for about five minutes. Rinse thoroughly. Then repeat the process. If you find your hair becoming dull and dry, wash it only about once a week. Use a gentle shampoo, followed by a good conditioner. If your hair is normal, wash it once or twice a week, with two sudsings and two rinsings. If you color your hair, use one of the shampoos developed especially for hair-color users.

As your pregnancy develops, you may find it difficult to wash and set your hair as often as you would like. So keep a dry, brush-through, instant shampoo on hand for such occasions. Nylon hairbrushes without rounded bristle tips can be extremely damaging. If possible, use a soft, natural-bristle brush. Teasing is not recommended during pregnancy, nor are brush rollers, since both tend to split the ends of the hair.

SKIN

Inasmuch as your skin is perhaps the most obvious indication of your good health and general well-being, it will pay you while pregnant to take scrupulously good care of it.

If your skin tends to be oily, use a good medicated soap, being careful to rinse it off completely with warm water and then splash on cold water. An astringent is often quite helpful

REALLY DO YOUR HANDS SOME GOOD.

DOES WHAT IT PROMISES

Chap-ans

MEDICATED HAND CREAM

NET WT. 3 OZ.

Caring for your baby is a soft job. For soft, smooth hands. Not hands made rough and dry by bleaches and detergents.

You need a hand cream that really works. Chap-ans®.

'Chap-ans' is medicated to soften and help heal rough, red hands. It even stays on in hot detergent water.

Just try it for three days. You'll see.

'Chap-ans' works.

© 1970 MILLER-MORTON COMPANY, Richmond, Virginia, a subsidiary of A. H. Robins Company.

STORE COUPON

SAVE 12c ON ANY SIZE CHAP-ANS®

MR. DEALER: For prompt payment of this coupon, please send to CHAP STICK COMPANY, P.O. BOX 1718, CLINTON, IOWA. You will be paid twelve cents (12¢) plus 3¢ handling, provided coupon is redeemed in accordance with our consumer offer. Invoices proving purchase of sufficient stock of 'Chap-ans' to cover coupons submitted must be shown upon request. Failure to do so may at our option, void all coupons for which no proof of products purchased is shown. Coupons presented through outside agencies, or others not retail distributors of our merchandise, will not be honored and will become void when so presented. The consumer must pay any sales tax involved. This offer void wherever taxed, restricted, prohibited, or license is required. Cash value 1/20 of 1¢. Limit one coupon to a customer. Chap Stick Company, P.O. Box 1718, Clinton, Iowa.

12c   12c

Does she...or doesn't she?®

Now! Your hair young again with new life...new lights ...new color

Mom. Sounds great, doesn't it? For this beautiful time in your life, you should look as beautiful as you feel. Happily, Miss Clairol has just the touch to make your hair come wonderfully young again. With all the healthy color and texture it should have. From palest blondes to deepest brunettes, there's a Miss Clairol shade to bring back your hair's natural beauty with lively color and a bright new shine. Just pick your formula—extra rich Creme Formula or extra easy Shampoo Formula. Go ahead. Let your hair be young again. With Miss Clairol. Consider it our baby present to you.

Miss Clairol®. Hair color so natural only her hairdresser knows for sure!™

Extra rich   Extra easy

© Clairol Inc. 1969

to an oily skin. It should be applied with a clean cotton pad or swab. You will probably be using a medicated makeup as well. Apply this with a clean sponge, using light, upward strokes.

Extremely oily skin can be helped by using beauty grains for deep cleansing. Or, as an alternative, try a beauty mask. In either case, be careful to keep clear of the area around your eyes.

If you have dry skin, it will benefit from a moisturizer. This should be applied under your makeup during the day and at bedtime after your face has been cleaned. Creams are the best aids for removing makeup from dry skin. Soap and water simply dry it further.

For dryness around the eyes, apply an eye cream or eye oil made especially for the purpose. The eye area is where so-called laugh lines become common wrinkles if you don't attend to them.

All skin types will benefit from a once-a-week steaming to cleanse and refresh. The procedure is to massage cream into your cheeks, chin, and forehead; wipe off the cream; then allow steam from a basin or mask to penetrate the pores. Rinse off with cool water or mild astringent if your skin is oily. Lie down. Place a pad soaked with witch hazel on the skin around your eyes. Relax for ten minutes. Then look in the mirror and see the difference. Follow up with a skin freshener used lavishly all over the skin. During the day and overnight, wear an oil-free moisturizer.

One skin problem associated with childbearing is the so-called mask of pregnancy. Here, brownish splotches appear on the cheeks, nose, or forehead. Such splotches are simply uneven deposits of pigment. Bright red spots due to dilated blood vessels may also appear on face, neck, and the upper parts of your body. Although both these conditions disappear after the birth of the baby, you may want to conceal them with an opaque cream. Choose a concealer to harmonize with your skin coloring and foundation. Then apply makeup. If discoloration still shows, additional concealer may be applied over foundation and blended in carefully. The cream can also be used alone when you don't have the time to make up completely. Notice whether the sun seems to accentuate the brown discoloration; if it does, you should obviously limit your exposure.

During the last months of pregnancy, you may notice striations or stretch marks on the abdomen. These reddish-colored lines appear on some women's abdomens as their skin stretches and are probably also a result of hormonal changes. After pregnancy the striations tend to fade and become whitish, but they seldom disappear completely. Physicians are by no means agreed that massaging and oiling the skin help this condition. Aside from such striations, the new mother's skin will usually resume its normal appearance soon after the baby has been born.

Another change to expect is enlarged breasts. They become firmer but are more sensitive. Due to the increased blood supply to the breasts, the nipples and the pigmented area become darker in color as pregnancy advances. These breast changes are in preparation for nursing the baby. A well-fitting uplift brassiere will provide good support for your breasts and will make you a lot more comfortable.

TEETH AND NAILS

Contrary to popular opinion, a woman's teeth do not usually suffer ill effects during pregnancy because of lack of calcium. Nevertheless, your diet *is* important to your teeth in other ways. So see your dentist early in pregnancy and again, as soon as possible, after delivery.

While you're carrying your baby, you may notice some change in your nails. They may become thinner. They may split, peel, or crack. Extra long nails aren't for a new mother. File your nails into gentle ovals and keep them from growing too long. Don't use a metal file; use an emery board instead; it's more gentle to delicate nail tissue. Don't file deep down at the side of the nail as this will predispose it to tearing. It's usually a good idea to apply a nail strengthener to the nails before using nail polish.

To help strengthen their nails, many women drink a daily glass of gelatin (an envelope of gelatin stirred into 8 oz. of orange juice or other liquid). A manicure once a week is also to be recommended. With the nails in good condition and pretty to look at, you'll be less likely to bite or pick at them.

DIET

Your diet during pregnancy is one of the most important factors in maintaining your health and good appearance, as well as the health of your child. If you eat the proper foods in the right amounts, chances are you'll have a healthy baby and will be able to furnish him with a good supply of milk. (The cliché about "eating for two" is quite erroneous and can only lead to overweight. It should be obvious that the fetus does not require the same amount of food as the mother.)

Liquids are extremely important to good health and good looks during pregnancy. You breathe more rapidly then. Your body perspires more. As a result, you lose more water. Therefore, doctors often recommend a liquid intake of up to two quarts a day. Liquids also aid in speeding up the elimination of body wastes.

Each day include the three essential body-building nutrients in your diet: proteins, minerals, and vitamins (and, to a lesser extent, fats and carbohydrates). No single food has all the nutrients you need; so variety is essential. When your physician prescribes a diet, he will of course take into consideration your weight, your age, and any allergies or special health problems you may have.

WEIGHT

A woman gains weight in pregnancy for several obvious reasons. Her appetite tends to increase. She is often less active. So her body is less able to work off the food she eats.

In addition, of course, there is the baby, who will generally weigh between seven and eight pounds at birth. The enlarged uterus adds another two pounds or so. The placenta and membranes add perhaps 1¼ pounds. The size of your liver and the volume of your blood increase. Your breasts become heavier. And your body tissues absorb and hold more water. The sum of these normal increases averages about twelve pounds. Your physician will probably advise you that 20-25 pounds is the most you should gain.

In the first three months of pregnancy your weight increase will probably be negligible. But after about 12 weeks, gains of about a pound a week are common, right up until the seventh month.

BATHING

The increased perspiration that occurs in pregnancy is partly the result of the baby acting as a small, internal furnace.

In cold weather, a daily warm bath will rid you of perspiration odor and will also work wonders in soothing tense muscles and serving as a general relaxer. In hot weather, a daily shower is the alternative. Be sure to use a good deodorant afterwards. Skin softeners are available for use in the bath water or for application directly to the body in the shower.

During the last six weeks of pregnancy, your physician may well advise you, for safety's sake, to take sponge baths or showers exclusively. Without your normal balance at this time, you might slip while getting into or out of the tub. The same safety precaution is often given to the new mother. She will usually resume tub-bathing about three weeks after delivery. (Some doctors recommend the comfort of tub-bathing much sooner in the event of hemorrhoids or an episiotomy.)

EXERCISE

Just as proper diet contributes to your health and appearance in pregnancy, so does a daily routine of exercise. Start with posture. This is something the pregnant woman can't afford to overlook. Above all, she must avoid allowing her pelvis to stick forward and her head to droop. If she doesn't, she will seriously strain her abdominal wall and the area between the pelvis and the lower spine.

Poor posture is, in fact, the most common cause of the backache that plagues pregnant women. There's also a tendency for the slump of pregnancy to become habitual. If it does, it is more than likely to cause chronic backache in later life, to say nothing of an assortment of other ailments such as fallen arches. So stand straight. Keep your head and your chest up. Hold your shoulders back.

Your physician will probably advise you to continue your daily routines during pregnancy but to stop as soon as you feel overtired. In other words, you can do light housework, drive a car, go shopping, dance, and so forth. Most desirable is a brisk daily walk (with correct posture!) for half an hour or so. It will make you feel better all over. It will stimulate your heart, lungs, and muscles, and it will relax you for sleep.

Lillian Rowen, a well-known exercise teacher in New York City, who has had years of experience with pregnant women, recommends this exercise: *Pull in your lower stomach and pinch your buttocks together at the same time.* Do this for about 3 seconds, then relax. Repeat. Breathe in through your nose and out through your mouth while contracting and relaxing your muscles (like blowing up a balloon). This "pull and pinch" exercise is exceedingly practical because you can do it as often as you wish, at almost any time of day or night, and whether you're standing up or lying on your back.

Miss Rowen has another exercise for the mother who has just delivered and who wants to get her abdominal muscles back to normal as soon as possible: *Lie on your back with arms over head, knees bent, heels close to buttocks, and feet anchored; then gently lift up your head.* Repeat.

This gentle exercise can be done during the first week after delivery. In the second week, and in the same position, lift both your head and shoulders. Later on, according to your strength, rise to a sitting position. Still later, touch your toes.

When doing this exercise, Miss Rowen warns, be absolutely certain that knees are bent and feet are anchored. If they are not, you may strain your back. Whether raising your head, shoulders, or whole torso, be sure also not to jerk up or down. Move slowly and deliberately.

Why you need the calcium protection of this little green pill... relief from leg cramps

Os-Cal®
"The Optimum Calcium"

Each Os-Cal tablet has 250 milligrams of working calcium to help protect you from leg cramps. This is more calcium than other tablets and means these little green pills help to meet the special need of pregnant and nursing mothers —also have supplemental Vitamin D . . . 125 U.S.P. Units per tablet.

Just by taking Os-Cal three times a day—morning, noon and night—you can give yourself calcium in an easily remembered, easily taken form. With Os-Cal you can take fewer tablets at less cost for calcium protection.

Ask your physician about Os-Cal tablets. Available at your pharmacy.

Another people benefit product from
Marion Laboratories
Kansas City, Missouri 64137

SIDE EFFECTS OF PREGNANCY

Some of the side effects of pregnancy may temporarily mar an otherwise healthy and radiant appearance. For example, excitement over the new baby, anxiety about the responsibilities, and hormonal changes often combine to produce a nervous, sensitive stomach. When nausea occurs, the doctor may recommend changes in your regimen—for example: Avoid eating three large meals a day. Instead, eat more often but in smaller amounts. Avoid fried or greasy foods. Luckily, nausea tends to subside after the third month of pregnancy.

Another side effect of pregnancy is so-called heartburn. This is a type of indigestion characterized by a burning or acid sensation in the chest. The condition may be caused or aggravated by pressure of the growing uterus against the stomach. It will generally yield to any one of the good antacids available from your druggist. If it persists or becomes severe, check with your physician.

Leg cramps, including muscle soreness, weakness, spasms, numbness, and tingling may occur during the latter half of pregnancy. This situation may be the result of a lack of the right form of calcium. So some physicians recommend a special calcium supplement in a form the body can more easily utilize.

Backaches are another common complaint as the baby grows. They usually disappear with frequent shifts of position and with the proper posture described earlier. If they don't, try this simple exercise: *Get on your hands and knees. Then put your forearms and elbows on the floor where your hands just were. Then rise up onto your hands again.* Repeat.

This exercise is equally useful for the woman who develops

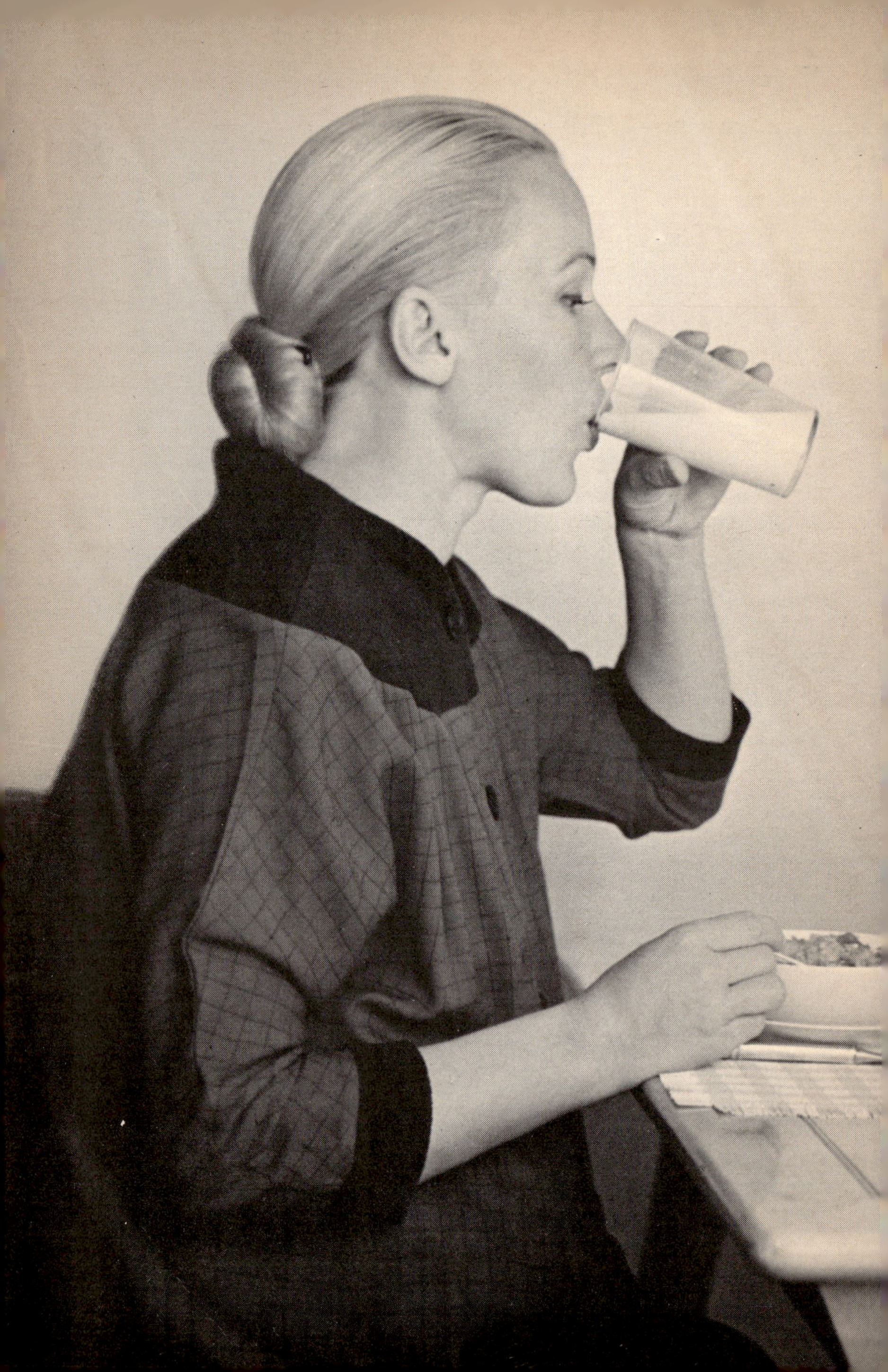

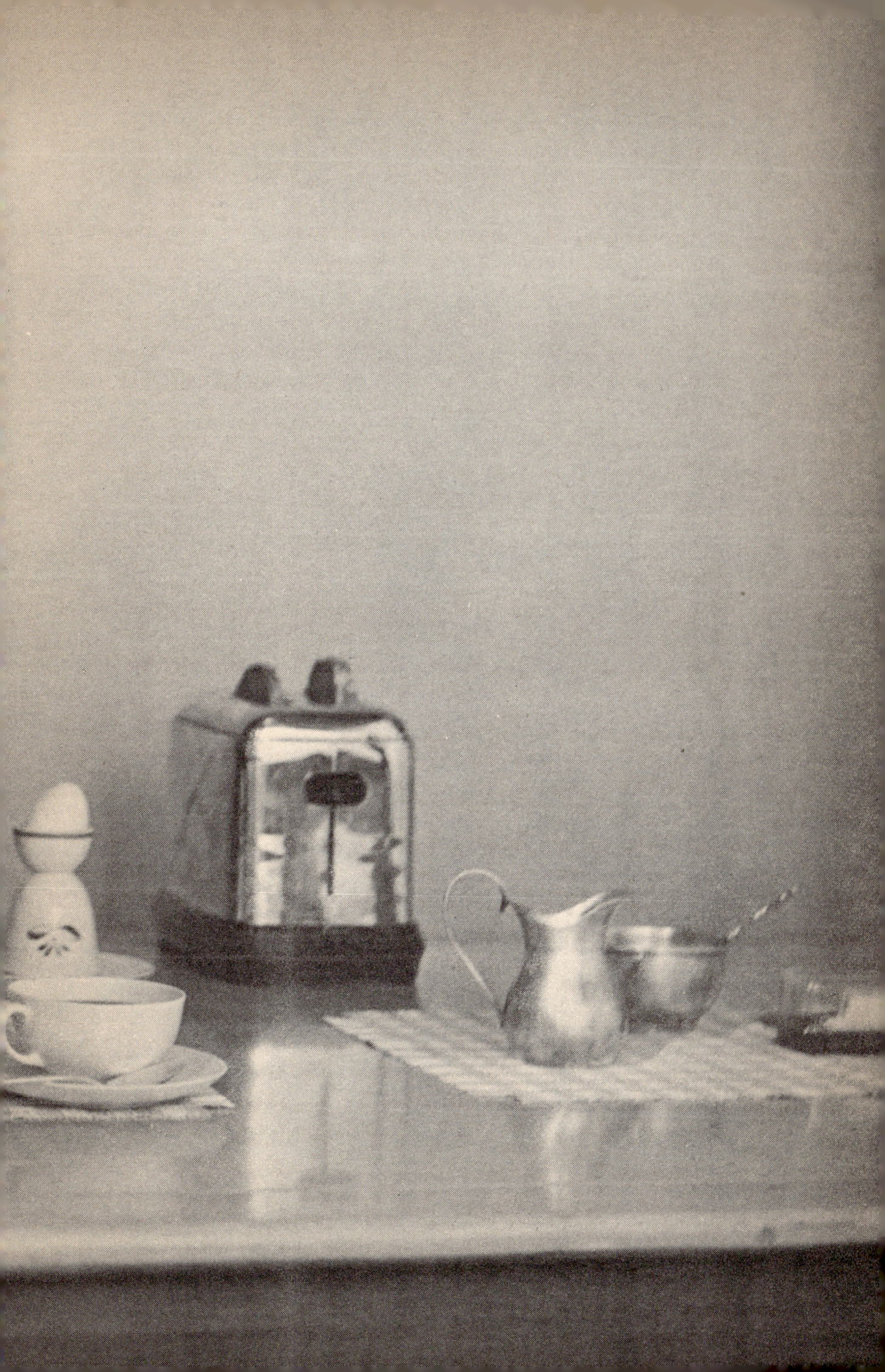

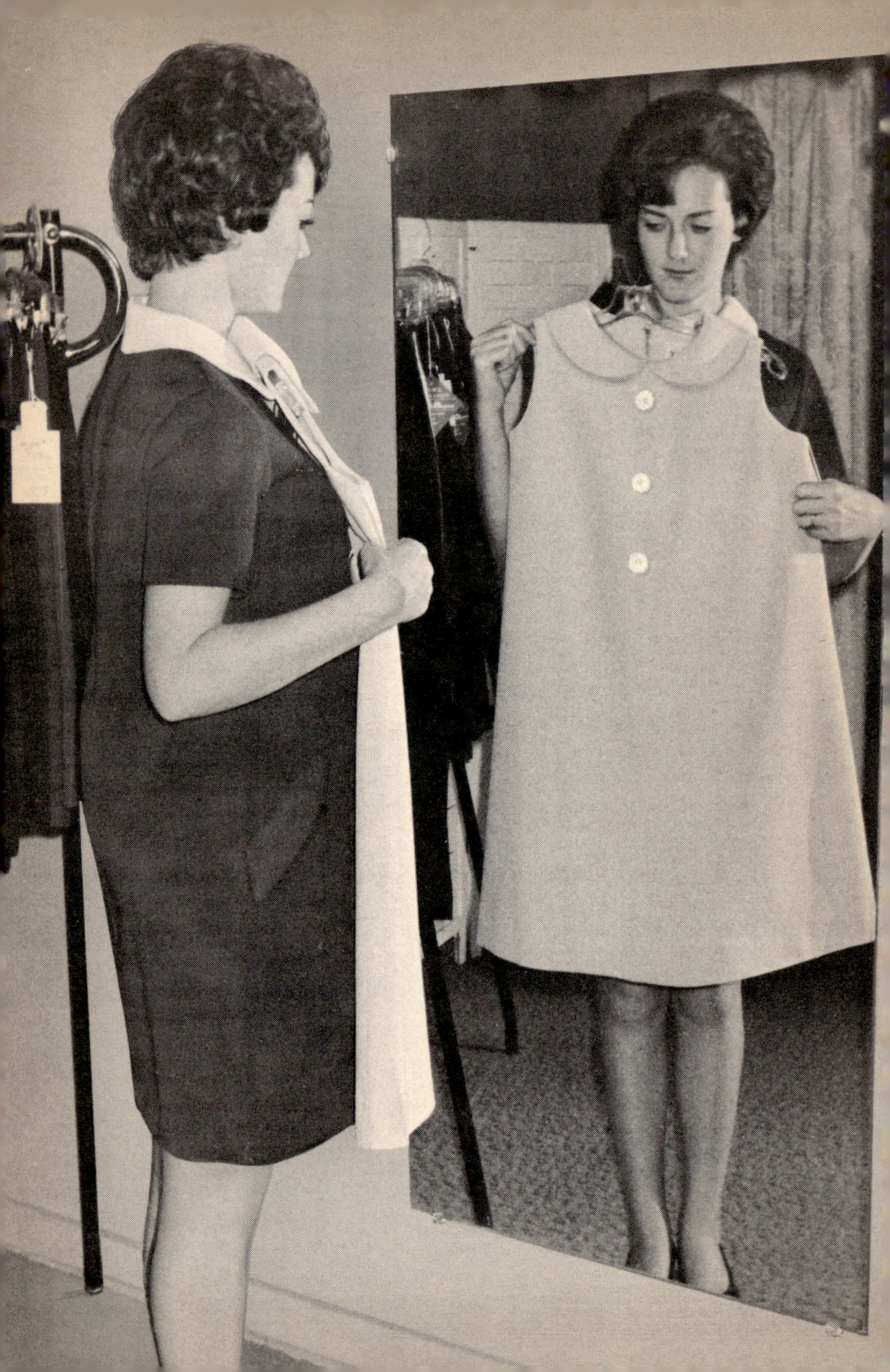

varicose veins. To relieve the venous pressure, she should also get into the habit of elevating her feet as often as possible. And she should wear elastic support stockings during the day, putting them on before she gets out of bed in the morning and before the veins have had a chance to fill. Varicose veins may be caused by the growing uterus pressing on the large blood vessels in the pelvis. Fortunately, the enlarged veins usually return to normal after the baby is born.

The growing uterus may also exert undue pressure on the lower intestine. A common result is constipation. The mother-to-be who exercises properly and who drinks enough fluids ought to have a bowel movement each day. If she does not, she should consult her physician.

CLOTHES

What to wear during pregnancy? Several items of dress should be avoided. First are high heels. Because carrying a baby affects your equilibrium, high heels may be all you need to encourage tripping or falling. Shoes should be chosen for comfort, making sure they have insteps firm enough to give good support to your arches. Since your feet are likely to swell a bit, you may find it desirable to buy your shoes a half size larger.

Something else to avoid at this time is tight garters, as they prevent proper circulation in the legs. Be careful in choosing brassieres, too; for as the breasts become larger in producing milk for the baby, they may also become heavier and tend to sag; and you don't want to overstretch the supportive tissues. The breasts should be lifted upward and outward—not pinched in together. A firm band or padded bone supporting each cup will help you to achieve this.

For the woman who wants more children.

Later.

We know what you have been looking for. A thoroughly tested means of birth control. Nothing to "wear" or remove. A product you can buy without prescription.

You have it now. DELFEN* Contraceptive Foam. A pure white foam that applies instantly, discreetly, in a single application. Undetectable in use. And it needs no douche.

DELFEN—cream or foam. Both available at drugstores throughout the U.S. and Canada. There is no nicer way to plan your next child.

Ortho

Delfen Contraceptive Foam.

WORLD'S LARGEST LABORATORIES DEVOTED TO FAMILY PLANNING RESEARCH FOR THE MEDICAL PROFESSION

*TRADEMARK

You may find you have to change brassiere sizes two or three times during pregnancy. It is advisable to buy cotton or cotton lace bras because they stay fresh and launder more easily.

Your doctor may recommend a maternity corset to relieve strain on the abdominal muscles. If so, it should be well-fitted and made of a non-elastic material. Many women prefer an all-in-one evening girdle which gives more mobility.

Maternity clothes should, first of all, be pretty. They should make you *feel* pretty. To be comfortable as well, a maternity dress must hang easily from the shoulders. The typical maternity skirt nowadays has an expandable waistline, so it can be worn from the first months right up to the time of delivery.

The woman with a larger-than-average bustline should avoid the empire style, with ties or shirring beneath the bosom. This type of dress looks chic on a non-pregnant, small-busted woman but ludicrous on a blossoming mother-to-be.

A number of women choose tent dresses. These are, to be sure, extremely comfortable and look well on a tall figure. But a small woman in such a dress will appear even billowier than she is.

By contrast, a well-cut coat dress is flattering to almost any figure. Many such dresses are buttoned over an inverted pleat. As time goes by, you may undo the buttons to allow more room.

Smocks are practical for daily use. And they can look attractive if they're not too full. Another answer for casual wear is the short-sleeved dress with stitched pleats that fall from a yoke at the bustline. Blouses with soft cowl necks are good-looking, as they frame your face nicely. Jumpers in the maternity wardrobe are indispensable. They double for day and evening wear and may be worn with or without blouses.

After the baby is born, you may find that you can't get into your regular dresses; yet you would swim in your maternity clothes. That coat dress you wore in the beginning months may now be an indispensable standby. Also, see if some of those pleated dresses can't be altered with a few tucks to fit your in-between figure. One thing is sure: Running around in your husband's old shirts, with the shirttails flopping outside blue jeans won't do your morale — or his — a bit of good.

TIME OFF

Even with the most becoming clothes, there are times — let's face it — when the new mother's spirits sag. This often occurs soon after she gets home from the hospital with her long-awaited baby. It's a period of her life when everything should be perfect, but sometimes is not. She may burst into tears at the slightest provocation and feel mildly or severely depressed a good part of the time. Her nerves may have been stretched pretty tight. Her hormone balance may not yet have returned to normal. She may be overtired, overexcited, worried about her husband's needs, concerned about her figure, anxious about her new responsibilities, and possibly even a little resentful of her lack of freedom.

The thing she must do is to keep reminding herself that these worries will pass in a few weeks. They are the rule with new mothers, not the exception. In the interim, she should, if possible, enjoy a change of scene, getting away from the situation for a few days or at least for a couple of hours a day. She needs this respite in order to gain perspective on her problems.

Having a baby is an exciting time in any woman's life. It can be the time of your greatest beauty. In creating a new life, you have fulfilled your own. Could you ask for more?

RECORD OF
WEIGHT AND GROWTH

Date	Age	Weight	Length

NOTES ON FORMULAS AND FEEDING

Date	Notes

IMMUNIZATION RECORD

(Your doctor may follow a slightly different schedule)

Date	FIRST YEAR	Recommended age
_____	DPT*	1½ to 2 months
_____		3 months
_____		5 months
_____	Polio vaccine	5–8 months
_____	Smallpox vaccine	Before 12 months
_____	Measles vaccine	12 months

SECOND YEAR

Give any injections not started or completed in first year

_____	Additional injection of DPT	12–18 months

Polio vaccine may be recommended by your doctor

BEFORE GOING TO SCHOOL

_____	DPT and polio vaccine	4 years
_____	Smallpox vaccine	5–6 years

THEREAFTER

_____	Booster doses of DT (whooping cough no longer needed) and polio vaccine	At intervals recommended by your doctor
_____		
_____	Smallpox vaccine every 5 years, before the child leaves the United States or if there is an epidemic	

*Diphtheria, pertussis (whooping cough), and tetanus.

RECORD OF DISEASES INCURRED

Date	Diseases	Physician

RECORD OF
TELEPHONE NUMBERS

Names | Numbers

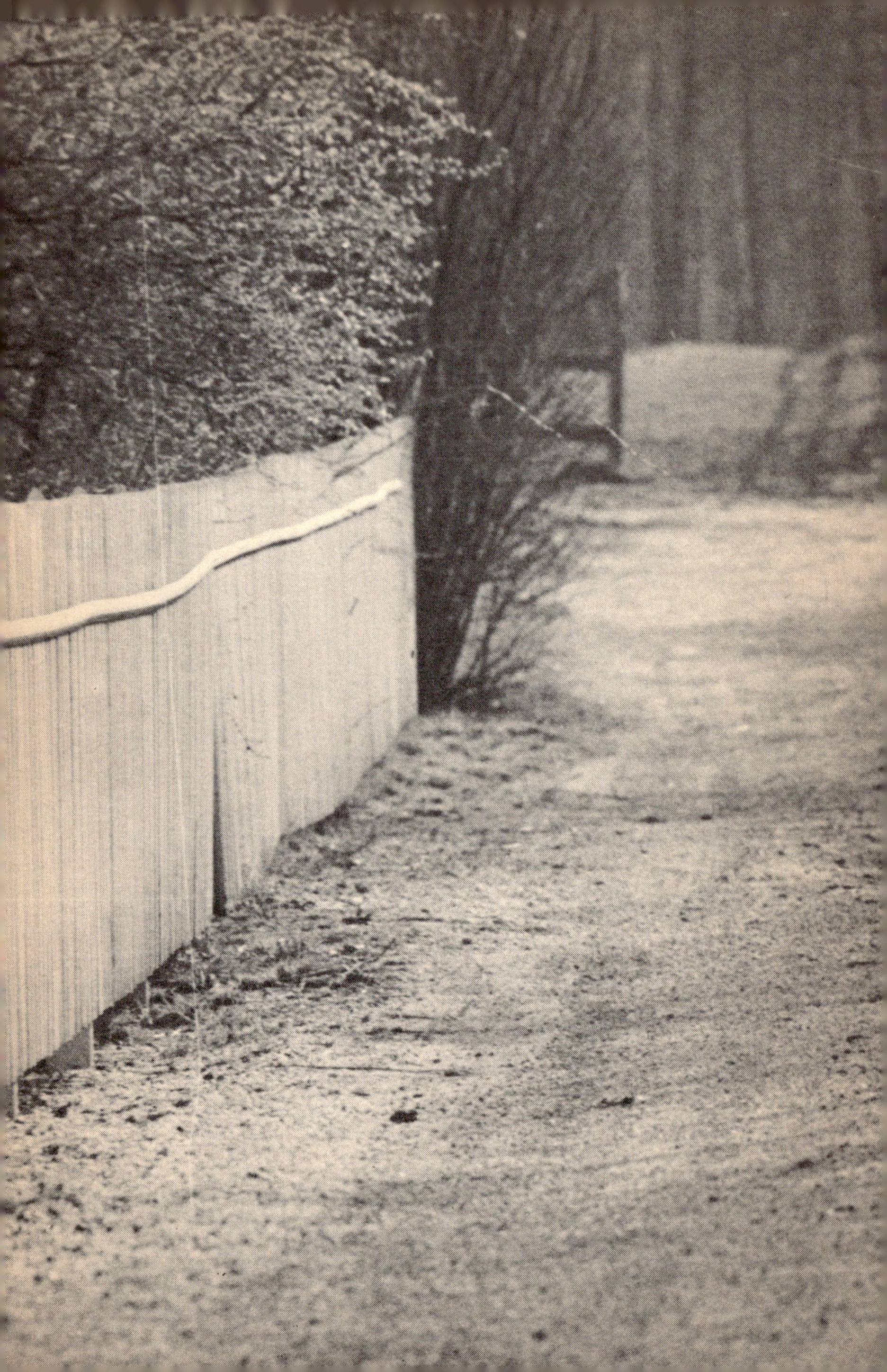

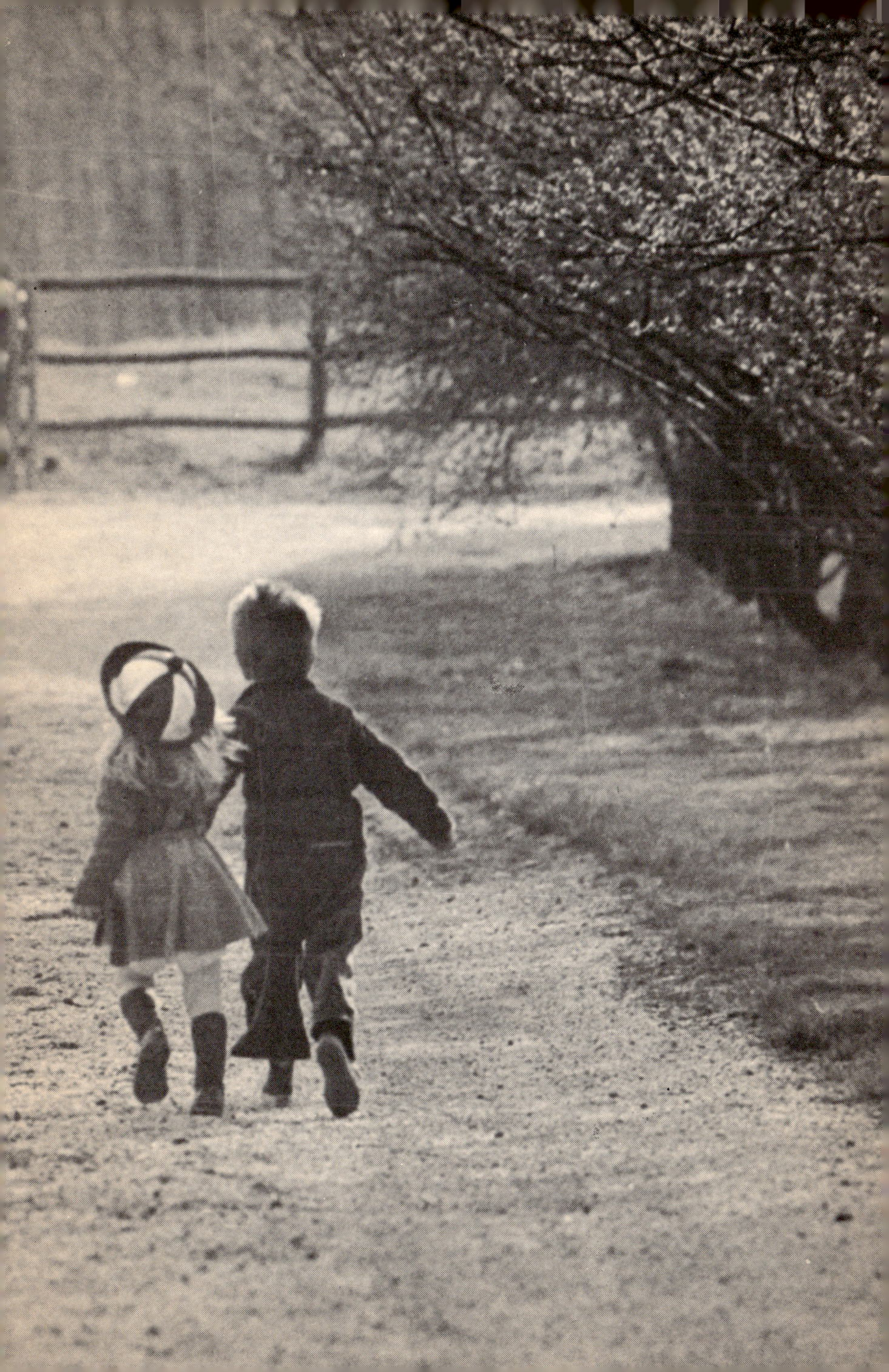

Index

Abdomen, 4, 10-11, 83, 85
  of mothers, 319, 322, 323
  stomachache, 133, 136, 176
  walking and, 217, 228
Accidents, 209, 228-230
  first aid, 163-171
  See also Safety; *and see specific hazards*, e.g., Poisoning
Adenoids, 150-151
Air, 65, 89, 131, 136
  allergies and, 152
  bubbles, 23, 28, 38, 66
  heart defect and, 155
  tetanus and, 164
Alcoholic beverages, 31
Allergy, 152-153, 157-158, 159
  chocolate, 198
  cow's milk, 42
  eggs, 196
  fruit juice, 36
  insect stings, 170
Antibiotics, 135, 175
Anus, 59, 161
Appetite, 102, 110, 111, 321
  of one-year-olds, 200, 235
  variations in, 113-115, 133, 135, 162, 202
Areola, 27
Arms, 6, 12, 180
  armpit temperature, 138
  broken, 171
Artificial respiration, 165
Ascorbic acid, 34, 36
Aspirin, 31, 120
Asthma, 140, 152-153
Automobiles, safety in, 132, 185-186
Axillary temperature, 138
Babysitters, 99-100, 186, 188, 269-270
Baby talk, 249-250
Back, 133, 171, 176
  in pregnancy, 322, 325
Balloons, 131

Banana, 182, 183
Baths, 68-75, 132, 158
  eye, 171
  fontanels and, 9
  in pregnancy, 321-322
  sick care and, 68, 89, 136, 140, 157, 322
  vaccination and, 118, 120
Beauty care, 16, 26, 312-332
Bed, 61-62, 136, 185, 194
  placement, 63, 65, 131, 231
  for premature baby, 87, 89
Bed wetting, *see* Bladder control
Bibs, 81
Bilingualism, 250-251
Birth, 8-9, 10, 11, 12, 22, 57
  disease resistance at, 117
  maternal depression after, 13, 15-16, 332
  premature, 87-88
Birth certificates, 18, 20
Birth defects, 15, 86
Birthmarks, 8
Bites, 125, 169-170
Biting, 261-263
Bladder control, 62, 63, 94, 240, 242-246
Blankets, 62-63, 78, 81
Blemishes, 6, 8
  "mask of pregnancy," 318-319
Blood, 81, 155, 163, 329
  birth changes in, 8
  in bowel movements, 59, 133
  circumcision wound, 12
  cuts and, 164
  vaginal discharge, 11
Bones:
  broken, 170-171
  development of, 8-9, 65, 90, 104, 215, 217
Books, 309, 311
"Booster" injections, 118, 120, 125, 335

Bootees, 81, 218
Bottle feeding, *see* Feeding; Formulas; Weaning
Bottles, 32, 36
   cleaning, 22, 46, 49–53, 54, 55, 145, 198–199
   refrigeration of, 51, 53, 55, 198–199
Bowel movements, 57–59, 82, 165, 329
   chopped foods and, 212
   control, 240–242
   signs of illness in, 133, 136, 140, 159–162, 176
Boys, 5, 104, 250, 274
   bathing, 75
   crib rocking, 233
   genitals, 11–12, 83, 163
   mumps and, 173
   toilet training, 242, 244
Brain, 9, 121
   See also Mental development
Brassiere, 26–27, 28, 329
Bread, 109, 110, 197, 198, 202
   in mother's diet, 33
Breast feeding, 21, 22, 24–27, 117
   bottle feeding combined with, 32, 34, 140–141, 198
   bowel movements and, 58, 59
   techniques of, 23–24, 27–30
   weaning, 212–215, 235, 237–238
Breasts, 27–30
   of the newborn, 10, 11
   pregnancy changes in, 26, 329, 331
Breathing, 6, 8, 13, 89
   artificial respiration, 165
   asthma and, 152–153
   respiratory infections and, 148–152
   in sleep, 61
   steam inhalation and, 140
Bronchitis, 140
Bruises, 8
Burns, 127–128, 163
   first aid, 168–169
   steam, 140, 151

Burping, 23, 28, 38, 66
Butter, 198
Buttocks, 68, 75, 76, 78
Calcium, 31, 319
Carriage, 184–185
Celiac disease, 161
Cereal, 33, 109, 110
   as first solid, 48, 182–183, 184, 195, 196, 197, 211, 235
Cerebral palsy, 90
Cheese, 31, 33, 109, 110
Chest, 10, 133
Chewing, 236–237
Chickenpox, 117, 155, 172–173
Chocolate, 198
Choking, 163
   first aid, 164–165
   prevention, 34, 48, 55, 59, 65, 130–132, 169
Circumcision, 11–12, 162
Citrus fruits, 34, 36
   See also Orange juice
Clay, modeling, 309
Cleanliness, 68–75, 117, 125
   of bedding, 62
   in bottle feeding, 22, 48, 49, 49–53, 55, 59, 145, 159, 198–199
   breast feeding and, 27, 28, 29–30
   in can opening, 41, 51, 53
   diaper, 76
   of genital areas, 75, 78
   mother's beauty care and, 314, 318 321–322
   of play areas, 258, 307–309
   premature babies and, 89, 90
   skin ailments and, 155, 157
   spitting up and, 38
   thermometer, 138
   thrush and, 144–145
Clinics, 3, 90–91, 116
   guidance, 251, 285
Clothing, 76, 132, 157, 271
   laundering, 81, 85, 159
   newborn needs, 10, 63, 68, 71, 78–81
   for mothers, 26–27, 28, 329–332
Colds, 58, 107, 148, 186

341

Colds (*cont.*)
    allergy and, 153, 157
    disease symptoms and, 172, 174, 176
    fever in, 138, 150
Colic, 66–67
Colostrum, 27
Communicable diseases, 117, 153, 172–177, 186
    early stages of, 133–135
    See also Immunizations; *and see specific diseases*
Condensed milk, 41
Constipation, 59, 159–161, 242, 329
Contagious diseases, *see* Communicable diseases
Convalescence, 142–143
Convulsion, 133, 140, 153, 176
    first aid, 169
Corn syrup, 43, 46, 161
Cornstarch, in baths, 157, 158
Cough, 133, 150–151, 172, 174–175
    in teething period, 202
Counseling services, 15
Cradle cap, 75, 76, 158–159
Cramps, 66–67
Creativity, play and, 302–311
Crib, 62
Crib rocking, 232–233
Crippled baby, 90–91, 126
Crossed eyes, 146
Croup, 140, 150–151
Crying, 21, 24, 65–68, 133
    for attention, 13, 61, 63, 66, 190, 232
Cup feeding, 32, 130, 141, 199, 212, 221
    milk and, 214–215, 235, 237–238
Cuts, 164
Day care, 99–100, 114
Death, 229, 293–294
Dehydration, 140, 159
Dentists, 104, 106, 107, 130, 319
Depression, 13, 15–16, 332
    of older children, 16–18, 278–280, 283
Diaper rash, 76, 78, 82, 157
    penis infection, 162–163

Diapers, 66, 79
    care of, 76, 78, 83, 85
Diarrhea, 58, 133, 135, 140, 176
    allergies and, 157, 159
    bottle boiling and, 199
Diet:
    bowel movements and, 58, 59, 161, 242
    children's daily needs, 107–116, 117–132, 141, 183–184, 196, 211–212, 235–238
    first solid foods, 48, 141, 181–184, 195–197, 214–215, 235, 236–237
    food allergies and, 152, 157, 158, 159
    mealtimes and, 197–198, 222, 231
    of mothers, 30–31, 34–36, 319, 320–321, 325
    sickness and, 135, 140–142, 148, 161–162
    teeth and, 104, 106, 202–203
    See also Feeding
Digestive tract obstruction, 162
Digestive upset, 38, 58–59, 67, 184
    allergies and, 157, 158
    malabsorptive disease and, 161–162
    in pregnancy, 325
Diphtheria, 117, 118, 120, 121, 335
Discipline, 261, 263–269, 280–284, 288–289, 295–301
    attempts to force babies, 22, 23, 43–46, 141, 206, 215
    bedtime, 205, 232, 233
    love and, 113, 114, 208–211, 224, 226, 265
    parental disagreements on, 274–276
    playrooms and, 257
    sexual attitudes and, 78
    sibling rivalry and, 17, 279
    sick care and, 96, 142
    stuttering and, 252
    thumbsucking and, 239
    toilet training and, 240–246
Diseases, 336

Diseases (*cont.*)
  common disorders and, 144, 148–153, 172–175
  less common, 176–177
  prevention, 3, 40, 90, 115, 116, 117–126, 173, 175, 177, 335
  See also specific diseases
Disorders, common, 144–171
DPT injections, 120, 121, 335
Drafts, 65, 71
Dresses, 81
  maternity, 331, 332
Drowning, 56, 132, 229
Dry milk, 30–31, 41, 44
Dysentery, 159
Ear, 72, 121, 148
  earache, 133, 152, 233
Eczema, 158
Eggs, 33, 109, 158
  introduction of, 195–196, 197, 211
Eight to twelve months old:
  development, 180, 207–220, 227, 240
Emergencies, 163, 177
Emotional needs, 2, 21, 68, 94, 221
  for companionship, 190, 203, 205, 207, 220, 222, 232, 256, 257, 276, 278
  for creativity, 303–308
  fantasies and, 285–289
  father's role and, 274
  of the handicapped child, 91–92
  hospital trips and, 95–97, 135
  for independence, 195, 199–200, 224, 230, 240, 243, 265, 288–289, 298
  of older children, 16–18, 278–280
  stuttering and, 251–252
  thumbsucking and, 206, 238–239
  of the toddler, 223–224, 229, 265
  toilet training and, 241, 242, 243–244, 246
  violence and, 263–264
  weaning and, 214, 237, 238
Enema, avoidance, 59, 136, 142, 161, 242

Epilepsy, 90, 169
Eustachian tubes, 152
Evaporated milk, 34, 41, 182, 198
  can opening, 41, 51, 53, 54
  measuring, 46
Exercise, for mothers, 321, 322–323, 325–329
"Expression" of milk, 29–30
Eyes, 133, 136, 171, 176
  crossed, 146
  mother's eye care, 318
  newborn, 5, 6, 9–10, 13, 146, 148, 178
Face, 68, 72, 133, 136
Falls, 106, 128, 170, 229
  walking and, 126, 217–218, 230
Family service agencies, 15, 86–87
Fantasies, 283–285, 311
Fathers, 15–16, 18, 100, 290
  toddler and preschooler relations, 222, 223, 273–274
Fears, 193, 218, 224, 281
  of death, 294
  imaginary, 285–289
  of medical care, 95, 96, 106, 116, 121–122
  of strangers, 188, 194, 222, 269–270
  toilet training and, 241, 243
Feeding, 21–38, 71, 140, 180–181, 182
  babysitter task of, 188
  crying and, 21, 24, 66, 67
  eight to twelve months, 211–212, 222
  formulas, 26, 40–55, 161 (*See also* Formulas)
  four to eight months, 195–199
  of premature babies, 88, 90
  records of, 334
  See also Breast feeding; Diet
Feet, 3, 115
  development, 12, 81, 180, 217, 218–219, 227–228
  in pregnancy, 329
Fever, 133–135, 136, 150, 151, 172, 174, 176
  convulsions and, 169

343

Fever (*cont.*)
    ear infections and, 152
    kidney infections and, 162
    skin ailments and, 155
    teething period, 202
    temperature taking, 136–140
    tick bites and, 170, 177
    vaccination and, 118, 120
Figs, 59
Fingernails, 75, 155, 173
    in pregnancy, 320
    scratching play and, 191, 193
Fingerpainting, 308–309
Fire, 127–128, 229
First aid, 163–171
Fish, 33, 109, 131
Five-year-olds, 106, 116
Fluorine, 107, 203
Fontanels, 9, 10, 72
Food, *see* Diet; Feeding; Formulas
Foreskin, 11–12, 162–163
Formulas, 26, 40–55, 66, 161, 334
    breast feeding supplement, 32, 35
    preparation of, 46–55, 141, 159, 181, 198–199
Four to eight months old, 178, 189–206, 247
Four-year-olds, 239, 244, 249, 271–311
    independence in, 114, 127
    medical care and, 95, 116
    toys, 142
Fractures, 170–171
Fruit, 34, 36, 109, 110
    bowel movements and, 59, 161, 212
    first solids and, 182, 183, 184, 195, 197, 211
    in mother's diet, 30, 33
    sickness and, 141
Gamma globulin, 121, 173, 177
Gas fixtures, 131
Gelatin, in nail care, 320
Genital organs, 11–12, 75, 78
    disorders, 162–163
    handling, 246, 291
German measles, 172–173

Girls, 162, 173, 274
    bathing, 75
    birth weight, 5
    diaper fold for, 82
    growth rates, 104
    talking, 250
    toilet training, 242, 244
    vaginal discharge, 11, 162–163
Glands, 133, 150, 176
    mumps and, 172
Glandular fever, 176
Glasses, 146
Goat's milk, 42
Growth, 3–4, 102–104, 114, 226
    colic and, 67
    at one to four months, 178
    of premature babies, 87, 88
    records of, 333
    walking and, 215, 218–219
Hair, 9, 65, 312–314
    shampoo, 75, 76
Handicapped babies, 90–91
Handling, 9, 13, 17, 59
    in bathing, 71, 72–75, 78
    broken bones and, 171
    earache and, 152
    rashes and, 157
    vomiting and, 132
Hand-removal of milk, 29–30
Hands, 12, 81
    use of, 180, 191, 193, 209–210, 221
Head, 133, 170, 172, 176
    banging, 232–233
    bathing, 72, 75, 76
    newborn, 5, 8–9, 65, 178, 180, 189
Health, 102–116
    mother's beauty care and, 312–332
Health departments, 20, 100, 125, 135
    special problems and, 87, 88, 90–91
Health examinations, for caretakers, 125, 188
Hearing, 3, 13, 90, 115, 152
Heartburn, 325

344

Heart defect, 90, 155
Height, 3, 5, 102–103, 221
Hepatitis, infectious, 176–177
Heredity, 2, 103, 106, 217, 227
Hernia, 10–11
High chairs, 128, 130, 199, 230
Hitting, 209, 263–264, 268, 300
Hives, 158
Homogenization of milk, 40, 41, 42
Hormones, 11, 15, 332
Hospitals, 71, 125
    birth care in, 12, 13, 15, 20, 22, 87, 88, 89
    children's visits, 94–97, 135
    emergencies and, 164, 165, 171, 177
    sick care and, 135, 155
Illness:
    convalescence, 142–143
    feeding in, 140–141
    home nursing techniques, 136–140
    symptoms, 133, 135, 148, 150–151, 152, 153, 155, 157, 159, 162, 163, 172–177
    See also Diseases; and see specific illnesses
Immunizations, 115, 116, 117–121, 173, 175
    poliomyelitis, 118, 177, 335
    schedule for, 335
    tick fever, 170
    typhoid, 125
Impetigo, 158
Incubator, 89
Individual differences, 2, 3, 88, 227
    in size, 102–103, 178
    in sleep requirements, 61
    talking and, 248, 250
Infantile paralysis, 118, 176–177
Infectious hepatitis, 176–177
Infectious mononucleosis (glandular fever), 176–177
Inoculations, see Immunizations
Institutions, 92, 250
Insect bites, 170, 177
Intestinal disorder, 159–161, 198, 199

Intussusception, 162
Itch, 173. See also Rashes
Jaundice, 8, 176–177
Jealousy, 16–18, 278–280, 283
Kettles, 48, 51, 52, 53, 128
    steam, 140, 151
Laryngitis, 140
Larynx, 150
Laundry, 62, 81, 132, 159
    diaper, 76, 79, 82, 85
Laxatives, 136, 143, 161
    for nursing mothers, 31, 58
Learning, 221, 273
    by imitation, 122, 191, 209, 217, 228, 247, 249, 250, 266, 274, 275, 280–281, 284, 302, 304
    love and, 2, 21–22, 190, 208–211, 222–223, 224, 226, 298, 300–301
    moral training, 261, 263–264, 280–284, 288, 295, 300
    play and, 191, 193, 253, 256, 302–311
    readiness for, 182, 215, 227, 240, 298
    See also specific learning tasks e.g., Toilet training
Legs, 6, 12, 180, 217, 228
    broken, 171
Lockjaw, see Tetanus
Lotions, 59, 68, 75
Maids, 125, 186, 188
Malabsorptive disease, 161–162
Manners, 261, 263–264
Mattress, 62
Meals, see Diet; Feeding
Measles, 120–121, 155, 172–173
    prevention, 117, 118, 121, 173, 335
Meat, 30, 33, 106, 109
    in baby's diet, 42, 183–184, 195, 196, 197, 211
Medicines, 135, 143, 242
    babies and, 59, 76, 120, 130, 131, 155, 163
    nursing mothers and, 29, 31, 58
Meningitis, 153, 155, 176–177

Menstrual cycle, 27
Mental development, 90, 189, 207–211, 273
    brain inflammation and, 121
Middle ear infection, 121
Midwives, 20
Milk, 21, 33, 117, 135, 182–183
    bowel movements and, 58, 59
    breast, 26, 27–28, 29–30, 34
    child's daily needs, 109, 110
    cup feeding of, 214–215
    in formula preparation, 40–42, 46, 51, 53–54, 198–199
    types, listed, 40–42
    vitamins in, 31, 34, 41, 184
Mineral oil, 59, 68, 71, 75
    for "cradle cap," 76
Ministers, 86
Modified milk, 42, 54
Mononucleosis, infectious, 176–177
Mothers:
    beauty care, 312–332
    children's hospitalization and, 95–97
    depression and, 13, 15–16, 67–68, 332
    nursing education for, 135, 163
    preschool children and, 274, 280
    special problems of, 86–101
    toddlers and, 214, 223–224, 237
    weaning period and, 214–215, 237–238
    working, 97–101, 224
    See also Nursing mothers; Pregnancy
Mouth, 6, 178, 180, 239
    temperature taking by, 138
    thrush infection, 144–145
Mouth-to-mouth resuscitation, 165
Moving, 92, 94
Mumps, 172–173
Muscles, 146, 176, 323
    development, 10–11, 90, 104, 178, 215, 219, 227, 305
Naps, 24, 203, 222, 230–231
    outdoor, 185
Nausea, in pregnancy, 325
    See also Vomiting

Navel, healing of, 10, 68
Neck, 5, 6, 8
    injury, 171
    stiffness, 133, 153, 176
Newborn, 5–20, 178, 280
    feeding, 21–55
    routine care, 57–85
Nightgowns, 81
Nightmares, 94
Nipples:
    bottle, 22, 48, 51, 52, 53, 145
    breast, 27, 28–29, 30
Noise, 193
Nose, 6, 148, 150
    nosebleed, 170, 176
    running, 133, 172
Nurses, 15, 27, 90, 91
    public health, 71, 86, 88, 89, 135
Nursing classes, 135, 163
Nursing mothers, 22–32, 237–238
    diet, 30–31, 34–36, 58, 320
Nuts, 113, 131, 212
Oil, poisoning, 168
Older children, 86, 130, 276
    handicapped babies and, 92
    infections and, 59, 145, 148, 186
    jealousy, 16–18, 278–280, 283
    room sharing, 231
One-year-olds, 104, 116, 219–220, 221–270
    aspirin and, 120
    diet and, 113, 114, 200, 211, 235–237
    vaccination, 121, 173, 335
    weaning and, 214, 237–238
Orange juice, 34, 36, 184, 197, 214
    bottles, 32, 48
Organizations, special problem, 91
Orthopedic problems, 90
Outdoor play, 258–259
Outings, 184–186, 244
Pacifiers, 206, 239
Pain, 95, 96, 288
    colic, 66–67
    signs of illness, 59, 133, 136, 152, 162, 176
    in umbilical hernia, 10

Paint, 258
  playing with, 305, 307–309
Paper, for play needs, 309
Parasitic diseases, 125
Parents, *See* Fathers; Mothers
Parties, 115, 261
Passive immunity, 117
Pasteurization of milk, 40, 41, 42, 198
Pediatricians, 3, 115
Penis, 11–12, 75, 162
Pertussis, *see* Whooping cough
Pets, 125–126, 142, 259
  death of, 293, 294
Phenylketonuria, 125
Pillows, 62
PKU test, 125
Plastic bags, 62, 131
Play, 191, 193, 253–264, 301–311
  solitary, 190, 222, 256, 257
  talking and, 249–250, 252
  See also Toys
Playmates, 92, 94, 190, 222
  imaginary, 285
  older children and, 18
  parties and, 115, 261
  sex differences and, 291, 302
  shyness and, 194
  toddlers and, 259, 260–264
Playpen, 194–195, 217, 229–230, 259
  crib rocking and, 233
Pneumonia, 56, 120, 151–152
Poisoning, 163, 229
  first aid, 165, 168
  prevention of, 32, 127, 130, 258
Poliomyelitis, 118, 176–177, 335
Popcorn, 113, 131, 212
Posture, 217, 228, 322
Potatoes, 33, 197
Poultry, 33, 109, 131, 196
Powder, 75, 157
Pregnancy, 1.1, 15, 87–88, 117
  beauty care in, 16, 26, 312–332
  birthmarks and, 8
  breast changes in, 26, 329, 331
  diet in, 30, 31, 319, 320, 321, 325
  explained to children, 290
  measles in, 173
  planned, 220
Premature babies, 86, 87–90
Preschool children, 270–311
  vaccination schedule, 335
Prickly heat, 157
Protein, 31, 195, 321
Prune juice, 59, 161, 183
Public health nurses, 71, 86, 135
  premature babies and, 88, 89, 90
Pulse, fontanel, 9
Punishment, *see* Discipline
Pyelitis, 162
Pyloric stenosis, 162
Quarrels, 261, 263–264, 274–280
Rabies, 125
Rashes, 8, 158
  diaper, 76, 78, 82, 163
  as sign of illness, 133, 153, 155, 157, 170, 172–173, 174, 176, 184
Raw milk, 41, 199
Records, 3–4, 115, 333–336
  birth registration, 20
  of fever, 136
  of inoculations, 121–122, 335
Rectal thermometer, 138
Rectum, obstruction, 161
Red Cross, 135, 163
Respiratory infections, 148–152
Rest, 135, 136, 148, 173, 175
  bedtime resistance and, 203, 205, 230–231
  birth and, 22
  meals and, 111, 231, 236
  for mothers, 15, 16, 24, 31–32, 67, 68, 323, 332
Rocking, in bed, 232–233
Rocky Mountain spotted fever, 176–177
Roseola, 174–175
Rowen, Lillian, quoted, 323
Sabin vaccine, 118, 177
Safety, 126–132, 297, 322
  in bed, 61–62, 185, 233
  bottle propping custom and, 56
  canned foods and, 183
  dusting powder, 75

347

Safety (*cont.*)
   household, 126–132, 199, 228–230
   play and, 131, 193, 195, 229–230, 258–261
   teething and, 202
   water bottles and, 32
   See also Accidents; *and see specific dangers*, e.g., Poisoning
Salk vaccine, 118
Sandbox, 258–259
Scalp, 72, 170
   "cradle cap," 75, 76, 158
Scarlatina, 174–175
Scarlet fever, 155, 174–175
Schedules, 15, 16, 18, 68, 100
   feeding, 21, 22, 23–24, 28, 43, 65, 180–181, 182, 197–198, 222, 231
   immunization, 335
   sleep, 203, 205, 222, 230–232
   in toilet training, 240, 243
Scratching:
   playful, 191, 193
   rashes and, 155, 173
Scrotum, 11
Self-confidence, 126–127, 190, 193–194, 297, 298
   imaginary fears and, 285–289
   toddlers and, 223, 224, 226, 230
Self-feeding, 110, 114, 115, 199–200
   preschooler, 271
   toddler and, 235–236
Septic sore throat, 174–175
Sex, 15, 17
   attitudes toward, 246, 274, 286, 289–293
   playmates and, 291, 302
   See also: Boys; Girls
Sheets, 62
Shirts, 79, 120
Shoes, 81, 218–219
   maternity, 329
Shots, *see* Immunizations
Sitting, 180, 189, 194, 205, 217
Six-year-olds, 104, 106, 217, 228
Skim milk, 31, 42, 110
Skin, 6, 8, 157–158
   care of baby's, 75, 76, 78, 157

   care of mother's, 313–319
   signs of illness, 133, 153, 155, 157, 176
Sleep, 4, 81, 102, 117, 222
   bed arrangements, 61–63, 65, 231, 233
   bed wetting and, 244, 246
   drowsiness, 133
   feeding and, 23, 24, 181
   nightmares, 94
   toddlers and, 230–233, 269–270
Smallpox, 118, 120, 121, 176–177, 335
Smoking, 31, 127
Smothering, 63, 130–132
Snacks, 108, 110, 181
Soap, 71, 72, 75, 314
Social workers, 15, 86, 91
Socks, 81, 219
"Soft spots," 9, 10, 72
Sore throat, 133, 172, 174, 176
Spanking, 209, 233, 268, 300–301
Sponge baths, 136, 140, 157, 322
   for newborn, 68, 75, 89
Stairways, 126, 128, 222, 230
Standing alone, 217, 227
Steam inhalation, 140, 150
Sterilization, *see* Cleanliness
Storytelling, 309, 311
Strabismus, 146
Strangers, fear of, 188, 194, 222, 269–270
Strep throat, 174–175
Stroller, 184–185, 230, 266
Stuttering, 251–252
Substitute mother, 99–100, 186, 188
Sucking, 6, 182, 206, 222, 238–239
   air and, 23, 28, 38, 66
   bottle feeding and, 56, 90
   breast milk flow and, 27–28, 31–32
Suffocation, 130–131. *See also* Choking; Smothering
Sugar, 22, 106, 109, 140,
   in formula, 42–43, 46, 53, 161
Sunshine, 78, 107, 185, 259
   overexposure, 128, 169, 186
Sweaters, 79, 81, 218
Sweating, 133, 321–322

Sweet foods, 106, 113, 182, 212
   baby desserts, 197–198, 211
Swellings, 11, 133, 150, 176
Tables, 111, 199, 230
   for bath, 71
   bedside, 135
Talcum powder, 75, 157
Talking, 115, 145–146
   of death, 294
   learning, 190–191, 207, 220, 222, 247–252
   of sex, 290, 291
   spoken directions, 266, 268
   toilet training and, 240, 241, 242
Tea, 135, 141
Tears, 10, 148
Teeth, 102, 104, 106–107, 110
   pregnancy and, 319
   rate of teething, 200, 202, 222
   solid foods and, 211
   teething problems, 145, 202–203
   thumbsucking and, 239
Telephone numbers, 337
   babysitters and, 188, 270
Temperament, 2, 215, 233, 250
   discipline and, 296
   signs of illness and, 133, 202
Temperature, 87, 89, 157
   bath, 70, 72
   bottle, 54
   of children's food, 110–111
   outings and, 185, 186
   room, 79, 142
   See also Fever
Testicles, newborn, 11
Tests, medical, 122, 125
Tetanus, 118, 125, 164
   immunization (DPT), 120, 121, 335
Thermometer, 89, 136–140
Three-year-olds, 102–103, 271–311
   medical care and, 95, 116
   talking, 248, 249, 250, 251
   teeth, 104, 106
   temperature taking, 138
   toilet training, 244
   violence and, 263
Throat, soreness, 133, 172, 174, 176
Thrush, 144–145

Thumbsucking, 205–206, 238–239
Ticks, 170, 177
Toddlers, 221–270
Toenails, 75
Toes, 12, 219
Toilet training, 182, 240–246, 273
Tomatoes, 34
Tongue tie, 145–146
Tonsils, 96, 150–151
Toys, 94, 96, 126, 191, 233
   preschooler favorites, 302–311
   safety and, 131, 193, 260, 261
   sick care and, 142, 143
   storage, 257–258
   teething and, 202
   toddler favorites, 259–261
Tuberculosis, 117, 122, 125, 188
Twins, 250
Two-year-olds, 18, 114, 221–270
   diet, 197–198
   growth rates, 103
   medical care and, 95, 116
   sleep and, 205
   talking, 248, 250, 251
   teeth, 104, 106
   vaccination, 335
Typhoid fever, 125
Umbilical cord, 10
United States Children's Bureau, 251
Urine, 133, 162, 176
   bladder control, 240, 242–246
Vaccination, 115, 116, 121, 173, 175, 177
   boosters, 118, 120, 125, 335
   schedule, 335
Vaginal discharge, 11
Vaporizer, 89, 140, 151
Varicose veins, 329
Vegetables, 30, 33, 109, 110
   bowel movements and, 59, 161
   introduction of, 183–184, 195, 196–197, 198, 211
   preferences, 111, 235, 237
   teeth and, 106
Ventilation, 65, 89, 131, 135
Vision, 3, 115, 148
   newborn, 13, 90, 146
Visiting nurses, 15, 88, 135

Visitors, 24, 59, 117
  older children and, 279–280
  toddlers as, 264
  visiting with babies, 185–186
Vitamins, 34–36, 38, 107–108, 184
  in mother's diet, 30, 321
  teeth and, 104, 203
Vitamin A, 33, 109
  in milk, 30, 38, 44
Vitamin B, 38
Vitamin C, sources of, 34–36, 184
Vitamin D, 33, 107–108
  in milk, 31, 34, 41
Vomiting, 38–39, 65, 132, 133, 172, 173
  allergies and, 157
  bowel disorders and, 162
  diet and, 135, 140, 184
  meningitis and, 155, 176
  pneumonia and, 151
  poisoning and, 165
  in pregnancy, 325
  sunburn and, 169
Walking, 81, 218–219, 323
  learning, 189, 194, 195, 207, 215–219, 220, 223–224, 226–228, 248
  safety and, 126–127, 128, 132, 228–229
Water, 22, 32, 90, 169, 321
  bath, 71, 72, 132
  fluorine in, 107, 203
  in formula preparation, 40, 42, 46, 51, 53, 54, 59, 141
  orange juice dilution, 36
  sick care and, 135, 136, 141
Waterproof materials, 62, 76
Weaning, 32, 182, 199, 212–215
  toddlers and, 235, 237–238
Weight, 5, 46, 215, 227
  growth rates and, 102–104, 178, 221
  low-birth-weight babies, 87–88, 89, 90
  of mothers, 30, 320, 321
  records, 4, 333
Welfare departments, 100
Well-baby clinics, 3, 116
Whooping cough, 117, 118, 174–175
  immunization (DPT), 120, 121, 335
Working mothers, 97–101, 224
X-rays, 130

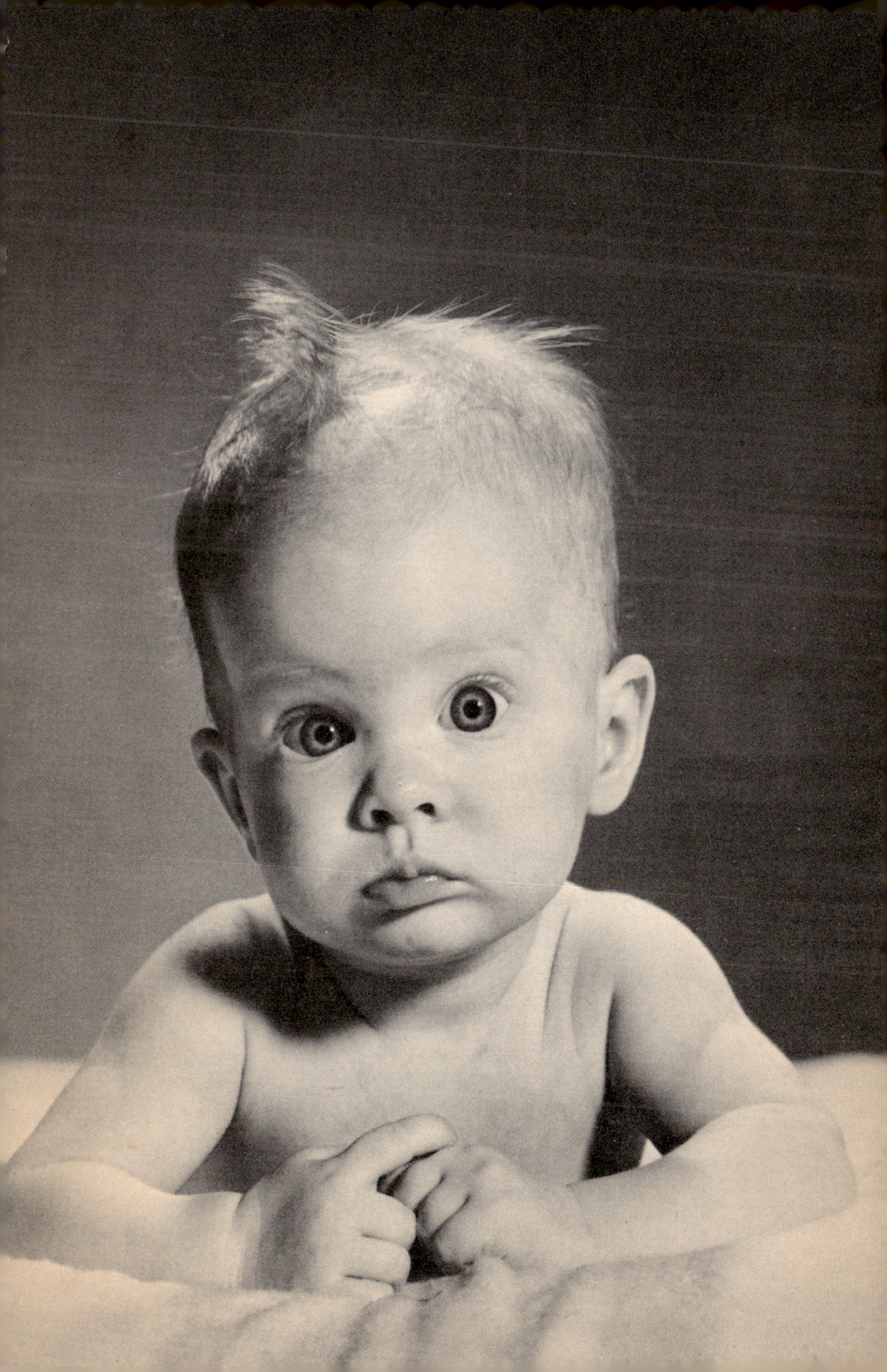

Notes

Notes

Notes

Notes

Additional copies of the American Guide to Infant and Child Care may be obtained at $1.35 each from the store where you received this copy or from

Robert McMichael, Inc.
12 East 44th Street
New York, New York 10017